The Complete Book of Dog Care

LEON F. WHITNEY, D.V.

The Complete Boo

OTHER BOOKS BY LEON F. WHITNEY, D.V

THE COMPLETE BOOK OF HOME PET C
FEEDING OUR D
HOW TO BREED D
BLOODHOUNDS AND HOW TO TRAIN TH
BASIS OF BREED

f Dog Care

BLEDAY & COMPANY, INC.

DEN CITY, NEW YORK.

Portions of this book have previously appeared in *The Complete Book of Home Pet Care*

PRINTED IN THE UNITED STATES OF AMERICA

LIBRARY OF CONGRESS
CATALOG CARD NUMBER 52-13792

To Kate

Contents

Part Two

Part Three

Diagnostic Table

THE following table is designed to help you use this book easily and well. It will make it possible for you to identify many of the common diseases of dogs and it will tell you where to look for information about them.

If your dog is sick it will exhibit certain symptoms—probably several. These symptoms are shown in the table in boldface, and under each of them there is a list of diseases or conditions with which they are most commonly associated. You will find in the book a detailed discussion of the symptoms, causes, prevention, and treatment of each of these diseases.

Here is an example of the way the table should be used: You notice that your dog is excessively thirsty, seems to be bloated about the abdomen, and shows signs of a soft swelling in his legs. *Excessive thirst, abdominal enlargement,* and *swellings* are all shown in the table as symptoms. The diseases listed under each of these symptoms vary greatly, but *dropsy* appears under all of them. By reading the discussion of dropsy, you will be able to determine whether your dog has the disease and, if he has, what you can do about it.

This table is *not* a cure-all chart. It will *not* make you a veterinarian. It *will* help you to recognize the signs of disease in your pet and show you where to get the information you need in order to decide whether you can treat the condition yourself or whether your pet needs expert veterinary attention.

ABDOMINAL ENLARGEMENT
Anemia (in young)
Bladder ailments
Bloat
Dropsy
Excessive thirst
Fat
Metritis
Organ enlargement (spleen, liver)
Overfeeding
Parasites (in young)
Pregnancy
Tumors

ABDOMINAL TENDERNESS
Colon impaction
Enteritis
Foreign bodies
Intussusception
Peritonitis
Poisoning
Porcupine quills
Stomach inflammation
Tumors
Ulcers

ANEMIA (Pale gums)
Hemorrhage
Iron deficiency
Lice
Parasites
Piroplasmosis
Poisoning
Tumors

APPETITE

Difficulty in Eating
Foreign bodies in mouth or throat
Insect stings
Lead poisoning
Mouth ailments
Teeth loose
Tongue injuries
Tonsillitis
Tumors in mouth
Ulcers

Loss of Appetite
Change of diet
Overfeeding
Parasites
Poisoning
Toxins
Tumors

Ravenous Appetite
Diabetes insipidus
Diabetes mellitus
Heat, onset of
Lactation
Pregnancy
Undernourishment

BLINDNESS
Cataract
Cornea, opacity of
Distemper, Carré
Eye ailments
Glaucoma
Vitamins

BREATH, BAD
Cancer
Constipation
Foreign bodies in or on teeth
Gum diseases
Kidney disease
Lip ailments
Poisoning, caustic or acid
Tartar
Teeth
Tongue injuries
Ulcers in mouth

BREATHING ABNORMAL
(Loss of breath from exertion)
Anemia
Emphysema
Heart ailments
Heartworm
Hernia of diaphragm
Hydrothorax
Pleurisy
Pneumonia

CONVULSIONS
Calcium-arsenate poisoning
Diabetes mellitus
Eclampsia
Encephalitis
Foreign bodies in stomach
Strychnine poisoning
Uremia
Worms

COUGHING
Bronchitis
Distemper
Emphysema
Esophageal worms
Heartworm
Housedog disease
Laryngitis
Pharyngitis
Pleurisy
Pneumonia
Worms

DIARRHEA
Enteritis
Exercise
Fiber, excessive
Parasites
Poisoning
Skim milk

DIZZINESS
Accidents
Cerebral hemorrhage
Ear canker
Ear mites
Encephalitis
Housedog disease
Middle-ear infection

EMACIATION
Diabetes
Diarrhea
Kidney disease
Liver disease
Tuberculosis
Tumors
Undernourishment

GAGGING
Foreign body in throat
Housedog disease
Tonsillitis
Worms

HEAD SHAKING
Canker in ear
Ear, ailments of
Ear flap torn
Ear mites
Fleas

Hematoma in ear flap
Lice
Middle-ear infection

HOARSENESS

Asthma
Foreign body in throat
Injuries to throat
Laryngitis
Paralysis
Throat ailments
- Streptococcus
- Virus

Tonsillitis

LUMPS

Abscesses
Bone tumors
Dropsy
Goiter
Hematoma
Hernia, inguinal
Hernia, perineal
Leukemia
Salivary fistula
Tumors

MOANING OR CRYING

Anal-gland abscess
Constipation
Ear ailments
Encephalitis
Fleas
Foreign bodies
Poisoning
Skin disease
Tooth abscess

NOSE, RUNNING

Distemper
Nasal discharge
Nasal tumors
Noseworms
Pneumonia
Salmon poisoning

PARALYSIS

Back broken or injured
Chastek paralysis
Housedog disease
Rabies
Stroke
Toxins

SHEDDING, ABNORMAL

Burns
Diabetes insipidus
Mange
Nursing puppies
Periodic shedding
Skin diseases

SHIVERING, TREMBLING

Cold
Eclampsia
Poisoning
- Caffeine
- Calcium arsenate
- Food
- Nicotine
- Strychnine
- Theobromine

SKIN AILMENTS

Acne
Alopecia
Burns
Dandruff
Fleas
Mange
- Demodectic
- Notodectic
- Sarcoptic

SLOBBERING

Convulsions
Encephalitis
Foreign bodies in mouth
Insect stings
Lip ailments
Papillomas
Poison
Teeth loose or broken
Tongue injuries

SNEEZING, SNORTING

Coryza
Distemper
Nose, ailments of
Noseworm
Pneumonia
Sniffles
Tumors

SWELLINGS THAT LEAVE PITS WHEN SQUEEZED

Dropsy
Edema
Heart ailments
Insect stings
Kidney diseases
Snake bites

THIRST, EXCESSIVE

Diabetes, incipient or sugar
Dropsy
Food too dry
Food too salty
Kidney disease

URINARY TROUBLES

Cloudy urine: bladder
Excessive urine: kidney disease, diabetes
Inability to urinate: bladder, urethra
Leaks (urinary incontinence): kidney disease, diabetes
Odor evil: bladder, blood, kidney
Over-yellow: jaundice
Sand in urine: bladder

VOMITING

Esophageal worms
Foreign body in stomach
Hair in stomach
Hernia, strangulated
Intussusception
Kidney disease
Parasites in stomach
Peritonitis
Poisoning
Tapeworms
Tumors, brain or other
Urinary ailments

YELLOWING TISSUE

Jaundice
Leptospirosis
Liver ailments
Piroplasmosis
Poisoning

The Complete Book of Dog Care

Part One

1. You and Your Dog

YEARS ago, when I began veterinary practice, I often wondered why it was that some people seemed to get so much more pleasure than others out of owning and handling dogs. As I talked with them, listened to their problems, and tried to answer their questions, it seemed to me that the difference lay largely in their general attitude toward animals, in their understanding of the nature of their pets and their relationships with them. All of these things were importan. factors in the choice of their dogs, in the way they handled them, and in the care they were able to give them. Having worked with thousands of pet owners, I am now more than ever convinced that a proper understanding of the nature of animals is the first and greatest need of most dog owners.

WHAT YOU SHOULD KNOW ABOUT YOUR DOG

The capacity to feel love for animals is a gift—to many people a gift as rewarding as any we have. There are those unfortunates—comparatively few, I think—who lack the ability to feel affection for animals just as surely as there are those who cannot distinguish red from green. They will never understand the pleasure and the gratification which every dog owner experiences, for the love of animals can never be truly taught. But most people—even those who have never owned a pet—do not have the sympathy and warmth and patience that it takes to get the most enjoyment from the care of a dog. What they lack more than anything else, I think, is a realistic conception of what they are to the dog and what their dog should be to them.

Just as so many humans feel the need of some higher power or individual and look to it or to him for support or guidance, so your dogs look to you, their provider, for their support. To them you are a god, you are Providence. The dog you own looks to you for leadership and food, even as his feral ancestors looked to their pack leaders and to nature for their guidance and sustenance.

If you are to get the most fun out of owning a dog, perhaps nothing is more important than that you learn to accept your pet for what it is, to cultivate the proper attitude of mind toward it. A dog is a dog. Glorifying him in your own mind, thinking of him or treating him as a human being, is a basic source of many of the difficulties some people encounter in dog owning. You must learn to refrain from the natural tendency of projecting yourself into the dog. It is poor logic; it will make your pet unhappy and you dissatisfied.

Though most people are willing to accept the laws of nature as they apply to wild animals, some of them are still reluctant to extend the same reasoning to the animals they keep as intimate pets. In principle, there is no difference. You should always try first to understand the nature of the species you are interested in, not just that of a particular animal. A pet's background in nature is still our most reliable guide to proper care. We learn our best lessons, particularly about food and feeding, from nature, and we would all be much better providers if we could bring ourselves to rely more on such guidance.

Take feeding, for example. Because we have learned to enjoy a great variety of food, we are inclined to project our tastes on pets. A horse will quite contentedly eat hay, oats, and a little salt for a whole lifetime. Wild dogs can live by eating what appears to be a single item, animal bodies. Even today, when cats become wild, they exist primarily on rodents. From a study of the natural habits of animals we can and should learn a great deal about the kind of food that is best for them. It would, of course, be foolish to suggest that we slavishly follow the natural diet of animals. Dogs have evolved with us for so long that they can exist on any food which a human can digest.

In every aspect of animal care it pays real dividends to know the natural requirements of the species—their breeding habits, the diseases they are subject to, the exercise they need. A dog is "The only true love money can buy," yet how many people really find it so?

If every dog owner understood the natural needs of all doglike animals and had the courage to treat his dog accordingly, we surely would never see fat, turtlelike dogs; we'd see no sick dogs being allowed to drag out their miserable existence; deformities would not be perpetuated. Dog breeders would refuse to breed another dog whose defects caused it or us inconvenience. Boston terriers who were unable to whelp normally would never be bred again, but only Bostons with large pelves would become progenitors. What suffering could be eliminated! Suppose no bulldog that snored because of his contorted nose would be used to sire another snoring pup? Or suppose that strains of wire-haired terriers were bred to be resistant to skin disease? How much more pleasure every dog owner would find in raising his pet!

Nature does not perpetuate defects; we do it in defiance of nature.

Nature doesn't allow animals to become fat and lazy unless for the purpose of storing food, to be used as we know it is in hibernating and semi-hibernating animals. We would be wise indeed to take the examples which nature has given us as our guides.

It is not too much to expect the owner to raise the kind of dog that won't bite under almost any provocation. It can be done and is done by people who have the proper feeling for animals. From the time a puppy is weaned he should be handled—handled at arm's length so that he begins to understand that he is on his own as nature meant him to be: a dog—not a part of a human's anatomy. He shouldn't be handled too much. A table is a splendid accessory. Place the new puppy on it. Put him at arm's length; stand him up. Brush him. Set him down. Make sure that he has nothing to lean against. Pose him in his correct show position for ten or fifteen minutes at a stretch, brushing and combing him all the time. If he tries to lean against you, move away and keep him learning independence. Open his mouth and feel around his little teeth. Let him know you mean no harm, and after a while you will find you can hold his mouth open for several minutes. Reward him from time to time with a tiny tidbit. If you do this, you will have a dog and not a nuisance—a dog that you can trust and one that will trust you.

THE DOG OWNER'S OBLIGATIONS

The obligations of dog owning are few, but you must fulfill them. All that the animal asks of you is *food, water, comfort, exercise, health,* and *protection.* If you can't fulfill these simple requirements, it would be better for you not to have a dog, for he will only be a burden.

As an example of what I mean, veterinarians often have people bring poodles to them with their coats solidly matted and fleas having a regular Old Home Week beneath the mat's protection. No one could possibly comb them. The owners lament, "Oh, why didn't somebody tell me what he would be like when he grew up!" A dog allowed to get in such a condition is a medical problem and a nuisance to the owner as well. When the dog has been clipped all over, de-flead, and the owner made to understand that from then on he must spend some time on the dog's grooming, he is likely to say, "But that's so expensive!" The owner should have known before he bought the poodle that a dog with a shorter nap is cheaper to keep.

Too often the prospective dog owner overlooks his own desires and tendencies when selecting a pet. A man who is of a sedentary and studious disposition not infrequently makes the mistake of selecting a dog which requires much more exercise than he is willing to give it. Let us say he has a Dalmatian. Every day he takes it for a walk around the block—thereby satisfying his own conscience but providing practically no exercise for the dog. All the owner has done is to give the animal a chance to relieve himself. He should know that sometimes a foxhound will run on a trail for as much as forty-eight hours. At ten miles an hour, he would have traveled four hundred and eighty miles in that time. The hungry wild dog may run one hundred miles to get a single meal. In the face of such facts, the owner's walk around the block to exercise the Dalmatian becomes ludicrous. What the animal really enjoys is a ten- or twenty-mile hike once a week—an outing that would probably do the owner as much good as it does the dog.

Beyond the few simple obligations which a pet owner assumes, there are a few things he learns to avoid. He soon finds that it doesn't pay to let his pets roam any more than he can help. It costs less to feed a dog or a cat on neighbors' garbage—but not for long does it cost less. Sooner or later the animal gets some tainted swill, sickens, and perhaps dies. Animals that are turned loose are in constant danger of being injured in accidents or hurt in fights. They may even join others and ravage the neighborhood. A pair of German shepherds in our community killed nineteen little pigs on one farm, seven sheep on another, three calves on another, and fifty-four rabbits on still another—all in one night. One of the dogs was shot and the other poisoned by the irate farmer who had lost the calves. Thousands of sheep are killed every year by dogs, and the dogs are, in turn, destroyed by the authorities. In places where the snow gets deep, dozens of roaming dogs are shot by wardens to prevent their killing deer which can't escape from them.

A final word on the danger of letting a dog run loose. Sooner or later he will be picked up by the dog warden and put in a truck with other strays. He will be lodged in the dog pound, and if there is any disease among the other dogs with which he is housed, he is sure to be exposed to it. It is true that he can be recovered from the warden, but he may well die or go through a long, expensive illness because of an infection he contracted in the pound.

HOW TO CHOOSE A VETERINARIAN

The failure to understand the simple processes of life, such as healing, bone knitting, and body functions, is to blame, I think, for those myriads of people who—possibly because of the habit acquired in taking their cars to a mechanic and ordering a new transmission or universal joint—take a dog to the veterinarian and say, "Kidneys out of order, Doc, fix her up." Or, "He's got kind of wobbly in the back end, sort of paralyzed. He's the only dog we have. We don't want anything to happen to him. Fix him up. When'll we call for him?"

A body just isn't like an automobile. You don't replace parts by taking something out and putting something else back. You remove causes and supply adequate nutrition; you may remove growths, but you must wait for the body itself to do the regenerating. Though it may disturb you to think of it, physiologically a dog is no different from Grandpa. You don't take *him* to the hospital and leave him with the admonition, "Fix him up, Doc.

He's the only grandpa we have and we don't want anything to happen to him."

People are inclined to expect either too little or too much of their veterinarian. Perhaps they have been misled in part by seeing too many movies in which the "vet" is depicted as a dirty, mussed, careless drunk, with a large cigar in his mouth, spilling ashes over his patient. This old gent is perfectly content to sleep in the bedding beside a sick horse, and his boon companion is always Dickie, the stableboy.

Most people today know, I think, that veterinarians neither look nor act like this caricature. They are men who have spent a good many years of their lives in rigorous study in order to be able to help you and your pet. Their skills and their abilities are of the utmost importance to the welfare of your pet and to your own comfort and enjoyment. It is well worth spending some little time and thought in selecting the one who can best help you with your problems.

What is the most important factor in your choice of a veterinarian? What makes you select one man, and only one, to take care of the health of your pet? It is *confidence.*

Before you place your confidence in a veterinarian the main thing you want to decide is: How much does he know? In addition it is often wise to inquire into how he got that information, because what a person appears to know is not always the truth. When the veterinarian talks about a "slight cold in the kidneys" or a "cold in the intestine," when he advises cutting out chunks of a dog's skin in order to eradicate red mange or the surgical removal of the cecum to eradicate whipworms, an occasional client may be deeply impressed. Conscientious and up-to-date veterinarians are ashamed that members of their profession can be so ill-informed or unscrupulous.

When a client visits two veterinarians and is given two diametrically opposite diets for his pet, how is the client to know which man to trust? In the first place, he should try to decide which of the two is a conscientious student. That man is the one to trust. Why? Because much education is thirty years behind the times. What veterinarians were taught in college is sometimes almost the sum total of what they know about veterinary medicine today *unless they have studied diligently since they left school.* What a man knows about the discoveries which have been made in recent years is the difference between a horse doctor of thirty years ago and a competent, modern veterinarian. Assuming that you know two men of equal educational background, one of whom has studied diligently since he finished his course while the other has not, you will have no difficulty in knowing where you can safely place your confidence. After you have read this book you will be able to tell without question whether or not your veterinarian talks in contemporary veterinary medical terms.

There are certain indications which you will look for immediately in choosing a veterinarian. You cannot fail to notice the cleanliness and efficiency of his office or of his hospital. You will probably see on his walls his credentials, which must include study at an accredited college of veterinary medicine and a state license to practice.

But the pet owner is looking for something more. He wants to know that his doctor lives up to the ethics of his profession. He will consult the man who is guided by the code of ethics of the American Veterinary Medical Association. Here are my ideas of what that kind of veterinarian should be.

He should be completely honest. There are many opportunities to dodge around the truth. The ethical veterinarian will avoid them conscientiously. He will not give unnecessary injections at exorbitant prices, using five cents' worth of vitamin concentrates. He will not exaggerate the seriousness of an illness. He will try to effect a cure in a single visit. Not only does he do what he can for the patient in his office, but he respects the owner by instructing him in the care of the patient. If repeated visits to the office will give you added confidence, that is a matter for you to decide. The wise veterinarian, however, knows that the pet which costs the owner too much is a burden rather than a pleasure.

The ethical veterinarian charges moderate fees. There are, unfortunately, a few who callously feel that "it's not unethical to charge all the traffic will bear." It is. To be ethical, the veterinarian should consider all the factors involved. If a bill must be too large for the value of the animal, or if it is beyond the owner's ability to pay without hardship, that person should be advised that the very purpose of owning a pet—namely, to have something to enjoy—is gone. Veterinarians who overcharge do infinite damage to their profession by reducing the number of pet owners.

The ethical veterinarian is democratic. He does not exclude from his attention the laborer in work clothes, or the man with a dark skin. Yet there are doctors who do exclude the poor, the laboring man, and the colored man. They should be reminded that when a pet needs care, *it* is the patient, not the owner.

The ethical man thinks first of the service he may render. He does not ask to be paid before treating his patient. Prepayment is not only unethical, it is unprofessional as well. Money is not and cannot be the veterinarian's first consideration.

The modern veterinarian shares his discoveries freely with the members of his profession. Through the presentation of studies at association meetings and in the proper veterinary journals, he makes his observations available to others so that they can be used to relieve suffering.

Finally, the ethical veterinarian does not advertise. Neon signs are frowned upon as are blatant window advertisements. Claims of unusual ability to effect cures by secret methods are not used. The veterinarian does not allow his picture to be displayed in undignified ways. He does not issue circulars advertising his low fees. However, if he operates a hospital on a standard fee basis, he may upon request give you a card stating those fees.

The man in whom you can place your confidence may not wear all these qualifications like shining armor. They represent an ideal, but more and more the conscientious veterinarian is approaching this ideal. The veterinary profession today is distinguished by many truly magnificent characters—men who have the most unselfish attitudes, who sacrifice themselves for their patients just as willingly and unstintingly as ever the family physician gave of his strength and knowledge. That should not be surprising to anyone. A veterinarian must of necessity love animals, and the man who truly loves animals must also love his fellow men.

2. The Dog's Body and How It Functions

SO MANY high-school and college graduates have managed to escape courses in even human physiology and anatomy that I have long ceased to be surprised that few dog owners have any conception at all of animal physiology. If you are to get the most out of this book, it will be necessary to review briefly both structure and function as they are related to our pets. Even though the study of the mechanism of the living body is to me one of the most fascinating in the world, the general attitude toward the subject is such that I feel I must warn you that you are not in for an "organ recital." All that will be necessary here is to learn enough about your dogs' bodies so that you may treat them sensibly.

The science which treats of the functions of living things or of their parts is called physiology. That which treats of the structure of the body and the relationships of its parts is called anatomy. Let us combine the two and see how the body is formed and how its parts function.

The body of every animal grew from a single cell. What is a cell? It is a unit of life smaller than our eyes can see. The whole body of some tiny animals is a single cell: the amoeba and paramecium, for example. Other animals consist of whole colonies of cells. All the visible animate creatures we see are immense colonies of cells, and each cell has some special function. Every one of these cells is composed of a covering within which is some protoplasm, a substance not unlike egg white, and a nucleus, which is its business part.

The first cell, which resulted from the uniting of a male cell (sperm) and a female cell (ovum), and thus started an animal, is complete in every detail. It is a favorite academic paradox to say that a cell multiplies by dividing, and quite true, of course. If one cell divides into two cells, it has divided, but because it is two, it has multiplied. The two become four; the four, eight. As they go on dividing and thus increasing, different cells become specialized at certain stages. Some may become skin, some liver, some heart, some germ plasm, some tonsils, and so forth. There are cells which never renew themselves; brain cells, for example. Then there are other very much specialized cells, like those in the hair and nails, which constantly renew themselves. They all live together in a happy community or colony, doing their work unless hindered by improper nourishment or crowding (from overfatness), or disease. That's what our dogs are—big colonies of cells.

THE BODY'S COVERING

The skin is composed of several layers, each made up of innumerable cells. Two main layers are recognized: the outer layer, *epidermis;* the lower layer or true skin, the *dermis.* Sometimes we hear the epidermis called the cuticle or the scarfskin and, colloquially, the scurfskin. The true

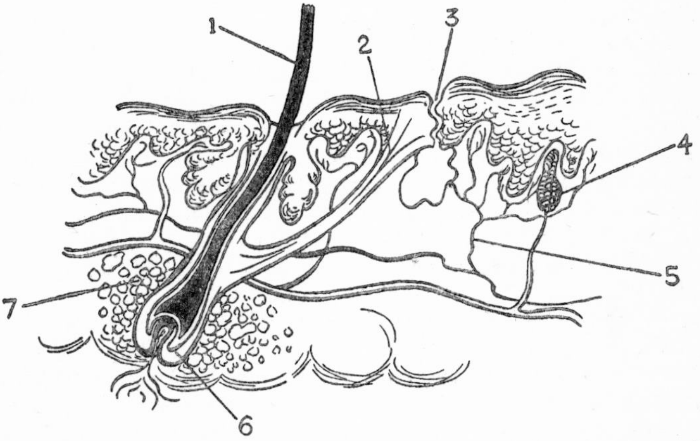

(1) Hair growing out of follicle. (2) Erector muscle. (3) Sweat duct. (4) Nerve end organ. (5) Blood vessels. (6) Bottom of hair follicle or papilla. (7) Subcutaneous fatty tissue.

skin, in turn, consists of two layers. The skin is constantly shedding and renewing itself, a fact that has an important bearing on the treatment of skin diseases.

Under the skin we find subcutaneous connective tissue, an interesting part of the body. It is made up of very elastic cells. Through it run nerves, lymph vessels, blood vessels, and fat is often deposited in it.

Out of the skin grow the appendages we call hairs in mammals, feathers in birds, scales in fish. Hair grows out of the skin from follicles. In the follicles (sacs or sheaths) are little muscles which, for example, cause a dog's hair to stand on end.

In some places on the bodies of dogs sweat glands are found, and everywhere in the skin there are sebaceous glands which usually discharge their waxy secretion into the follicles. As the hair grows, it comes out coated with this sebum, a substance with an acrid smell, which, in dogs, partly accounts for the doggy odor. This is the substance which gums dogs' collars brown, in time, with so heavy a coating that it can actually be scraped off with a knife. Other glands secrete oil, which helps the dog to shed water.

These protective coats, plus its natural resistance to water, make the skin waterproof. It is not, however, resistant to all oils, some of which can soak through it. In fact, the skin can absorb a good many drugs and substances which can be toxic (poisonous) to the dog.

In addition to its function as a protective covering, skin is also an organ of touch. Some parts are extremely sensitive. Through it, too, the dog responds to variations in heat and cold outside.

The skin heals by growing outward from the lower layers if it is not wholly destroyed by a gash, scald, or other injury. (Blisters usually are pockets of fluid between layers of skin.) When all the layers are destroyed, growth occurs from the sides. It is for this reason that your veterinarian, in case of injury to your pet, will want to bring the sides of the destroyed area as closely together as possible, so that the space to be covered over will be as narrow as he can make it. Moreover, if left open, the newly generated skin will be devoid of glands and hair. Great scalded areas become covered with skin, but not skin with the usual accessories.

THE BODY'S FRAMEWORK

The Skeleton. The skeleton is the framework of the body and protection for the organs. The ribs cover the lungs, heart, liver, stomach and kidneys, pancreas; the skull covers the brain and such delicate organs as the hearing mechanism and the organs of scent. These services which bones perform are not always fully appreciated, because we think of them primarily in their role of support.

Each species differs from the next in form; breeds within species differ from other breeds, and individuals vary in some respects. The skeleton on which the soft tissue of the body hangs is the basic cause of these form differences. In some animals, for example, the mere shortness of certain leg bones can cause a startling difference in appearance—witness the basset hound's difference from the foxhound, the two breeds being alike in all other major respects except leg length.

Some bones are solid, others hollow or filled with marrow in which red blood cells may be generated. Some are mere beads and others long and strong. The way they are joined is an interesting study in itself. There are ball-and-socket joint (hips), hinge joints (knees), others made by one bone abutting another with a cushion between (vertebrae), and modifications of all three kinds. Some animals are more agile than others; some have difficulty turning around in a short radius, while others, because of their skeletal construction, can "turn on a dime."

The skeleton is a marvelous framework,, replete with strength where strength is needed, rigidity where rigidity is needed, flexibility, swivels, and hinges where stretching, bending, and rotating are required.

Each long bone is made up of a shaft of hard, brittle material with a soft center of marrow and ends of spongy material with a covering of dense, hard bone. Around the whole is a sort of skin called *periosteum.* On top or on the bottom of the spongy end—if the bone terminates at a joint—is a springy, cartilaginous pad, called the *epiphyseal cartilage,* which takes the shocks. All through the bone small spaces form tunnels which carry blood and nerves; nourishment is also furnished by the periosteum.

Some bones are flat; ribs, head bones, and shoulder blades are examples. They are not so solid as they seem, but are well fortified with nourishment.

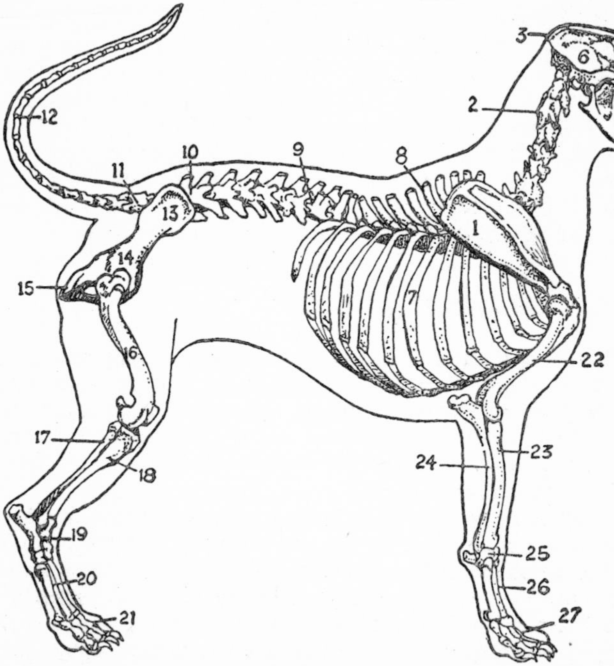

Skeleton of a dog. (1) Shoulder blade. (2) Neck vertebra. (3) Occiput. (4) Nasal bone. (5) Mandible. (6) Cranium. (7) Ribs. (8) Cervical vertebra. (9) Lumbar vertebra. (10) Lumbar vertebra. (11) Sacrum. (12) Tail vertebra. (13) Ilium. (14) Ischium. (15) Pubis. (16) Femur. (17) Fibula. (18) Tibia. (19) Tarsus. (20) Metatarsus. (21) Rear toes. (22) Humerus. (23) Radius. (24) Ulna. (25) Carpus. (26) Metacarpus. (27) Front toes.

The ribs join at the lower extremities with cartilages. These look like true ribs but are only extensions upward from a flat "bone"—the *sternum* or breastbone—to which all but one or two of the last ribs in some species are joined. The sternum is not actually a bone, but is composed of cartilage of a springy, tough nature, which is fortunate as the breastbone needs to be flexible, considering all the strains it undergoes.

At the points where ribs and these cartilaginous extensions of the breastbone meet, one sometimes finds enlargements which may stay throughout life. These enlargements are an indication of rickets, or, in

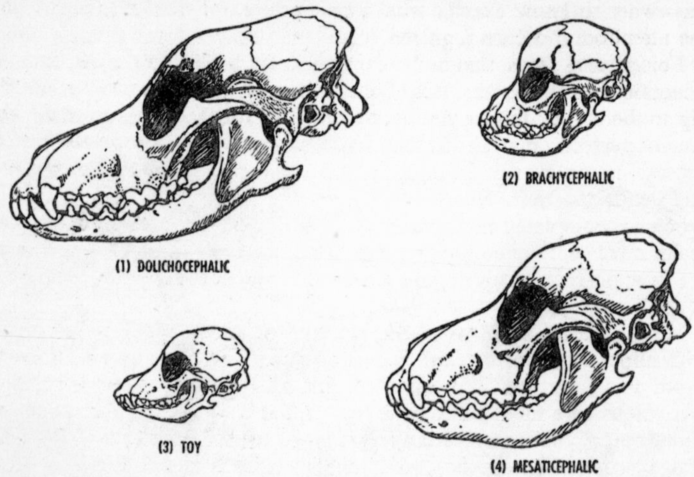

Skulls of dogs of different breeds. (1) Collie or Greyhound type skull. (2) Skull typical of Boston Terrier. (3) Skull of midget or toy types such as Pomeranian or Chihuahua. (4) Average-type skull characteristic of hounds, Dalmatian, et cetera.

other words, evidence that the dog was inadequately fed or was sick for a considerable part of his growing period. Coupled with these one generally finds abnormal enlargements on the lower end of the *radius,* a large bone of the forearm, where it joins the wrist joint. The spongy end may be so abnormal as to turn the leg, making it crooked (bandy leg), or weak, so that the leg from the wrist down bends out sideways. Some dogs are born with hereditary "bench" legs. Many basset hounds and dachshunds used to be raised intentionally with this deformity, but one seldom sees it any more.

The process of bone healing is most interesting, and it is worth while to understand it in case you have to manage a dog, one or more of whose bones are fractured.

Let us suppose that your dog, for example, suffers a break in the bones of the forearm. The break is a simple one, and when your dog returns home after his accident the broken leg is obviously shorter than the others. He holds it up, cries with pain. Your veterinarian waits until the dog has recovered from shock, then makes a splint from a round aluminum rod, well padded with cotton where it passes under the leg, or he may pin the bone or apply other devices, such as a cast. The dog is anesthetized and the splint or cast applied. Considerable traction—force in drawing—is required to pull the leg out so that the ends of the bone may be brought together; *in apposition,* your doctor calls it.

Now the ends of the bone must knit. Here is where it is worth while for the owner to know exactly what happens, so that he can give the pet all the attention and care required.

For several days the body decalcifies or withdraws lime and other minerals from the bone ends. Gradually they become soft, like cartilage. Up to the end of this period it doesn't make much difference if the bones are not perfectly matched at the break. The second step, after the softening process, is the growth from each end of connective fibers which join the bone ends together, whereupon it shrinks, pulling the ends closer. This process is completed in fourteen or fifteen days. Up to this time it doesn't make much difference how straight the bone is kept, so long as the ends are in apposition. At any time during this interval it is possible to bend it at the break.

Next comes a stage when the junction or callus becomes impregnated with mineral salts of calcium and phosphorus—in other words, it hardens. From this point on it is essential that the bone be kept straight, and meticulous care must be given to seeing that it is. If the splint slips or the tapes loosen, your veterinarian will want to see the dog at once. Remember that a crooked leg he has set is a poor advertisement for him—to say nothing of its effect on the dog's future, with which both you and the veterinarian are concerned. You owe both your pet and your doctor the co-operation of careful attention at this point. Once the callus is strong enough so that the bone will not bend, the splint or cast can be removed.

The last period involves the shrinking of the callus. Some bones will set with what appears to be a disfiguring bulge about the break, but in time this largely disappears, leaving a strong repaired bone even stronger than the adjacent unbroken parts.

Many injured bones can't be set properly. Some are so badly shattered that chips must be removed and nature be trusted to pull the pieces together. The *pelvis,* that girdle of bones forming a framework for the rear part of the abdomen, is often broken into many pieces which, without any attention, set by themselves without too much constriction of the passage.

There are breaks of such a nature that the bone breaks but stays in place; others where part of the bone breaks and part does not. These are called *greenstick fractures. Compound fractures* are those in which the broken bone protrudes through the skin.

Muscles. Skeletal muscles help hold the framework together and co-operate with it in locomotion. But there are two kinds of muscles, the skeletal being obvious. The others, not seen outside of the body, are called the *smooth muscles.* Under a microscope, fibers of a skeletal muscle appear to have bands or striations, which do not exist on the smooth muscles. The striated muscles are under voluntary control. The duties of the smooth muscles are generally restricted to the functioning of organs and digestive tract. The gullet, intestines, bladder, blood vessels, and sphincter muscles, which act more or less involuntarily, are all smooth.

THE CIRCULATORY SYSTEM

Heart and Vessels. The body is nourished by the blood. It delivers to the cells the substances they need, picks up the bad and useless, and

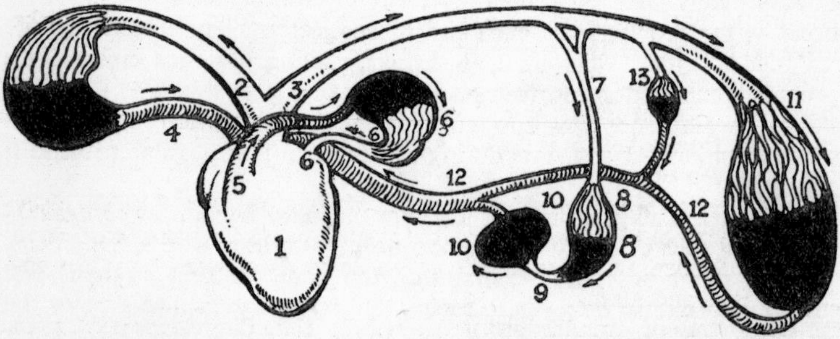

Heart and circulatory system. (1) Heart. (2) Anterior aorta, supplying front end of body. (3) Posterior aorta, supplying rear of body and organs. (4) Anterior vena cava, *returning blood from front of body. (5) Pulmonary artery, carrying blood to lungs. (6) Pulmonary vein, carrying blood from lungs. (7) Celiac and mesenteric arteries carrying blood to (8) , (9), and (10) stomach, spleen, intestines, liver, and other organs. (11) Blood supply to rear of body. (12) Posterior* vena cava *returning blood from rear of body. (13) Kidney circulation.*

delivers waste to the organs of excretion. At the center of this marvelous system is a pump, the heart, an organ situated in the chest, as we know, and which for efficiency is not excelled by any man-made device.

The heart receives blood into two sides, then squeezes or contracts, so that the blood is driven into two large tubes (vessels). One leads to the lungs; the other divides and carries blood fore and aft into smaller vessels which, in turn, carry it about the body. In the lungs the blood liberates a gas, carbon dioxide, takes up another gas, oxygen, and is hustled back to the heart to be pumped around the body to distribute the oxygen and pick up cell wastes.

The great arteries which carry the blood from the heart start dividing into smaller arteries, these into other smaller and smaller ones, called *arterioles,* and thence into capillaries. From the capillaries the blood returns to the heart via *venules,* veins, and finally large veins. It also returns in lymph tubes or vessels. (The lymph is blood without red cells.) So blood leaves by arteries and returns by veins and lymph vessels.

The pump keeps up its contracting squeezes and relaxations rhythmically for the life of the animal. It says *lubb, dubb, lubb, dubb,* and, in a forty-pound animal, pumps about a gallon of blood every minute. Everything about it is wonderful: the delicate *valves,* the strength, its four *chambers,* the skin around it, called the *pericardium,* the nervous mechanism which causes it to beat.

The Blood. The blood is an organ. Even though it is fluid, it is a colony of specialized cells in a specialized fluid which, as we have seen, discharges carbon dioxide and picks up oxygen and nourishment, which it transports.

The liquid part is called *plasma.* In the plasma float red cells, disks concave on two sides. These contain a chemical called hemoglobin, whose job it is to handle the oxygen, as mentioned above. When arterial blood gushes from a cut it is bright red, the hemoglobin being rich in oxygen; when it runs from a vein it is darker and almost bluish, because the hemoglobin has given up its oxygen.

Then there are white blood corpuscles of various sizes. Usually they appear spherical, but because of their softness and elasticity they can move through small openings, changing shape to do so. Moreover, they can engulf impurities and germs.

Platelets, oval or circular disks which help blood to coagulate or to clot, are another tiny component of blood.

Besides these visible entities there are chemicals, such as *fibrin.* Fibrin stays in solution until an injury allows blood to escape; then a ferment called *thrombin* causes the fibrin to clot.

Spleen and Lymph Nodes. All along the path of the blood and lymph are filter organs, chief of which is the spleen. This varies in size with the size of the animal. A dog's spleen weighs about one ounce for every twenty-five pounds of body weight. It is a flat, long, narrow organ, more purplish than red, which lies close to the stomach. The spleen's function is chiefly that of an organ of blood purification. Great numbers of bacteria are destroyed by it. When red blood cells become aged, the spleen breaks many of them down into liquid; but, in addition, red cells as well as white are made in its tissue. The blood spaces in the spleen are very large compared with ordinary capillaries; and when the organ is ruptured in an accident, hemorrhage into the abdomen may result in death, though not necessarily.

While the spleen is the principal filter organ of the blood, other smaller glands are situated along the lymph vessels and, by their construction, remove solid impurities, such as bacteria, from the blood fluids. Lymph does not move about by blood pressure, but rather by the body's movements. Muscle movement, breathing and the consequent expansion and contraction, intestinal movements and others, all force the lymph through the nodes and along its course. Valves in the vessels permit flow in but one direction, which is also true of veins.

THE RESPIRATORY SYSTEM

A pair of organs situated in the chest, one on each side, the lungs function in co-operation with the blood in the oxygen-carbon-dioxide transfer and, to a certain extent, in body temperature control as well.

In all mammals a partition—strong in some and almost gossamer in others—divides the chest cavity so that the lungs are separated. In the dog the membrane is extremely thin, and if the chest cavity is broken open on one side, so that air can enter, not only does the lung on that side collapse but the other as well. In humans, where the partition is stronger, if one lung collapses the other may not.

From the throat a tube made up of many rings of tough cartilage runs down into the chest and branches into two bronchial tubes, one for each lung. (Bronchitis is inflammation in these tubes.) They, in turn, branch and subdivide into bronchioles, and finally into air sacs, each of which is surrounded by a network of blood capillaries so thin that gases can be absorbed or escape through them.

THE EXCRETORY SYSTEM

The Kidneys. Blood disposes of certain chemical substances, other than gases, through the kidneys. All the blood travels through their intricate mechanism, disposing of waste. These wastes are principally urea, sugar, poisons, and substances such as carbonates, which can be got rid of in no other way.

Urea is the end product of the breakdown of the proteins in the body. The nitrogen, which is the principal constituent of protein, is also the principal component of urea. Everyone knows how urine gives off ammonia when hot. Ammonia also contains nitrogen.

In most animals the kidneys are located under the protection of the ribs and on either side of the body close to the backbone. They constitute one of the most delicate and ingenious filter plants possible to imagine. Everyone who has eaten kidneys or fed them to animals knows in general what they look like. But few have observed, microscopically, the minute inner workings, or even wondered at their marvelous construction. If one slices a kidney lengthwise, one sees a "*pelvis,*" so called, which constitutes a pocket for collecting urine, from whence it is conducted via a tube—the ureter—to the bladder. That is about all one does see of the mechanism with the naked eye. The microscope reveals the most interesting features: the blood vessels, which divide to become capillaries, in tiny containers called *glomeruli,* and minute collecting *tubules* into which the urine filters and is conveyed to the pelvis. There are beautiful and ingenious arrangements to effect the transfer and reabsorption into the blood of certain useful substances and rejection of the useless—all of which is accomplished while the blood is passing through the kidney, entering under high pressure and coming out under much lower pressure.

Diseases can easily upset the normal function of the kidneys so that they cannot retain the useful nitrogenous substances like albumin or may lack absorptive capacity, so that too much water is secreted from the blood, causing great thirst. Albumin found in urine and excessive thirst are both indications of kidney disease or dysfunction.

Kidneys that function properly regulate the amounts of blood ingredients in considerable degree. If too much sugar is present, some will be found in the urine. The same may be said of salt. Urine is composed mostly of water (95 per cent). Urea constitutes about 2.3 per cent, salt 1.1 per cent, and the balance, 1.6 per cent, is composed of other solids.

The bladder is a storage reservoir with elastic walls. It is amazing how it can stretch. I have removed as much as seventeen ounces of urine from the bladder of a thirteen-pound dog and had the dog recover.

Other Excretory Means. Other impurities and surpluses from the blood —some mineral salts, for instance—are also excreted into the intestines; some gases are excreted by the lungs, and still other substances by the skin in sweat. The excretory system actually is composed of four parts, and not of the kidneys alone, as the average layman thinks.

THE DIGESTIVE SYSTEM

As we have seen, one of the functions of the blood is to transport nourishment to the body's cells. The nutrients are made ready for the blood by the digestive system.

The Mouth and Teeth. Mouths of animals differ markedly among the several species, yet there is a general similarity. The lips are the portal to the mouth. They are also remarkably sensitive organs of touch for some animals. The horse is an excellent example of this point. If he can, with his coarse lips, feel among a lot of debris in a manger for a single oat grain, think what our pets can do with their more delicate lips! Monkeys use their lips with singular effectiveness. Watch one eat and you will see. Fishes rely on them. Dogs, cats, rabbits, guinea pigs, mice, and rats, on the other hand, seem to use their lips almost entirely for their primary purpose—to retain the food, as it is chewed, and the mouth juices or secretions.

In each of our pets the teeth are unique in some respect—number, arrangement, length—yet in major respects there is an unusual similarity. Whereas humans frequently need dental care for cavities in their teeth, dogs develop very few such painful defects. Nearly all their tooth troubles are either germ infections or are due to defective diet. Our pets almost never have their teeth cleaned, so this care does not account for their sound teeth. Nor can chewing hard foods be the reason, because many pets are fed on soft, mushy food all their lives, and their teeth, while becoming covered with tartar, do not decay; the difference is to be found in the structure.

The dog has two sets. The first, or milk teeth, fall out after their roots are partially resorbed by the body at about halfway through the growing period. The eruption of the new teeth takes place so rapidly that it often causes loss of weight in growing animals and fever may sometimes accompany the teething.

Anatomists and students of natural history have a method of representing the number and arrangement of teeth of a species which tells the story, graphically, at a glance. Examples of the dental formulas of all our common pets follow.

The front "biting-off" teeth are called the incisors. A dog and a cat have three on each side of the mid-line of the upper jaw and three on the lower. Observed from the front, there appear to be in the upper and lower jaws six nice even teeth in a row. So the formula for these incisors is $I\,\frac{3-3}{3-3}$. Behind the incisors on each side is a long, strong canine tooth in both upper and lower jaw: $C\,\frac{1-1}{1-1}$.

Next we find premolars: $P\,\frac{4-4}{4-4}$. Finally there are the molars: $M\,\frac{2-2}{3-3}$.

We write the whole formula:

$$I\,\frac{3-3}{3-3}\quad C\,\frac{1-1}{1-1}\quad P\,\frac{4-4}{4-4}\quad M\,\frac{2-2}{3-3} = 42.$$

In contrast, see how the formula differs in an unrelated species—the opossum: $I\,\frac{5-5}{4-4}\quad C\,\frac{1-1}{1-1}\quad P\,\frac{3-3}{3-3}\quad M\,\frac{4-4}{4-4} = 50.$

The following table shows the dental formulas for the common species of pets:

Dog	$I\,\frac{3-3}{3-3}$	$C\,\frac{1-1}{1-1}$	$P\,\frac{4-4}{4-4}$	$M\,\frac{2-2}{3-3}$	= 42
Cat	$I\,\frac{3-3}{3-3}$	$C\,\frac{1-1}{1-1}$	$P\,\frac{2-2}{2-2}$	$M\,\frac{1-1}{1-1}$	= 28

Mouse and Rat $I\ \frac{1-1}{1-1}\ M\ \frac{3-3}{3-3} = 16$

Rabbit $I\ \frac{2-2}{1-1}\ P\ \frac{3-3}{2-2}\ M\ \frac{3-3}{3-3} = 28$

Squirrel $I\ \frac{1-1}{1-1}\ P\ \frac{2-2}{1-1}\ \text{or}\ \frac{1-1}{1-1}\ M\ \frac{3-3}{3-3} = 20\ \text{or}\ 22$

Raccoon $I\ \frac{3-3}{3-3}\ C\ \frac{1-1}{1-1}\ P\ \frac{4-4}{4-4}\ M\ \frac{2-2}{2-2} = 40$

The part of the tooth above the gum is called the crown, and that part between the crown and root is called the neck. The part embedded in the socket is called the root. Some teeth have one straight root, some several. At least half the length of each canine tooth is embedded inside the gums; their roots are strong and exceedingly difficult to extract.

The tooth structure is interesting because of its toughness. When one sees a cat become angry and shear the end off a hardwood stick with its small, sharp teeth, as I have seen one do; or a dog crush a large, flinty hard bone; or a squirrel gnaw through a hickory nut; or a raccoon crack a nut that few of us would want to risk our molars on, our respect for animal teeth deepens.

Enamel adds to the hardness and strength and covers a softer substance called dentine. The root has no enamel covering. Inside each tooth we find the pulp, a structure with nerves and blood vessels. These structures seldom give way, but pets can and do have tooth and gum troubles even though they are only rarely of the cavity sort.

If a dog is sick with a fever disease during teething, the enamel fails to deposit on the teeth. By observing the pits or rings on the canine teeth, for instance, anyone can tell at what time the puppy was sick. The whole period of replacement is not more than forty-five days. In dogs the upper middle incisors erupt at close to fourteen weeks of age; the canines at about eighteen weeks. Thus, if we see a five-year-old dog with just the tips of his canines devoid of enamel and the lower part of the enamel missing on the incisors, we know he was sick at about four months of age. In short, the teeth may thus form a chart of puppy sickness.

It used to be said that pitted teeth in dogs were "distemper teeth." Today we know that is not necessarily so. Pitted teeth can be caused by any one of several diseases, some quite mild.

The teeth of no two species are exactly alike. It has been said that the natural diet of any species of animal can be told by examination of the teeth. This is probably true. With long, sharp tusks like those of cats or raccoons, it is logical to suppose that the animal's natural prey was some small animal easily killed and eaten. Dog's teeth are those of carnivores. The long, powerful tusks help a dog to pull skin off a carcass, to tear muscles loose or rip out the organs, while the arrangement of the back teeth as cutters or shears would seem to indicate that they were once meant to cut off pieces which the canine teeth had torn loose. The molars also have some flat surfaces which might lead us to believe that they were useful in crunching grains.

A dog bolts his food, usually without making any pretense of chewing. He will swallow anything small enough to go down his extraordinarily elastic gullet. I once threw a piece of tripe three feet long, eight inches wide, and over half an inch thick to a fifty-five-pound hound. A few minutes later I saw him swallowing it, with only a few inches still sticking out. I pulled it out to see how much chewing had been done on it and found that it was whole. He swallowed it again—all the way—and the next day his stool was normal. All that huge piece of tripe had been well digested.

It is because a dog does bolt everything we give him that he may not digest some foods very well. All other pets, except fishes, do a much better job of mastication. Fishes swallow other fishes whole. Birds, of course, have no teeth, so the problem of chewing doesn't arise.

Into the mouths of all animals is poured a fluid (saliva) from glands below or behind the mouth. Some animals have a starch-digesting substance in the saliva. Dogs and cats have very little. This explains in part why it is so important to cook such foods as potatoes before feeding them to these pets—to break up the starchy granules.

The roof of the mouth has a hard surface, the hard palate, going as far back as the last teeth and made up of ripples or bars extending across the mouth. Behind the teeth, the roof (soft palate) is flabby. By the time a pet's food is chewed and reaches the soft palate, it is practically in the throat.

The Tongue. The tongue is the principal organ for moving food into the mouth and for taste. Taste is experienced by the reaction to chemical stimuli of "buds," or sensitive areas, which stud this organ and produce the sensations of saltiness, sweetness, bitterness, and acidity. The taste buds are situated all over the tongue but are more abundant in the tip and at the back, in the throat proper.

The Throat. In the throat the delicate business of getting food properly started down the gullet instead of down the windpipe is accomplished by the pharynx and larynx (pronounced larinks, not larnicks). The gullet and windpipe are located one above the other, with the gullet above. An arrangement called the epiglottis, which is part of the larynx, kicks the food over the windpipe and down the gullet, then drops down to allow the passage of air. The gullet, when not stretched, has an inside diameter of perhaps half an inch in a forty-pound dog, so it will be appreciated how much it can stretch to take that piece of tripe I mentioned.

Peristalsis. In order to understand how food moves along through the body, one must realize that those smooth muscles we mentioned earlier are at work carrying out this function. The only so-called voluntary muscles concerned are in the lips, the throat, and the anus, and these are partly involuntary. Physiologists regard the inside of the alimentary tract as continuous with the skin on the outside of the body. Actually the lining is of the same origin as the skin. The tract constitutes a tube with valves and enlargements. The food is swallowed. At once a constriction in the gullet starts behind it and, as it progresses, forces the bolus (lump) of food into the stomach. The progress may be upward. A dog drinks with his head downward, and the water is moved upward for some distance before it goes downward into the stomach. The contraction which passes along the tube is called peristalsis.

In the stomach this wavelike movement continues. It mixes the stomach juices with the food. The exit valve of the stomach, the *pylorus,* opens and lets the food out into the intestine in sausagelike gobs into which constrictions have divided it. Soon other constrictions may start which cut the sausages in half, but all the while this marvelous process pushes the intestinal contents along through the whole length of the intestine as digestion continues.

The Stomach. Down the gullet goes the swallowed food and into the stomach, which has walls sufficiently elastic to accommodate the varying amounts of food swallowed. Here in the stomach some digestion of food takes place, for it is a reservoir into which glands pour an acid liquid that helps digest proteins and fats. Starch digestion stops when the food in the stomach becomes acid, but few animals rely on such digestion.

The Intestines. The *duodenum* is a thickened area of intestine between the stomach and *small intestine.* It is important because into it two *ducts* or tubes discharge their contents. One is *bile,* which is made in the liver and stored in the *gall bladder.* Bile splits fat up into tiny globules so small they are invisible and at the same time affords a laxative effect to the food. When an animal vomits a yellow substance, it is stomach secretion together with bile which has been pumped backward into the stomach by the regurgitation.

The second duct conducts from the *pancreas* more starch-digesting substance, which the pancreas, as one of its duties, manufactures. Starches are turned into dextrin, and then, as the food is pushed along, it is broken down into glucose by another substance excreted by the small intestine and thence absorbed through the intestine. Glucose is blood sugar. It is also the sugar of grapes and an article of commerce as corn syrup. And so in this way digestion transforms the carbohydrates in the food into a form in which they may be transported by the blood. Proteins and fats are also reduced to their component parts, amino acids and fatty acids—forms in which they, too, can pass through the intestinal walls and into the lymph and blood.

Absorption of materials from the intestine is increased by a unique arrangement. The inner surface feels—and indeed is—almost like velvet, being studded with microscopic, short, hairlike projections called *villi.*

Each one, while minute in itself, increases the surface of the intestine by a little, and in the aggregate these tiny projections increase the area of the intestines immensely.

This efficient "factory" of the digestive system is like an automobile assembly line running backward, with the cars being taken to pieces bit by bit, instead of being built up. As it passes through the digestive system

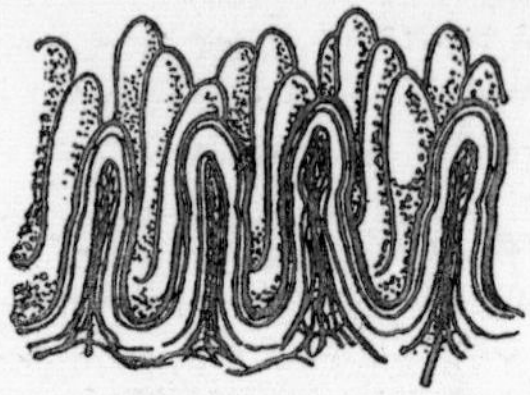

How the inside of an animal's intestine appears when magnified to show the villi. This arrangement enormously increases the absorbing surface of the intestine.

the whole mass of food which entered the mouth is reduced to its essential parts—fatty acids, glucose, and amino acids—and these disassembled products are absorbed into the blood.

The Liver. The liver is the largest organ of the body. It lies in front of the stomach and just behind the diaphragm, and is constantly massaged by the regular inhalations and exhalations caused by breathing. In color the healthy liver is a dark red with a glistening surface and several lobes, the number differing among the species.

All its activities are not concerned with digestion. Besides turning old red blood cells into bile pigment, it is a prime organ of regulation and manufacture. Bile, as we have said, comes from the liver. Urea is made in the liver by converting ammonia left over from protein metabolism (chemical changes). Bacteria are destroyed in the liver to some extent, too, as they are in the lymphatic system and spleen.

As a sugar regulator for the body, the liver is essential. Suppose glucose is absorbed from the intestine in greater quantities than the body can use. The liver then changes it into glycogen (actually animal starch) and stores it. When the blood sugar level gets too low, the liver obliges by releasing glucose from the conversion of the glycogen.

When the gall duct or gall bladder becomes plugged or the bile cannot escape, the pigment gets into the blood, producing a yellow color known as jaundice. Jaundice is not a disease but a condition.

Fats are absorbed and not acted upon by the liver. Fat is deposited in the tissues of the body to be used when called upon, or it may be used at once for energy if needed.

The Pancreas. We cannot leave the subject of digestion without mentioning an important function of the pancreas, besides that of furnishing enzymes (digestive ferments). That is the regulation of the power of the body to handle blood sugar. In this task it functions with the liver, which, as we have seen, stores up or liberates the sugar (glucose). In the pancreas are tiny islands that manufacture *insulin,* and it is insulin which in some way regulates the percentage of glucose in the blood. If there is too much, it sees that the liver stores it; if too little, the pancreas sees that glucose is called out. A lack of insulin causes *diabetes mellitus,* or sugar (or honey) diabetes. The excess sugar escapes into the urine and may be measured. The disease also causes an increase in thirst and amount of urine excreted.

Final Steps in Digestion. What is left of the food after it has traveled through the small intestine is deposited through a valve into the large intestine, where it may contain large amounts of water. Here water is absorbed, and here a huge growth of bacteria takes place. In some species it has been estimated that over half of the feces is living and dead bacteria. The more unassimilated food ends up in the colon, the more there is for bacteria to work on and the more products of bacteria there are to be absorbed by the body along with the surplus water. This is another good reason for not overfeeding and underexercising pets.

THE GLANDULAR SYSTEM AND REGULATION OF BODY FUNCTIONS

Ductless Glands. The blood acts also as a vehicle for transporting the products of the body regulators, only one of which has thus far been considered—the pancreas. The spleen and lymph glands are also ductless glands but, so far as we know, do not secrete regulators. A ductless gland is one which does not have an outlet except back into the blood.

Some glands, like the pancreas, are mixed ductless and ordinary glands. Salivary glands are good examples of ordinary glands because they have ducts which lead their products away from the glands, secreting saliva in the mouth. The important, strictly ductless glands are the pituitary, the adrenal, thyroid, and parathyroid. The important mixed ductless and ordinary glands are pancreas, ovaries, and testicles.

The Pituitary. Probably most important as a body regulator is the pituitary gland, located at the base of the brain, to which it is attached by a stalk. It has a front and a rear lobe. It seems incredible that such a tiny organ could be capable of performing such feats as it performs. Yet its direct and indirect chemical influence on other glands and organs persuades them to extraordinary accomplishments. Here are a few of its capacities; it can:

Cause an animal to come in heat.
Make an unmaternal animal become maternal.
Affect the shedding of the coat.

Cause a pregnant female to commence labor.
Stimulate growth and cause giantism, if overactive
Cause stunted growth if underactive.
Cause sexual development.
Help regulate metabolism of carbohydrates.
Cause overfatness if underactive.
Raise blood pressure.

Because it is so potent, the amount of chemical required for these tasks is very small.

The Adrenal Glands. These glands, situated near the kidneys, are also known as the suprarenal glands. They produce epinephrine—also called adrenalin—a potent chemical concerned with blood pressure by its effect on the heart and vessels right down to the capillaries. They also determine in some manner the amount of salt in the urine and affect the use of fat and sugar. Their outer layers secrete a substance now being used in the treatment of arthritis.

The Thyroid. This gland lies in the neck on either side of the windpipe, the two parts being connected by an "isthmus." It is attached to the larynx, so that with every swallowing movement the thyroid is moved too. An important chemical regulator, thyroxin, is secreted by it, and this is known to contain about 60 per cent iodine. Animals whose diets are low in iodine content become sick, and some young animals grow into cretins—peculiar abnormalities not often seen among pets. A cretin is a dwarf, stupid, slow, dull, gross in appearance.

Thyroxin regulates the speed of living in any animal. Slow, poky animals, overweight and phlegmatic, respond by quicker actions, more rapid pulse, restlessness and sleeplessness when given the drug. When the gland secretes too much of its regulating substance, the animal becomes nervous, develops a ravenous appetite, wastes away, exhibits protruding eyeballs and usually an increase in the size of the gland itself. Any such increase is called goiter in man or in animals.

Parathyroids. Located beside the two parts of the thyroid are two small glands whose concern is with the regulation of calcium metabolism. If they are removed, a condition known as tetany, involving violent trembling, is established and death ensues. It has been thought that they are also concerned with eclampsia, characterized by trembling and rigidity in nursing mothers. Injections of parathyroid extract increase the percentage of calcium in the blood, even when none is fed, by forcing the body processes to draw it from the bones.

The Ovaries. Located behind the kidneys in bitches and connected by strong tissue to the kidneys are small organs—the ovaries. They have several functions. Their first and most important task, of course, is that of perpetuating the animal, but that function we shall deal with later. Here we are interested in the secretions which regulate the animals behavior.

That the ovaries, even before reproductive functions begin, are concerned with body development no one can doubt. Even such a thing as mental interest is controlled by them. If the ovaries are removed before puberty (sexual maturity), the animal grows somewhat ungainly and tends to put on fat more than a twin whose ovaries have not been removed. This propensity continues through life. The pet tends to become an intersex. A female chick grows hackle feathers like a cock; a female puppy loses some of the charm and grace of the whole bitch; a female kitten tends to grow larger and lazier than her whole sisters.

Working in co-operation with the pituitary, the ovaries initiate the sex cycle, but there is some question as to which gland is of the greater importance. Once started, the actions of the female, as we know them during the sex cycle, are produced by an ovarian-secreted hormone in the blood known as the follicular hormone. It is also called estrone and is known by trade names, such as Theelin, Amniotin, and others. This hormone produces the swelling of the vulva, the bleeding well known in bitches, and, after several days, the desire for mating.

If we could observe an ovary through a window in the female animal's side, we would see some interesting changes take place. Let us consider the ovary of the bitch. At times it might appear about the shape of a yellow-eye bean. The visible surface would seem smooth and glistening. A week after commencement of bleeding from the vulva, we would see small bumps protruding from the ovary's surface. These would continue to grow. Eventually, at about the eleventh to the eighteenth day of the period (counting from the first faint showing of blood), they would look like peas in size and shape. The time of this ripening varies in different bitches. Perhaps we would see half a dozen of these pea-shaped bumps completely distorting the shape of the ovary. Each one of these is called a follicle, and it is they which secrete the follicular hormone (estrone). At first they were tiny, almost invisible bubbles growing within the ovary, secreting their hormone. It took them several days to become large enough to push up a bump on the ovary's surface. But when they reach their maximum size, their internal pressure causes the surface, which has grown thin, to rupture. All during the growing period an egg (ovum) has been contained in each follicle, so that the rupturing sets the egg free. In dogs the rupturing (ovulation) occurs spontaneously, but cats have to copulate (mate with a male) to ovulate. Usually, if the animal has been mated, there are male sperm waiting to fertilize the eggs.

As soon as the rupture (ovulation) occurs, a blood clot forms in the follicle and then the growth of yellowish cells begins. These grow until they have filled the follicles with a solid mass. We call them luteal bodies. This mass secretes a hormone. It puts a brake on the mating behavior, not suddenly, but in the space of a few days. The female is no longer receptive, nor does she attract the male. It is my theory that her attraction is lost because of a positive odor which the luteal bodies secrete. Males lose interest in her often after no more than a single sniff.

Whether or not the aging of the ovary is responsible to some extent for the aging of the animal was partially settled by the author in an ovarian transplanting experiment. Ovaries from aged bitches were transplanted in place of those of young bitches. These caused no premature aging in the recipients. Instead the ovaries themselves became rejuvenated and have functioned for six years as this is written.

The Testicles. Besides producing sperm, the testicles secrete the male hormone, testosterone, which functions in connection with the pituitary gland. Some grave errors were made in the use of testosterone in the mistaken notion that it stimulated the testicles to greater activity. Much was administered until it was learned that its use actually lessened testicle activity and caused the deterioration of the testicles. It was the pituitary gland whose secretions caused testicle activity and production of testosterone, which in turn affected the maleness of the animal. Some good stud animals have been temporarily sterilized by the indiscriminate use of testosterone, some possibly permanently. The natural secretion does affect the male animal profoundly, and without it he would be little good as a sire.

THE NERVOUS SYSTEM AND ORGANS OF PERCEPTION

The nerves are the telegraph wires of the body. Thousands of miles of these fibers control the body's activities. They stimulate the muscles to contract, and each of even the tiniest muscles has its nerve supply. The brain is the central station from which the nerves radiate through several pathways, the principal one being the spinal cord. Most of the conscious body movements are regulated by the brain and cord. These two wonderful organs are exceedingly well protected, entirely enclosed in bone—the skull and spine.

Nerves carry impulses to the brain from distant parts of the body. Organs of sense, such as the delicate nerves in the skin, may telegraph to the brain. For example, feeling is a function of these nerves of the skin—sensitivity to temperature, to electrical stimuli, to wetness or dryness, to sharpness, as in the case of a pin prick. Some disease—rabies, for example—may destroy the skin's sensitivity, so that a rabid animal may not even feel the bites of another animal.

Whereas telegraph wires carry messages both ways, nerves conduct impulses in only one direction, some *to* the brain and some *away from* it. Suppose a dog touches a hot electric-light bulb. His sense organs tell the brain with the speed of electricity, and instantly the muscles are given an impulse which pulls them away from the hot object.

We used to talk about the five senses, but today, besides the ordinary five, psychologists recognize many more: the kinesthetic sense, or muscle sense, the sense of balance, which can be demonstrated even while animals are embryos, the sex sense, to mention only a few.

The Brain and Cord. The nerves are unlike other cells in that they are long, thin fibers. Many fibers may be associated in bundles, and the largest bundle of all is the spinal cord, which gives out and takes in pairs of nerves between every vertebra of the backbone. The bundles of fibers branch here and there (the trunk divides into branches) until the final divisions are tiny individual fibers innervating some small area of the body.

Besides the cord there are other nerves which leave the brain, running to organs and other parts of the body. All of the body—organs, muscles, glands, intestine—is controlled by the cord and by these "cranial" nerves.

For every sensitive area in the body there is a corresponding center in the brain. Sometimes when a dog has a twitch in a leg it is difficult to realize that the origin of that twitch is a part of the brain or spinal cord. Nor, when we see a pet scratch, do we think that a nerve somewhere in the skin telegraphed the brain which set in motion the pet's hind leg. Have you ever scratched a dog on the back close to the tail and had the animal scratch his shoulder? This is due to the so-called reflex action. A human knee jerk is a reflex, and animals are not unlike us in having such areas. Everyone who has groomed a Scottish terrier knows that there is a large patch on each of his sides which, when combed or clipped, makes the dog scratch involuntarily.

When compared with our own, the brain itself is small in dogs, chiefly because the fore part, called the *cerebrum,* is so much smaller in lower animals. The positive, willing, conscious actions are evolved in this portion of the brain. Ordinary living is a concern of the lower part, called the *cerebellum.* There are other parts, most of which, like the two mentioned, are in pairs.

Animals can function mechanically without the cerebrum, but have no memory, can't learn or will to do anything. Their existence is almost like that of a vegetable. They can breathe, eat if their faces are held over the pan, defecate, urinate, sleep, wander aimlessly around, bite or growl when hurt. But by the way some of our pets are trained (or not trained) one might conclude that all they had were cerebellums.

The cerebrum is the part of the brain which responds most to training. Let no one think a pet can have its brain "cluttered up" by the training. Once a pet learns what is wanted of it and is properly rewarded, each succeeding act or trick taught it is easier to teach than the acts before. Those most highly educated of all dogs find learning easier and easier. Unfortunately our pets do not live long enough. Just as they become "almost human" mentally, they break down physically and die or must be destroyed.

The Eye. Many misconceptions exist about the eye. It is not so complicated as many think and is much tougher than most people believe it to be. From the front of an animal one sees a big, round, transparent part of a globe, the *cornea*. Surrounding it we see a ring of clear white glistening tissue, the *sclera*. In the lower part of the eye some animals have a third eyelid, the *nictitating membrane*. Inside of it, next to the nose, dogs have a small gland (*Harder's*) which often becomes inflamed and causes the membrane to tip over and exhibit a swollen, red, spongy-looking tumor, which usually has to be removed surgically.

In the middle of the eye we see the *pupil*. This really is only a name for an opening between the two chambers of the eye. The pupils get larger or smaller, depending on the amount of light the eye needs for vision, or on

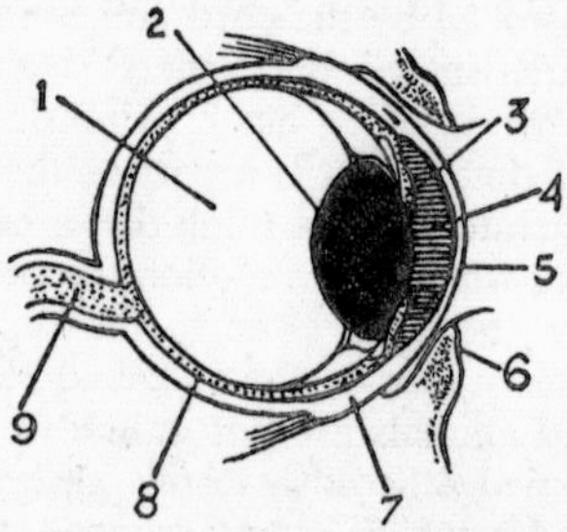

Cross section of the eye. (*1*) *Vitreous humor.* (*2*) *Lens.* (*3*) *Iris.* (*4*) *Aqueous humor.* (*5*) *Cornea.* (*6*) *Lids.* (*7*) *Sclera.* (*8*) *Retina.* (*9*) *Optic nerve.*

drug action, or on orain disease. An animal looking at a bright light shows a very small pupil. If his vision is unimpaired, the dog shows a round spot. When it gets dark, the pupil enlarges. The colored tissue we see around the pupil is called the *iris*. It ranges from pearl in some pets, yellow, green, blue in others, to blood color in albinos and dark brown in still others; dogs rarely may have each eye of a different color.

Behind the pupil lies the *lens*. It is tough, crystalline, and fibrous. Through it light rays are bent so that the image comes to rest on a sensitive area behind the lens, known as the *retina*.

People so often think that scratches on the cornea constitute a cataract that it should be stated a cataract is an *opacity in the lens*. When you look through the pupil and see a white spot it is a cataract. The spot should enlarge and contract because the iris will react to light, but the pupil appears white no matter how dilated or contracted the iris is. Really all we see is the white lens, since, as we have said, the pupil is actually an opening in front of it.

Dogs, in particular, show their age best in the color one sees through the pupil. The fluid in front of the iris and pupil is a thin liquid called *aqueous* (watery) *humor;* the fluid behind is called the *vitreous humor.* It is much thicker and cloying. If one looks at the pupil one sees a dark, clear blue in a young dog. If one observes a very old dog, free of cataracts, the blue has become almost white. Dogs of intermediate ages show gradings of the whitish tinge. Five-year-old dogs show enough white so the blue is a lighter, cloudier shade. There is no better way of approximating roughly a mature dog's age than this. Teeth cannot be relied upon.

The *retina* is the part of the eye which receives the light impressions on nerves imbedded in it, which in turn transmit those impressions via the optic nerve to the brain. Most pet animals are color-blind (see colors as shades of gray), but fish are not; they see colors as we do.

The Ear. Though the eye is a marvelous organ, the ear excites even more wonder. Here is a truly marvelous device for catching sounds and carrying the impressions to the brain on nerves. The natural four-legged animal has the cupped erect ear to enable it to pick up distant or faint

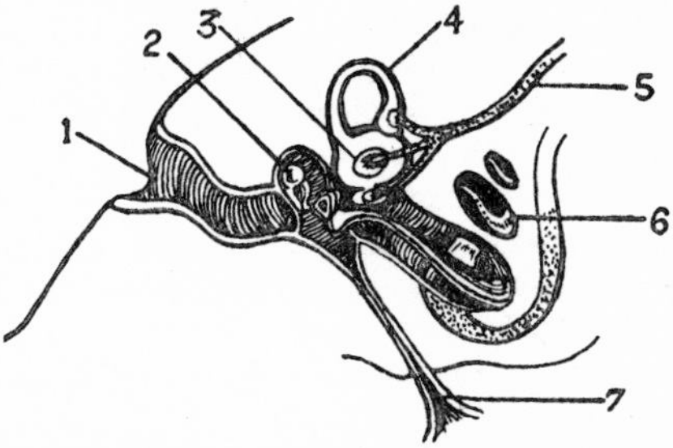

Cross section of the ear. (1) Auditory opening and canal. (2) Middle ear with mechanism for feeling vibrations. (3) Tympanum. (4) Semicircular canal. (5) Auditory nerve. (6) Cochlea (a spiral represented in sections). (7) Eustachian tube.

sounds. By turning the head, the sounds can be captured as by a trumpet or radar antenna. The sounds are conducted downward through the external canal. Surely, every dog owner has looked down into his pet's ear, probably cleaned it, and knows the projections to be found there. And that is all of the ear most people do know about. They often wonder if they might not pierce the drum when they are cleaning the canal. So long as they clean downward, they do no harm. The tube becomes smaller at the bottom, then turns upward slightly and terminates in a very delicate membrane, the *drum.* All the rest of the ear is within the solid bone of the skull.

Behind the drum are three tiny delicate bones. A delicate mechanism via the *semicircular canal* communicates the impressions of vibration registered by these bones to the nerves, which carry impressions or stimuli to the brain via the auditory nerve. From the small cavity in which they are found, the *middle ear*, a tube called the *Eustachian*, runs into the throat. By means of it, pressure on the drum is equalized. If we go up a high hill or mountain or under a river in a subway, we feel a sensation in our middle ear. If we swallow, the pressure is relieved or, in other words, equalized. If it were not for this provision, the delicate drum might be broken from the changes of atmospheric pressure.

Suppose some ear medicine is dropped into the ear canal of a dog. The canal is rubbed and squeezed by the fingers, to mix the wax with the medicine. While that is being done, the pet sticks out his tongue as if he has experienced an unpleasant taste. Perhaps we open his mouth and smell his breath. There is the odor of the medicine. This is a certain indication that the eardrum is broken. Some of the worst cases of ear disease, and hardest to cure are due to infections in the middle ear. When the drum is broken, special medicines are required to effect a cure.

The Nose. That part of the animal's face which we call the nose is only a small part of his smelling apparatus; all the important parts are out of sight. These consist of a complicated pair of cavities with a partition or *septum* between. The front part is called the *anterior nares;* the back part, the *posterior nares*. The bones of the face cover the anterior nares. This part of the cavity is called the *vestibule*.

In warm-blooded pets the inspired air passes through the vestibule and thence through a remarkable shelflike arrangement made up of *turbinate bones* covered with erectile tissue which can become engorged with blood. A mucous membrane overlies this tissue.

When the air is cold, the erectile tissue fills with extra blood which helps to warm the air before it passes to the lungs. The arrangement of bones and erectile tissue also filters the air at all times, removing dust and bacteria from it.

Before animals can smell odors, the odors, which are gases, must be dissolved in the watery secretion which is present in the olfactory organs. A chemical stimulus received by large numbers of nerve fibers terminating in olfactory hairs in the mucous membrane goes to the brain via the olfactory nerve. At the first stimulus or acknowledgment of the new odor, most animals begin to sniff, which, of course, brings more of the odor into contact with the mucous membrane where it dissolves. The stimulation is thereby increased.

It is difficult for us to realize how minute an amount of odor is required to effect this remarkable recognition by dogs. When we see a pointer dog smell a bird perhaps fifty yards away or a bloodhound follow a human foot track three days old, we know that the smelling ability of these animals is of a different order from ours. Not a little research has been done on scent and the conditions under which scenting is most efficiently done. Wind direction and velocity, moisture content of the air, and the strength of the stimulus are important. So is heredity; it is quite well established that certain breeds excel in scenting ability. How much of this ability is actual scenting keenness and how much stick-to-itiveness has not yet been determined.

THE REPRODUCTIVE SYSTEM

The sex organs exist as a means of producing the next generation. Eggs are produced by the female; sperm by the male. An *egg* and a *sperm* unite and the plans for a new individual are completed. The architectural scheme awaits unfolding. Mammals are arranged so the egg or eggs develop within the female. In reading scientific literature, you may see the words *ovum, ova,* or *spermatozoa.* The word *ovum* is the singular, and *ova* is plural; they mean, respectively, *egg* and *eggs*—not an egg with a hard shell, to be sure, but an egg nevertheless. *Sperm* is short for *spermatozoa.*

Female Organs. The female's ovaries contain her heritage—the germ plasm of which she is the custodian and which created her. At certain times, as we saw when we discussed glands of internal secretion, the ovaries produce eggs in blisterlike follicles. The eggs are conducted to a resting place, but before they arrive they are generally fertilized by the sperm—a tiny tadpolelike cell containing the male's heredity. Yes, all the heredity from the male is in a "package" so small we would have to multiply one a hundred times to be able to see even its crudest details.

The female mammal has a *uterus* in which the fertilized eggs rest. This organ is their home for nearly nine weeks. In the bitch it is shaped like a letter Y, but the stem is short and the two horns long and capable of growing much longer. In a sixty-pound bitch which has not yet matured the *horns* may be five inches long. While she is in heat they may be ten inches long; and at the time of delivery of her pups they may have increased to four feet each or even more. In a fifty-five-pound bitch which had eighteen puppies each pup was six inches long, making the horns of the uterus four and a half feet. How large must they have been in the St. Bernard which whelped twenty-two puppies each seven inches long?

The Y-shaped uterus of the bitch is referred to as being bifurcated in contrast to the pear-shaped type of the human. At the lower end of the uterus is a muscular ring which constitutes its mouth and is known as the *cervix.* And the cervix is at the upper end of the *vagina,* that part of the reproductive tract into which the penis of the male is inserted during copulation. Close to the opening of the vagina (the vulva) is the *clitoris,* a small glandular organ known to be the equivalent of the penis of the male. If a female puppy is regularly injected with enough of the male sex hormone, this clitoris will grow to be almost as large as the penis of a male of the same species. The function of the clitoris in mammals is not known. Being of erectile tissue, it becomes somewhat enlarged at times.

Probably it assists in making the sexual act pleasant for the animals and, if so, is helpful in stimulating procreation.

The *vulva,* which one sees below the anus, is the termination of the reproductive system of the female. Into it, urine is discharged, so that it serves two functions. During the mating cycle it enlarges considerably.

The *breasts* of the female mammal are glands of the skin. Richly supplied with blood, they make milk. Many people have an entirely erroneous idea about the process of milk production (*lactation*). The young take hold of the teats and suck. Milk may not come at first, or if it does, not more than a few drops at best. Then it begins to come so fast in some animals that it may actually run out of teats to which no young are attached. This is because the mother exerts a positive pressure which forces the milk out easily. Milk is made by glands, from blood *while* the young are nursing and not made up in advance and then drained out. The breasts could not possibly hold such amounts. If each of a litter of nine six-weeks-old setter puppies takes eighty to one hundred cubic centimeters each time they nurse, their mother's udder would have to hold nearly a

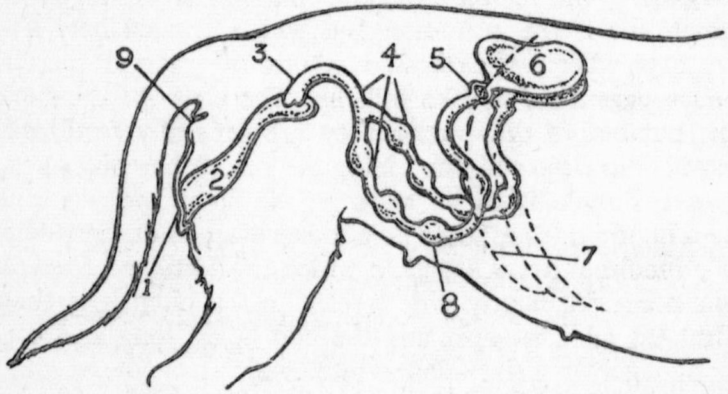

Reproductive system of a bitch. (1) Vulva. (2) Vagina. (3) Cervix. (4) Uterus. (5) Ovary. (6) Kidney. (7) Location of ribs. (8) Lump consisting of embryo and placenta. (9) Anus.

quart of milk. She would have to produce five quarts a day, and many bitches do. Proportionally, then, she can outproduce the world's champion Holstein cow, who would have to give three hundred quarts to equal her, and the best cow on record has given no more than eighty. When it comes to butter fat, the bitch's milk is nearly three times as rich, so she is an infinitely better producer.

Male Organs. The male organs are pairs of the following: the *testicle,* in which the sperm are produced, an *epididymis,* in which they are stored and which is connected directly on the outside of the testicle, a *vas deferens,* through which the sperm are transported to a common duct. Anyone with a knowledge of human organs may wonder why the seminal vesicle is not mentioned. Most male pet animals have none. The vas deferens from one testicle joins the one from the other side, and the *urethra* forms the passage by which the sperm are discharged during copulation. The penis runs out through the pelvis, under the anus, bends around between the hind legs, and emerges through its covering, the

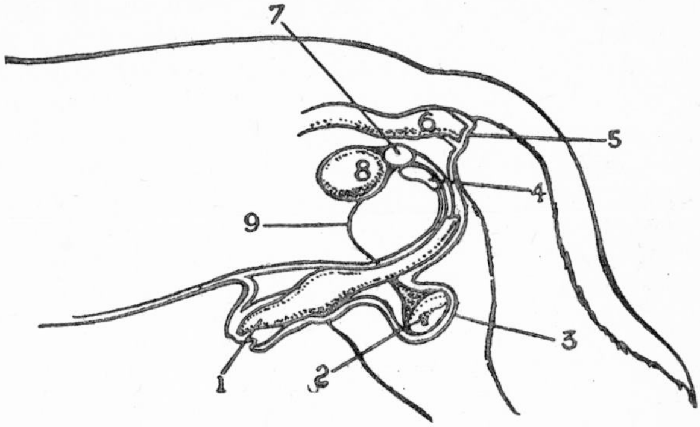

Reproductive system and neighboring organs of a dog. (1) Penis. (2) Testicle. (3) Scrotum. (4) Pelvis. (5) Anus. (6) Rectum. (7) Prostate. (8) Bladder. (9) Vas deferens.

sheath. In mammals, the testicles must be located outside of the body since body temperature is sufficient to prevent the production of sperm. A strong muscle draws the testicle up close to the body if the external temperature is too cold, and lets it down when the weather is hot. Notice in a dog how the testicles are low or high depending on the weather.

In puppies, the testicles are descended at birth, which is not the rule in some species—humans, for example—in which they descend considerably later through two slits in the abdominal muscles. Each testicle, besides having the vas deferens leading away, has a vein and artery and the muscle (*cremaster*), which together compose the spermatic cord, which enters the body through the same opening in the abdomen through which the testicles descend.

3. What You Should Know about Food and Feeding

ANIMALS are usually divided into three classes—flesh-eating (carnivorous), plant- and seed-eating (herbivorous), and those which eat both plant and animal matter (omnivorous). These classifications are made not only on the basis of the food which the animal eats, but also on such characteristics as teeth and digestive apparatus as well.

The distinction between these three general types of animals is not so sharp and clear as most people think. There can be no doubt, of course, about the group to which some animals belong. Having observed large numbers of rabbits and cavies without finding a single instance in which they ate food of animal origin—even crickets—the scientist can be certain that they are as herbivorous as the cow or deer. But the classification of most household pets is not so simple. The layman is likely to think of dogs, cats, rats, and raccoons, for example, as carnivorous animals. The zoologist, however, very properly considers them omnivores, because he has observed that they eat *all* of the animals they catch—including the partially digested vegetable matter in the intestines. Despite the fact that their teeth are typical of carnivorous animals, well adapted to tearing the flesh and puncturing the skull and vital organs of the smaller animals on which they prey, studies have shown that dogs and many dog-like animals are nearly as omnivorous as we are. With one notable exception, there is practically nothing that we eat which these animals cannot digest as well as humans. This one exception is, as we have seen in Chapter 2, that, since dogs bolt their food, they must have certain starchy foods crushed for them. When wild dogs consume the stomach and intestinal contents of their prey, they are getting the benefit of the chewing and mastication which has already been done.

Today we are beginning to doubt whether any of our pets, in fact, can live for very long on flesh alone without deficiency diseases developing sooner or later. It is fortunate that this is so—fortunate that our dogs can assimilate foods of vegetable origin. It may well become increasingly so in the years to come, when the earth has more people and less to feed them.

Nearly all the information we have about nutrition has been provided by the great laboratories of the world since 1900. And much of our knowledge of food values and human nutritional needs has come through feeding experiments with pets. Yet we have been extremely slow in applying this knowledge in the care of household animals. Recently, as I was reading through a volume on dogs published in 1872, I found that the directions given in the section on feeding are just about what the average dog owner thinks of as the proper way to feed his dog today! There is no excuse for not keeping up to date. We have put into daily practice innumerable scientific findings with regard to our own food requirements, but we still cling stubbornly to outdated ideas in feeding our dogs.

No one should assume, of course, that because we are interested in adopting scientific methods in the feeding of animals that we intend to depart from their natural habits and tendencies. We have previously stressed the point that if we want to keep pets healthy and happy, it is essential that we understand and consider their native inclinations. A dog is a dog, we said, not a human being. Nobody would want to take an old meat-covered bone, scratch a hole in the ground, bury the bone, and later dig it up and eat it. It might not hurt us to eat it; it seldom hurts a dog. But, being human, we have other preferences. To a dog, however, that old bone is a delicacy which he finds much more tasty than breast of chicken or devitalized dog biscuits. While it is true that we should interfere as little as possible with an animal's natural mode of life, it is also true that when we refuse to use what knowledge we have of their care we are being foolish and wasteful.

We know that modern dogs differ from their remote ancestors because human selection of certain odd characteristics has made them most unnatural in many respects. Their mildness and ease of domestication are the most interesting illustrations of that fact. No similar form of animal can be domesticated to such a degree of dependability as the dog. Many of what we consider the finest characteristics of dogs and many of those most useful to us are the very ones which would make them unable to survive if they were suddenly dropped back into a wild existence. Can you imagine a sweet, lovable, long-haired Japanese spaniel living and reproducing if it were raised by a she-wolf in the natural environment of a wolf?

Dogs have been evolved to be useful to man, and while they were being developed they lived closely enough to man to share his food. They became accustomed to it as time went on, and those which could not manage it died off, while those which could lived and reproduced. Partially as a result of that selection, we find that dogs, large and small, today thrive on a variety of diets that is almost unbelievable—such a wide variety of diets, indeed, that we may safely say they can digest anything a human can digest. So the problem boils down to how to feed our pets *best* and most *completely* with the foods we have available, rather than to consider what they *must* be fed.

Let us see first how our dogs' digestive apparatus differs from our own. Starting at the mouth, we find that the teeth are different. The teeth useful for ripping an animal apart and cutting the tissue off are longer and sharper than the equivalent teeth in our mouths. Our back teeth (molars) are flatter and more useful for grinding grain into powder. The dogs' habits of eating consist of tearing their food apart, cutting off pieces with the back teeth, and gulping them with only sufficient chewing to make them small enough to swallow.

The next difference is in the saliva. We have a starch-digesting enzyme —*ptyalin,* now called *salivary amylase*—which does something toward splitting the starch we eat into one step nearer sugar. The dog, it's true, has very little of that enzyme. It was this discovery that caused the early students of dogs to say that they couldn't digest starch. Probably such students never saw a human eat a huge mouthful of doughnut and wash it down with a gulp of coffee—and stopped to think that that too is digested.

Let's see how starch digestion works both for man and for our dogs. Our pets' stomachs secrete somewhat stronger juice than do ours. When dogs eat bones, they are acted upon by this juice which is rich in hydrochloric acid and pepsin, and actually dissolved in the stomach. A bone in a healthy dog's stomach becomes soft and pliable in less than an hour. Actually the same thing might happen in the human stomach, but it would take much longer.

Upon emerging from the stomach the food is mixed with the same kind of juices—pancreatic and bile—which affect our food. Here, then, is where most of the digestion of starch takes place. The boy who washes down the half-chewed doughnut and the dog who gulps his starchy meal both live and thrive because digestion takes place in the small intestine. But here is the important difference to remember: we usually chew our foods, so that we crack the starchy grains and nuts into a fine paste, but the dog doesn't. When the pancreatic enzyme (amylase) works on these starches, in our case, they are so fine that the enzyme has little trouble. In the dog, when the starchy foods are fed in too large lumps, the enzyme cannot do its work effectively. To some degree the same thing happens in the human digestive tract if a person fails to chew a nut or a kernel of sweet corn—neither is digested any more than it would be by a dog. Occasionally a dog will regurgitate any such indigestible material, but more often he will not.

In feeding dogs, it has been found that it indeed pays to feed either very finely ground raw starch or precooked starches. Corn meal fed raw is an inefficient food, but corn meal which has been boiled until the starch granules have been cracked open, so that they are vulnerable to the attack of the amylase, is an efficient, if incomplete food. Another point of difference between dog owners and their dogs is the length of the small intestine. Dogs' food travels through more quickly and there is less time for absorption—another reason for feeding easily digested foods. Cooking makes for this ease in digestion, especially with those foods which pets do not chew—raw cereals, vegetables, fruits. Meats are digested as easily raw.

FOOD AND SKIN DISEASE

It is often said that certain foods are too "heatening to the blood," that they cause skin disease. There is very little truth in that idea. We used to be (and still, alas, are) advised too often that we must never feed fat or starches in hot weather because they cause eczema. Remember that the fungus spores which are everywhere in nature float around in the air, are found in dust, in grass and hay, and that they grow best during warm, moist weather. It has been found that many of the skin diseases of dogs, except those of insect origin, are caused by these fungi. Many kinds have been isolated from dogs' skins. Let us suppose that an infection gets started on your dog's skin close to the tail. You had not noticed it during its incubation. Then suddenly your dog starts to chew at the infected area. He furnishes saliva to add moisture needed for rapid growth of the fungi. The infection seems to you almost to have boiled out of the skin. You might very logically conclude, as did early students, that it was moist eczema. Eczema means "boiling out." Something had to boil. Blood is liquid. Something must have made it boil. Food! That's what caused it. Some foods must be "heatening to the blood"—not an unreasonable conclusion for those who didn't know better.

In time students began to inquire and reason further. If we can cure this disease by external applications, while at the same time feeding the same food, the problem cannot be a dietary one. I was one of those who tried such treatment. I have never yet found a single food that causes this breaking out on dogs, although I have read studies which seem to show that dogs in rare cases are allergic to certain proteins. I believe that nearly all dog skin diseases are caused by external infections. I have cured thousands and have yet to find one that I couldn't cure by external applications of a skin remedy, of which several excellent ones are available to every pet owner.

So don't worry that what you feed, if it is a complete diet, is going to cause breaking out, itching, eczema, or mange.

Now, there are certain known requirements which must be fulfilled in the diet of every dog of every breed. These are the essentials without which our pets develop nutritional deficiencies. First of all, it is obvious that each must have *enough* food. This is another way of saying that there must be sufficient food to furnish energy for his day's living. We measure this energy in the food by burning it in calorimeters to see how many heat units it holds. The heat units are *calories*. It is now known how many calories any resting animal of a given size requires. He needs more, of course, as he exercises or works more. Living, exercise, or work all require energy, and this energy is extracted from the food. If he gets too few calories he will live on his fat; he'll get thin. If he gets too many, he may discard the surplus in the feces or he may use some to make fat to store for a time when his food will be scanty. In other words, he puts it away for a rainy day. Laymen often forget that the pet doesn't have to consume food to obtain nourishment when he is carrying it around in the form of fat. But more about this when we take up the very common problem of how to reduce a pet.

Besides having enough food, our pets need these essentials: water, minerals, amino acids, fatty acids, vitamins. Some species can live without consuming certain essentials which other species must have. (Cavies need vitamin C; dogs make their own.) Knowing what the requirements are makes feeding simpler and at the same time permits us to ensure that our dogs get enough of everything.

WATER

That water is essential to living is obvious. Everybody who observes at all has seen what its absence produces in the way of dehydration, knows the sensation of thirst, the dry mouth, the way some sick, dehydrated animals develop skin which stands in folds when it is squeezed together, the sunken eyes. And since blood, the very vehicle of transportation of nutrition to the cells, consists mostly of water, the need for water is patent. Besides its internal uses, its evaporation regulates temperature.

Water carries out waste products; it bathes the cells and totes off their excreta as it carries useful substances to them, to mention only a few of its uses. But supplying water is so easy that it is not a problem. A pan from which the pet can drink at will is all he asks. Then if there is enough water in his food so he needs no more, he is satisfied, and if his food is of such a type that he must have additional water, he drinks.

Seventy per cent of our pets' bodies is water. Here are the percentages for the separate parts:

Teeth	10%	Brain	79%
Cartilages	55%	Blood	88%
Bones	60%	Urine	93%
Skin	72%	Lymph	96%
Muscles	75%	Gastric Juice	97%
Ligaments	77%	Saliva	99%

Nearly all the water drunk is absorbed. Normally about 20 per cent passes out with the breath, and in hot weather more is thrown off in this manner. Almost all the rest is passed in the urine. Very little water is used in combination with other substances. It acts as a solvent or vehicle. As water it enters the body; as water it leaves.

In foods, water content varies greatly. The juiciest meat contains about 75 per cent water. So do many brands of canned animal food. Dehydrated meals and baked biscuits contain about 7 per cent water. If they are dried below that, they often absorb enough water from the air to build up to 7 per cent. It is important that these facts be known because, when they are, the dog owner understands that some feeding schedules require that more water be fed. High water consumption need not be indicative of kidney disease or diabetes, as some pet owners surmise; perhaps the diet is too dry

Probably every dog owner has at one time or another wondered whether it is harmful if animals eat snow. Not at all. Some dogs prefer it. In the Far North dogs eat snow as they would eat food. Even in areas where water and snow are simultaneously available, dogs often prefer snow.

MINERALS

Some uncombined chemical elements are called minerals. You learned about the elements in your high-school chemistry course. A chemical element is a substance, made up of atoms, which cannot be decomposed by chemical means. Some of these elements are minerals, some gases. Most of the dogs' nutrition is in combinations of elements, very complicated combinations, chemically.

Minerals compose about 6 per cent of the animal's body in the following proportions:

Calcium	40
Phosphorus	22
Potassium	5
Sulphur	4
Chlorine	3
Sodium	2
Magnesium	0.7

with many minerals in lesser amounts. Among these are: iron, manganese, copper, iodine, zinc, cobalt, fluorine, boron.

Table I—Minerals: Their Functions and Sources

	FUNCTIONS IN BODY	PRINCIPAL SOURCES
Calcium		
90% of body calcium is in the bones; 1% in circulation Stored in body	Bone building. Rickets preventive Blood component Reproduction Lactation Muscle function Nerve function Heart function Tooth component	Bones and bone meal Alfalfa-leaf meal Milk

	FUNCTIONS IN BODY	PRINCIPAL SOURCES
Phosphorus		
Bones, blood, muscles, and teeth	Bone building Tooth component Carbohydrate metabolism Fat metabolism Blood component Rickets preventive Liquid content of tissues	Cereals Meat Fish Bones Milk So abundant in pet diets it is of little concern to owners
Iron		
Composes only 4/1000ths of the body weight Needed in minute quantities Is stored in body	Component of red blood cells Transports oxygen in blood 65% is found in blood 30% is found in liver, bone marrow, and spleen 5% is found in muscle tissue	Egg yolk Liver Kidney Gizzard Heart Bone marrow
Potassium		
	Body-fluid regulator Helps regulate blood Muscular function	Blood Potatoes Vegetables
Sodium		
Found in body in combination with phosphorus, chlorine, and sulphur	Regulates body fluids Blood regulator Component of gastric juice Component of urine	Table salt Blood
Chlorine		
Found combined with sodium and hydrogen	Component of gastric juice Blood regulator Regulates body fluids Component of urine	Table salt Blood

	FUNCTIONS IN BODY	PRINCIPAL SOURCES
Iodine		
Most of iodine in body is found in thyroid gland	Thyroid health and normal growth Regulates metabolism Prevents goiter and cretinism In formation of thyroxine	Foods grown in iodine-rich soils Iodized salt Fish meal made from salt-water fish Shellfish
Magnesium		
Needed only in minute amounts	Muscle activity Bone building Normal growth Nerve function Blood function	Bones Vegetables Epsom salts
Copper		
Needed only in minute amounts	Forms hemoglobin with iron	Blood Copper sulfate
Sulphur		
Minute amounts required but needed regularly	Body regulation Combination in salts as sulfates	Meat Egg yolk Any food which, when decomposed, smells like bad eggs

You can refer to Table I for information on the functions of the minerals in the body, the daily requirements, and the best sources of them.

PROTEINS AND AMINO ACIDS

A second general group of essentials for every diet is proteins. These complex chemicals always have the element nitrogen as a component. Every protein is composed of amino acids, which contain the NH_2 group as chemistry students know it. Proteins differ in that they contain different amino acids.

There are twenty-two amino acids, each of which has been studied both for its composition and its essentiality. There are ten without which life cannot go on. They must be part of the diet of all pets so far as is known. These are: arginine, histidine, isoleucine, leucine, lysine, methionine, phenylalanine, threonine, tryptophane, valine. In Table II you will find some of the commoner proteins listed, but no breakdowns into amino acids.

Two of the amino acids, cystine and methionine, contain sulphur. The most satisfactory way to feed sulphur is not as the element, because as such it is not absorbed, but as one of these two amino acids, for with them ample sulphur is available. Wheat, meat, fish, milk, yeast, egg are excellent sources of both cystine and methionine.

We have made note of some interesting properties of protoplasm—the principal ingredient of protein. The same may be said of the amino acids which compose it. There is so much sulphur sold to pet owners—little sulphur dogs or bricks to go in drinking water, or sulphur tonics to be added to food—that it is necessary to say here that practically all of it is wasted. The way to feed sulphur—more than pets can use—is to feed foods containing amino acids which have sulphur in their composition. Chances are you are feeding them anyway.

The proteins found in various foods have unequal properties. Milk proteins possess all of the essential amino acids, and all are digestible. But corn, with its protein called zein, is not complete and is less valuable in feeding. Here, taking milk as a standard, are relative values of the proteins found in some common animal foods:

Beef	104	Yeast	71
Milk	100	Casein	70
Fish	95	Peas	56
Rice	88	Wheat flour	40
Potato	79	Corn meal	30

Most proteins contain more than one amino acid. Some have one complete and others incomplete. Proteins, with their different assortments of amino acids, can be mixed to produce complete rations of amino acids. Corn meal and horse meat, milk and cereals, alfalfa with wheat or oat flour—all are compatible mixtures. Even meat protein can be supplemented to advantage. It is the mixtures of proteins which produce the almost limitless variety in diets, varying flavors, aromas, and appearances.

Protein Requirements. If we could feed just the minimum of complete proteins, the average adult dog of any breed could probably get along on a diet which included 4 to 6 per cent of protein and the growing animal on 15 per cent. Nearly all pet foods and rations contain over 20 per cent of protein mixtures, some complete, some incomplete, some supplementing others so the results are excellent.

Protein is used primarily in building the body. Some is burned as energy, the nitrogen passing out in the urine, but protein foods, such as meat, are not primarily energy foods. Hunters mistakenly think they must feed their dogs great quantities of meat while the dogs are hunting, but, as we shall see, all species get their energy best from fats and carbohydrates.

Table II lists the most important proteins together with their most common sources and some of their properties. It will be useful to those interested in checking the protein content of diets.

Table II—Some Common Proteins and Sources

PROTEIN	RICH SOURCES	PROPERTIES
Albumin	Egg white Milk Meat Blood	Soluble in water Does not precipitate by dilute acids or salts Coagulates when boiled
Casein	Milk Cheese Cottage cheese	Does not coagulate when boiled Coagulated by renin Coagulated by pepsin Coagulated by acids
Fibrinogen	Blood	Soluble in weak salt solutions Coagulated by heat Forms scabs Elastic Dissolved by weak acids
Myesin	Muscle meat	Dissolved by weak acids Flexible only while alive Semifluid consistency Coagulated by heat Shrinks Easily digested
Syntonin	Muscles and organs End product of digestion of other proteins by gastric juice	Dissolved by weak acids Next step in digestion is to a peptone
Peptone	An end product of protein digestion by gastric juice	Leaves stomach and enters intestines after protein digestion Can diffuse through intestinal walls Has more hydrogen and oxygen than proteins
Gelatine	Well distributed throughout animal body	Becomes solid on boiling Three per cent or more in a batch of food will solidify it Trick ingredient often used in dog food to give appearance of solid goodness Precipitated by tannic acid and alcohol

PROTEIN	RICH SOURCES	PROPERTIES
Chondrin	Ligaments, cartilage	Similar to gelatine in properties Requires longer boiling of the tissues which contain it to bring it out
Keratin	Horns, hair, nails, hoofs	Tough fibrinous indigestible, useless in pet feeding but sometimes found in foods Manufactured in hair follicles, etc. Contains much sulphur
Vegetable Proteins	All vegetable matter Richest in seeds, especially legumes	Very similar to animal proteins In legumes one protein is found like albumin in milk Some are like fibrinogen, some like albumin with similar properties

CARBOHYDRATES

All carbohydrates are derived from plants. The chlorophyl of the plant leaf (much like the hemoglobin in the animal's body) is able to take six parts of carbin dioxide (CO_2) from the air, combine it with five parts of water (H_2O) and produce starch, $C_6H_{10}O_5$, and then have some oxygen left over which it passes out into the air. Aquatic plants do the same thing, but pass the surplus oxygen into the water where it may be used by fish. Starch granules are built up, layer on layer, the primary factor in nutrition. Plants add nitrogen to starch and make proteins.

The starch granule has two substances in its composition: cellulose and granulose. The cellulose is fiber and gives plants their rigidity. When boiled it becomes soft but does not dissolve. Granulose will dissolve in boiling water. We find the starch diffused all through plants, some in seeds, some in tubers or roots, et cetera. Some starchy food has large amounts of water (potatoes), some very small amounts (grains). When we buy starches we compare them on the basis of their dry components.

As a practical matter, it is important to remember this: raw starch is not soluble in cold water but it does dissolve in boiling water. However, about twenty times as much water must be added for the dissolving to take place. Mixed with an equal amount of water, it does not dissolve. Dissolving starch does not materially alter its composition, but when dissolved starch cools it becomes solid. This unimportant change explains why pet-food canners like to add to their products some starchy foods which are poured into the cans before processing and come out solid chunks. Many are excellent food but are not the solid goodness the buyer might think, since they contain 70 per cent or more of water.

In order to make starch digestible for some species—dogs and cats—it is necessary to crack the granules by cooking. It can then be handled quite easily. Rabbits, cavies, and others digest part of the cellulose by enzymes and liberate the soluble starch. Because lumps of potato were sometimes found in dogs' stools, it was once commonly believed that dogs couldn't digest starch. We now know, however, that when potato, carrot, or any other starch food is cooked and mashed, dogs can utilize it perfectly well.

Baking starch to 400°F. changes it to *dextrin* (not dextrose)—a gummy, sweetish substance, not unlike sugar, which dissolves easily. Biscuits taste good to animals because the heat has converted the starch to dextrin. They are sweeter but actually very little different from starch; they have one more molecule of water (H_2O), $C_6H_{12}O_6$ where starch is $C_6H_{10}O_5$.

Starch is found in the animal liver and muscles as *glycogen* or animal starch. It is soluble in hot or cold water. Animals quickly convert vegetable starch into animal starch, and they are able also to convert protein into glycogen.

Fasting uses up stored glycogen, eating replaces it, and quickly. Within a few hours after a meal of starch there are abundant stores to be found in the liver. As it is circulated for the nourishment of the body, glycogen is converted into blood sugar, *glucose*. And, as the blood leaves the liver, it may contain as much as 3 per cent. Sometimes animals are fed so much sugar they cannot store it. The excess is found in the urine; allowances for this must be made in tests for diabetes.

Besides the starches there are several carbohydrates common to most diets.

Milk sugar (lactose) is found in its only natural liquid form in milk. It is not, as a matter of fact, particularly sweet. Lactose is the food of acidophilus bacteria in the intestine. Many very difficult cases of intestinal trouble have been greatly helped by the simple expedient of adding milk to the diet or some food like bread, which has considerable milk in its composition. Lactose is easily dissolved by the acid digesitve juice. Its action on the bowel is laxative, which explains the effect of skim milk.

Cane sugar is good for animals but spoils their appetites as candy spoils those of children. It is, of course, usually fed in artificial forms. Honey is composed of cane and fruit sugar. The latter is the sweetest sugar known.

FATS

The fatty acids are carbohydrates in a sense—being composed of carbon, hydrogen, and oxygen, but they have much less oxygen and more carbon than starches.

Unlike protein, fats contain no nitrogen. Like protein, they too are combinations of components, known as fatty acids. Only three of these are essential so far as we now know—*linoleic, linolenic* and *arachnidic* acids, all believed to be concerned with our pets' health in several ways. All are so very common in nature they may be almost neglected in our thoughts of nutrition. Some other nonessential ones are *butyric acid, caproic acid, lauric, oleic, palmitic, stearic acids.*

Fats melt when heated, are smooth, lubricating when warm. Some fats like tallow are comparatively hard and crystalline; some, like vegetable oils, are extremely soft and fluid. All are made by the plant and the animal body.

When an animal consumes fat he stores it in his body largely in the same form in which he ate it. A dog eating lard mixed with his food in a sense first becomes part hog. Later his body slowly changes the lard to dog fat. Dogs fed mutton tallow, which melts at 40°C., become part sheep until they change the sheep fat into dog fat, which melts at 20°C. The same applies to vegetable fats. Dogs first starved and then fed corn fat become part corn for a while. All the fats in the body are fluid and pliable because they melt at body temperatures and harden after death when the fat chills.

Fats have a number of interesting properties which should be remembered by the dog owner:

Fats are able to emulsify; when acted on by bile salts, for instance, they can split into tiny invisible particles which stay in suspension in water or gastric juice.

Fat acts as a vehicle for carrying some of the vitamins—A, D, E, K. Because of this fact, mineral oil can absorb them from food in the intestines and prevent their absorption.

Fat slows digestion and renders it more complete. It spares vitamin B in the diet, is concerned with fertility.

A balanced diet should contain not less than 20 per cent fat. An animal living on prey often eats 30 per cent or more of fat. The amount of fat animals can utilize depends on the amount of exercise they are getting. Sled dogs can eat pemmican consisting of 70 per cent fat which would sicken a house dog. Bitches giving huge amounts of milk fat to their puppies need higher percentages in their food.

Cows' milk, with the water omitted, contains about 25 per cent fat, and milk is an excellent food for many pets—almost a criterion of what a food should be. But note that it contains a goodly amount of milk sugar. Feed milk sugar alone and the pet's stools become almost liquid. Feed fat alone and the same thing happens. Feed the two as whole milk and the stool is perfect.

Physiologists say: *fat burns in the flame of carbohydrates.* When you feed fat always see that there is sufficient carbohydrate present. On the other hand, if you fail to provide enough fat, the pet has to manufacture his own from proteins and carbohydrates in his diet—a less efficient and more costly process.

The economy of fat in pet food can be easily and conclusively demonstrated. One pound of rendered suet contains about four thousand calories; one pound of the best dehydrated foods contains about one thousand five hundred and fifty calories; and the fat costs less than the dog food. Fat in the diet contributes two and one quarter times as much energy as either proteins or carbohydrates.

For those who wish to compute the calories in any food formula, this is how it is done. Consider only the protein, carbohydrate (which may be expressed as nitrogen-free extract), and fat. Disregard the rest. Multiply the protein and carbohydrate by four, because a gram of protein, when burned, yields four calories. Multiply the fat by nine; a gram of fat burns to yield nine calories. This will give you the number of calories in one hundred grams of food. Since there are 454 grams in a pound, you can convert the answer to pounds by multiplying by 4.5.

How many calories in a one-pound can of a certain canned fish food? The guarantee says:

Protein	9%
Carbohydrate	11%
Fat	2%
Fiber	2%
Water	74%
Ash	1%

Protein	9 × 4	equals	36
Carbohydrate	11 × 4	"	44
Fat	2 × 9	"	18
			98 × 4.5 equals 441 calories in a pound.

How many calories in a pound of top round? It contains about 21 per cent protein, 10.5 per cent fat, and the rest is mostly water.

Protein	21 × 4	equals	84
Fat	10.5 × 9	"	94.4
			178.4 × 4.5 equals 802.8 calories in a pound.

How many calories in a pound of a certain dehydrated dog food? It has 25 per cent protein, 57 per cent carbohydrate, 4.5 per cent fat.

Protein	25 × 4	equals	100
Carbohydrate	57 × 4	"	228
Fat	4.5 × 9	"	40.5
			368.5 × 4.5 equals 1658.25 calories per pound.

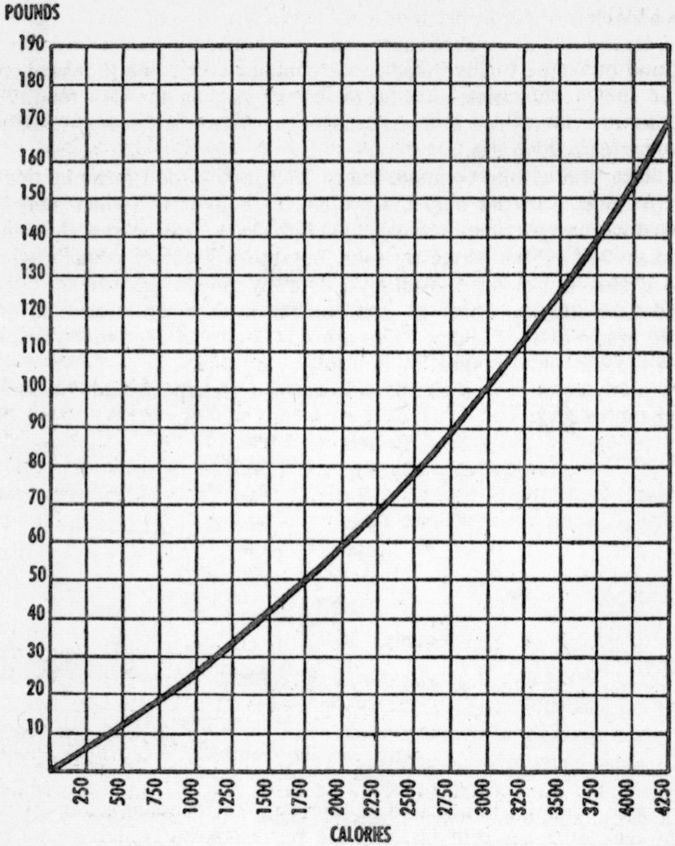

Approximate caloric requirements of dogs by weight. Find the weight of your dog on the left-hand side and follow the line toward the right to its point of intersection with the heavy black line. Then drop downward to the bottom line, where you will find the daily calorie requirement.

It is also necessary, however, to consider what part of the total caloric volume is actually usable, because sometimes the protein and carbohydrates may not be so completely available as those in other foods. Even so, a dehydrated ration which furnishes sixteen hundred calories certainly should recommend itself for our consideration, especially since some fat could readily be added to it.

LAXATION

Which brings us to the subject of residue. There often is considerable residue in the indigestible fiber and in part of the proteins and ash in many ingredients of pet foods. For a long while it was thought that the amount of this fiber was one of the criteria of how laxative a food would be. Tables containing this information were published. It is now known that it is more a matter of the character of the fiber than the amount. If alfalfa meal is powdered like flour and used in food, it is not laxative; if it is ground coarse, like fine bran, it is exceedingly laxative; but if the same amount is fed as whole leaves, then it again is constipating.

The question of residue in animal food is of considerable practical importance to the dog owner. Dogs eating mice pass much of the hair and stomach contents and skin, but are not constipated by it. Some pets—rabbits and cavies—eat only vegetable food, which if fed alone to dogs would physic them. The natural food habits of the canine species have to be considered. In general, however, it is quite well established that animals are kept in better health where the stool has considerable bulk. It is unwise, therefore, to try to figure diets with as little indigestible residue as possible. Some residue is definitely an advantage.

VITAMINS

Another class of essential elements in food is vitamins. It may sound like heresy, but there is good evidence that far too much stress has been placed on this subject. Too many people drew rash conclusions from the scanty information available to them. We are now finding that we will need a great many more facts before we can speak with the confident tone many adopted some years ago. New vitamins are in the process of being tested daily, and there will be many others. Our knowledge will be incomplete and inconclusive for some time yet. Table III gives a brief review of the vitamins about which we do know something.

The definition: A vitamin is one of a class of substances, existing in minute quantities in natural foods, and necessary to normal nutrition and growth, whose absence produces dietary diseases. Some are made synthetically.

Some vitamins are soluble in fat and are found only in foods containing appreciable amounts of fat. Some are water-soluble. Some are destroyed by heat, some by rancidity, some by age.

Vitamins are necessary only in minute quantities. With a few exceptions, all essential vitamins are present in the normal diet. When all our information is boiled down it seems certain that our dogs can get all the vitamins they need if their diet contains yeast, fresh alfalfa-leaf meal, and some form of vitamin D. This may be percomorph oil, in minute amounts, irradiated yeast, et cetera. It is as simple as that. Is it an exaggeration to say that the talk about vitamins, essential as they positively are, has been too free, and often misleading?

Many vitamins have individual but very similar functions. In maintaining health some are useful only in conjunction with others. It is often difficult to break down the better sources into their individual components. For our purposes it is quite unnecessary to discuss each of the vitamins individually in order to understand the effects of the groups in which they occur and in which we handle them. The B complex is an excellent illustration. It embodies many essentials. All may be found together and are used together medicinally. A veterinarian seldom gives thiamin, rather the whole complex, when he is using vitamin therapy.

Table III gives in outline form the major properties, functions, and sources of the principal vitamins and vitamin groups.

Table III—Vitamins: Their Properties, Functions, and Sources

VITAMINS	CONCERNED WITH	SOURCES
A (and carotene)		
Stable at boiling temperatures	General metabolism	Alfalfa-leaf meal
Spoils with age if exposed to air	Growth	Butter
Body stores it	Skin health	Carrots
Fat soluble	Muscle co-ordination	Egg yolks
	Fertility	Fish livers
	Calcium utilization	Glandular organs
	Digestion	Leaves of plants
	Hearing	Milk, whole
	Vision	Spinach
	Prevention of infection	Many dark green vegetables
	Nerve health	
	Prevention of one type of bladder-stone formation	
	Pituitary-gland function	
	Prevention of one form of diarrhea	
B Complex		
Biotin	Growth promotion	Yeast
Pantothenic acid	Nerve health	Cereals
Riboflavin, thiamin	Heart health	Milk
Folic acid	Liver function	Eggs
Niacin	Appetite	Liver
Pyridoxin	Gastro-intestinal function	Alfalfa-leaf meal
Animal protein factor	Intestinal absorption	Rapidly growing plants
Water soluble	Lactation	Bacterial growth
Body storage—small	Fertility	Cattle paunch and intestinal contents
Some destroyed by	Muscle function	

VITAMINS	CONCERNED WITH	SOURCES
high cooking temperatures, but not riboflavin Biotin effects robbed by raw egg white	Prevention of anemia Prevention of black tongue Prevention of Vincent's disease Kidney and bladder function Blood health Prevention of one type of paralysis	
C		
Ascorbic acid Water soluble Unstable at cooking temperatures	Prevention of scurvy in some pets *Not necessary in dogs*	Fruit juices and vegetables Alfalfa-leaf meal
D		
Irradiated ergosterol Well stored by body Stands considerable heat Resists decomposition Fat soluble	Regulation of calcium and phosphorus in blood Calcium and phosphorus metabolism Prevention of rickets Normal skeletal development Muscular co-ordination Lactation	Fish livers and oils extracted Some animal fats
E		
Tocopherol Fat soluble Body stores it Perishes when exposed to air Stands ordinary cooking temperatures	Muscular co-ordination Fertility in some species Muscular development in puppies Sound hearts Survival of young animals Growth Pituitary gland health	Seed germs
K		
Fat soluble	Blood-clotting Young puppy health	Alfalfa-leaf meal
Unsaturated Fatty Acids (sometimes called vitamin F)		
Linoleic acid Linolenic acid Arachnidic acid	Coat and skin health Young puppy health	Wheat-germ oil Linseed oil Rapeseed oil Many seed oils

Scientists have made careful studies of what they often call "nutritional wisdom" in animals. In doing so they expose animals of one species or another—children, rabbits, dogs, cattle, poultry—to separate dishes of all kinds of foods. Each day they measure what is left and keep track of what the appetite dictates the animal needs. In making these studies the scientist tries to rule out "conditioning." He knows that once an animal is conditioned or habituated to eat only certain foods he is almost useless for experimental study of nutritional wisdom.

If dog owners had only a little realization of the effect of food habits on animals, those who judge the value of a food by how greedily a dog eats it would revise their opinions completely. Students have consistently found that the taste test is nothing but a test of previous conditioning. It is difficult to understand why dog owners should sometimes be so reluctant to accept this fact. Anyone working with humans knows that undesirable habits in food selection are amazingly difficult to eradicate. A man is asked, "Why don't you eat cabbage? It's good for you." "Because if I ate it I might like it, and I hate the stuff," is his reply.

How many people prefer bread made of patent flour to whole-wheat bread! And yet it is distinctly inferior. Most of the better proteins, iron, manganese, magnesium, copper, calcium, thiamin, riboflavin, are removed. But white flour keeps better, so flour and bread manufacturers have conditioned the public to like it better. Fish is as valuable a food as meat and costs much less, yet many people refuse to eat it—and some have even trained their omnivorous pets to reject it.

A remarkable number of people have projected their own peculiar food habits to their dogs. Animals can't reason, even as poorly as the man who wouldn't eat cabbage, but it is extremely easy to build up likes and dislikes by habit formations which are difficult to break. I have seen many dogs, raised on complete dehydrated dog foods, which had to be starved several days to make them eat meat, and vice versa.

The point is—every pet should be trained to "eat what we set before it," so long as we know our provisions are wholesome and nutritious. All experience indicates that, given a very large assortment of foods, any unconditioned puppy will settle down to a certain diet of foods he likes, mostly what is good for him. Among these might be the smelly contents of a steer's intestines, or overripe meat. But since most of us can't offer such tidbits, or live in the same house with a dog which has eaten them, it behooves us to remember how important training is in the cultivation of appetite. A puppy reared on a diet of just one dehydrated-meal dog food mixed with water, and given nothing else, gets a treat in every meal. He's hungry for that diet when mealtime comes around. After he has become accustomed to it for a year, try offering him a porterhouse steak. He probably will have forgotten it is meant to be eaten.

HOW MUCH TO FEED

There are some general principles of feeding which are important to the health of every dog regardless of breed. Next to our consideration of what to do when the end comes, this is the most ticklish subject we have to tackle.

Nobody should have any difficulty understanding the fundamental rule: *In feeding mature pets, the less they eat,* compatible with keeping them in sound condition, *the healthier they'll be and the longer they'll live.* It goes without saying, of course, that they should have a complete and balanced diet. They should not be allowed to get too fat or too thin. If you try to keep them too thin, they may get too little of some essential ingredient; if you permit them to get too fat, you will shorten their lives.

In growing pets, the faster they grow the cheaper it is to raise them. Yes, *but*—will they live longer, be healthier? Probably the best rule for sound health and longevity is to grow them moderately fast, but not to force them.

Nearly everyone overfeeds. And almost every animal will eat 20 per cent more than it needs. There are some animals, like some people, which never get fat even though they are chronically overfed. The way to feed —the way people who are good feeders feed their pets—is to find just the amount which will maintain your pet's weight and feed no more. No rule in feeding is as important as this one. Your dog is happier if not burdened with unnecessary fat.

If only Mrs. Jones and all others who allow pets to become obese knew a few truths about food storage in the body and something about fasting—which some people call starvation—how much better off their pets would be.

Starvation is the long-continued deprivation of food.

Fasting is total or partial abstinence from food.

Starvation is forced; fasting is voluntary. A sick animal fasts; an obese animal must be starved but not necessarily deprived of all food. When an animal is too fat he won't really starve, even though he takes no food until his fat is consumed. We say "he lives on his fat." In the winter the raccoon fasts. Not that he reasons what he is doing. He lazily lives on his fat. He has stored sufficient vitamins and minerals along with the fat and moves about very little except during the warm spells of winter. No one need be sorry for raccoons. Why, then, pity our fat dogs when they have to forego the habit of overeating for a while?

Most of this feeling sorry for pets which are reducing stems from the idea that starvation is painful. But it is not, so long as there is a reservoir of food in the stored fat of the body. If a little protein and a little carbohydrate is fed—say a slice of bread a day—to help burn the fat, there is no danger of acidosis developing. If a vitamin-mineral supplement is added, there is no danger of starvation at all.

Anyone who thinks starvation is painful need only try it. I once lost forty-two pounds in less than two months and smaller amounts on many other occasions, and I have never felt a pang of anything but hunger. Hunger pangs are habit pangs—not pain at all.

Starvation is painless until it reaches the point of emaciation, so humans tell us. There are many instances of dogs living with only water for two months. One dog lived 117 days. So don't think your pet is going to die if he doesn't eat for a few days while you are accustoming him to what is good for him. His taste can become re-educated so he will like the diet you choose, and he will thrive on it if it is complete.

Clients whom I have advised to feed a certain diet ask if a dog doesn't need variety. How can a certain canned food or meal-type food which is fed day after day still be palatable? The reason is that our pets can smell each ingredient in a food. You and I smell hash. The dog smells separately each of the ingredients of which hash is composed. If you doubt this, watch a finicky pet trying to separate finely ground ingredients from each other in a mixture of foods. It isn't difficult to understand this ability if one thinks about it for a moment. My bloodhounds can smell a man's track a day after he has walked down a path, even when that track has been trampled all over by many other people. Why should we doubt that it is as simple a matter for any dog to smell the ingredients of a dog food and to enjoy its various components?

It is far more cruel to overfeed than to reduce. It is a discredit to the owner. It shortens the life of the animal to be obese, and makes him sluggish and no longer fun to have around. It often brings great misery and suffering to pet and owner alike, because of the paralysis which so frequently sets in as the pet grows older.

Loss of weight can be accomplished in two ways: by reducing the amount of food or by exercising the pet. With most pets a decrease in food consumption is the more practical and effective means. With dogs, however, the close personal feeling between the master and the dog sometimes makes it difficult for the owner to reduce feeding sufficiently to achieve the purpose. Admittedly this is a vexing problem which is too much for some weak-willed persons to surmount. With dogs, obesity is a serious matter, and if the owner cannot bring himself to limit the amount of food the animal gets, he should certainly be willing to exercise the pet enough to prevent its becoming dangerously fat.

Dogs can be exercised in many ways without great inconvenience to the owner. There is no problem with the hunting breeds. Their love of hunting makes it necessary only to turn them out and their energy expenditure "melts the fat away." With other dogs, going for increasingly longer walks does wonders. Swimming is fine exercise. Retrieving is best of all. Nearly any dog can be taught to retrieve. Have you ever thought how many miles a dog can be made to run while you stand in one spot and exercise only your arm and back? You take Darwin, your spaniel, to the park. There you throw a ball fifty yards. He races and retrieves it. That's one hundred yards. Repeat it seventeen times and Darwin has run a mile. A hundred times and he has run over five miles. Perhaps at first he will become tired, but gradually you'll have him retrieving by the hour.

Or, to exercise Darwin *and* yourself, teach him to retrieve a golf ball, Go to a golf links after the playing is over and pretend to throw a ball into the rough. Darwin will dash in, sniff around for the golf-ball odor, and bring one out. I know a man whose dog retrieved forty-two in one trip around a course. Such exercise puts and keeps a dog in tiptop condition.

4. Diseases and How Your Dog Catches Them

If your dog contracts pneumonia you will know that he is sick. But unless you know more than that, there is little that you can do for the animal. On the other hand, when you know something about the types of diseases and their causes and your pet becomes ill, you can handle the situation much more intelligently. You may be able to recognize the symptoms well enough to diagnose the condition and treat it yourself. If you do not recognize the symptoms, or if it is a serious disease which you cannot treat, you will realize the importance of having the pet properly cared for by a veterinarian. You will also be much better able to give the veterinarian the specific, accurate information he needs to treat the animal quickly and effectively.

A knowledge of the causes of the diseases to which our dogs are subject and of the ways they contract them is even more important from the standpoint of prevention. Many diseases can be avoided by observing a few simple precautions. Some of these maladies, once contracted, are difficult or impossible to cure. To the pet owner and to veterinary medicine, the prevention of disease in animals is as important as it is in the case of humans. A dog that is kept well is a good pet—a lively, active companion.

A simple understanding of the basic facts about disease is sufficient for the pet owner. He doesn't need to learn and remember a series of medical names or technical terms. He should know the broad general classifications into which all diseases are divided, he should be familiar with the common characteristics of each, and he should have a general knowledge of the way each affects animals. This is hardly too much to expect of any person who is really concerned with his dog's welfare.

To most pet owners all animal diseases are more or less alike—the result, they think, of some vague thing called "germs." Actually, of course, there are a number of distinct types of diseases, and they are classified according to their causes. Some are caused by bacteria, some by viruses, and others by fungi, or parasites, or growths, or deficiencies. To understand the diseases themselves it is necessary to know something about these causative agents.

BACTERIA

Bacteria are single-celled organisms; those which cause disease are called *pathogenic*. There are many forms causing disease, and all are, in some way, transmissible from one animal to another.

Since bacteria are too small to be seen without magnification, they must be studied through the microscope. There they appear as different from each other as the various farm animals. Some are spirals, some are little balls, some have whiplike attachments, and some look like baseball bats.

(1) Streptococci (grow in strings); (2) Staphylococci (grow in bunches); (3) Bacteria; (4) Bacteria.

Coccal bacteria are round. *Streptococci* (pronounced strep-toe-cox-eye) are round bacteria which grow in strings. They produce such diseases as pneumonia and pus infections. *Staphylococci* are round forms which grow in groups like bunches of grapes. They are notorious pus producers and abscess formers.

Bacilli are rod-shaped bacteria, many of which are mischief-makers, sometimes complicating other diseases. Rod-shaped forms, of which there are many, cause bubonic plague, tularemia, and some poultry

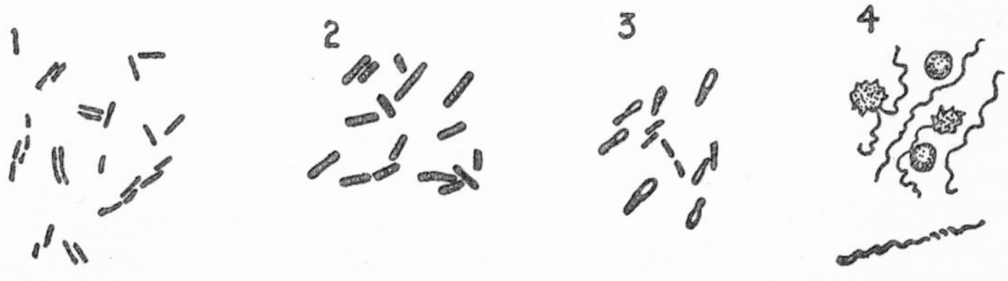

(1) Bacilli (rod-shaped); (2) Bacilli (rod-shaped); (3) Clostridia (form spores); (4) Spirochetes (among blood cells).

diseases. *Salmonella* organisms cause food poisoning in man and other diseases in animals. *Shigella* cause dysentery in puppies; *Clostridia* cause lockjaw, food poisoning (botulism), gas gangrene; *Mycobacteria* cause tuberculosis.

Spirochetes are corkscrew-shaped organisms which cause diseases such as trench mouth and leptospirosis.

Since these are all comparatively large forms, too large to enter the cells of the body, bacteria float or propel themselves about in body fluids or remain stationary. Some invade the blood; some are specific for certain tissue, such as pneumococcus types for lungs; others are found confined to the stomach and intestines.

RICKETTSIAE

Rickettsiae are different from bacteria. They are smaller—so small that they have been found inside of cells. They are responsible for such diseases as Rocky Mountain spotted fever, which is spread by the parasites of rodents, dogs, and humans.

FUNGI

A third class of infecting organisms most interesting to the veterinarian and to the pet owner is the fungus (plural, fungi or funguses). Fungi are plants of a low order; they produce spores which are like seeds.

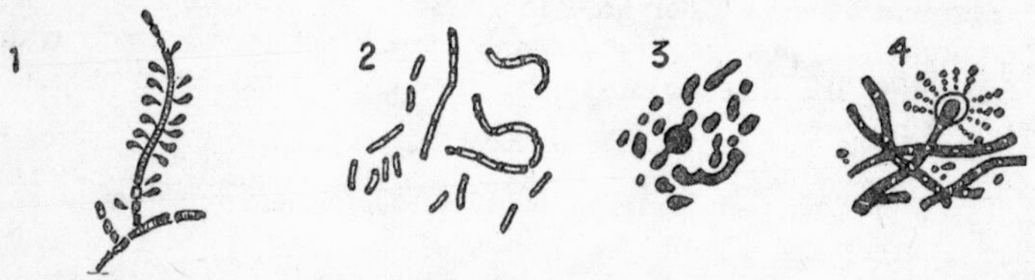

(1) Mold; (2) Rickettsia (greatly magnified); (3) Fungi (grow by budding); (4) Fungi (grow in threads).

Spores resist drought, heat, cold, and other environmental factors. When conditions of moisture and temperature are right, they grow into mature forms.

Many skin diseases in dogs are of fungus origin. Ringworm which grows in individual cells is a fungus. Molds are fungi. There are a great many kinds of fungi—good, bad, and neutral types. Penicillin, one of the most extraordinarily effective drugs ever discovered, is made from a mold.

VIRUSES

Viruses live *in* the cells. They are so small that they are invisible through an ordinary microscope. Photographs of them made through the electron microscope indicate that, like bacteria, they grow in various forms. Their exact nature is not understood, nor has a cure for the diseases they cause been discovered. If your veterinarian diagnoses your dog's disease as a virus disease, and tells you that he has no medicine which can cure it, believe him. Don't run to another doctor expecting him to cure it with drugs. If he does effect a cure with drugs, your pet did not have a virus disease. At least this is true on the basis of what we now know about viruses.

Viruses, even more than bacteria, have affinities for certain tissues in the body. Rabies, for instance, is neurotropic, which means that it attacks nerve tissue. Distemper has an affinity for the epithelial tissue (skin and mucous membranes). Some viruses attack the lining of the nose and throat, and others attack lung tissue.

One of the tragic facts about viruses is that they so weaken tissue that bacterial diseases can get a start and develop. Certain bacteria are such constant companions of viruses that we once believed that bacteria caused a number of virus diseases because bacteria were constantly present. This was true, for example, of distemper, which we thought was caused by a bacterium called *B. bronchisepticus.* In housedog disease, bacterial pneumonia is a frequent secondary complication. Of course veterinarians should and do try to cure any part of the disease they can. If penicillin or sulfa drugs will destroy bacteria which complicate virus diseases, they should be used, *but not to treat the virus,* because they are worthless against it.

DISEASE TRANSMISSION

Before animals can contract a disease, they must in some manner be exposed to the infecting organism. Exposure can come about in many ways.

Bacterial diseases may be contracted by an animal's eating infected food, by getting the bacteria into cuts or puncture wounds, or by inhaling them. If a dog is bitten by another dog, the wounds may fester by the multiplication of bacteria inserted by the tooth. Bacteria may be drawn into the system, or they may be present in air passages, waiting for a virus or general loss of resistance to weaken tissue and set up conditions favorable to their growth.

Some virus diseases can be passed from one animal to another by inhaling one brief sniff of a sick animal's breath, or even by inhaling air in a room in which a sick animal has sneezed and left minute droplets floating about carrying the virus. Other virus diseases can be transmitted by bites, as in rabies.

Fungus diseases are spread in several ways: by contact, by wind, by water. Suppose your collie develops a concentric bare spot on his nose. How did it get there? Well, he may have pushed his nose against a spot on your infected cat, or he may have rested in a couch where the cat had been lying previously, or a breeze may have blown spores on him. Somehow they settled on his nose and grew. Some of the worst skin diseases a dog gets can be contracted by his lying on a lawn, or rubbing against another dog, or from dust blown on him containing spores that find entrance to his skin in fleabites.

IMMUNITY

Some knowledge of the body's defense against diseases and of immunity is necessary in understanding methods of prevention and cure.

When a dog which has been bitten develops an abscess, his body builds a dam around the area and walls it off from the rest. The next time he is bitten other infections may develop from the same bacteria. But if, instead of developing a localized abscess, the bacteria invade the blood stream, a different condition develops. *If the dog survives by its own bodily mechanism or chemistry,* it will be immune to that species of bacteria for a long time afterward. But if the dog is treated with medicine such as sulfathiazole, which destroys every bacterium of that type in the body within a few days, then solid immunity may not be developed. Why?

Because the body builds up defenses to overcome bacteria or viruses in several ways: white cells may engulf them, or the body may develop antitoxins which counteract the toxins elaborated by the bacteria. All animal bodies have the power to develop specific counter-chemicals which will act to destroy invading bacteria. We call these defense chemicals antibodies. It is amazing how specific they can be. The antibodies against one disease organism are seldom of value against another. If a dog recovers from Carré distemper, for instance, he can still contract housedog disease. If he recovers from one species of coccidiosis, he can still contract another form. But if the dog is to develop immunity, he has to recover without medication. If the recovery from a bacterial disease is due to chemicals added to his blood, he does not always develop antibodies which will solidly protect him against that form of disease in the future.

There are different kinds of immunity. *Passive immunity* is conferred by additions of biologics to the blood which insure temporary protection. *Inherent or inherited immunity* is transmitted from parent to offspring. *Acquired immunity* is acquired after birth. *Active immunity* is produced by an animal's own tissues or fluids. It may be produced:

By having a disease and recovering.
By constant mild exposure to the disease-producing organism.
By injection of dead bacteria, or products of dead bacteria.

By injection of attenuated or dead viruses
(a) Attenuated by the addition of chemicals to live virus.
(b) Attenuated by passing the disease through another species.
By injection of toxins.

PARASITIC DISEASES

Parasitic diseases from which our pets suffer are real diseases, often tragic in their consequences. Have you ever thought of lice infestation as a disease, or hookworms, or mange? Fortunately these are the easiest diseases to manage, so long as we remember that the cure is only half of the job; the important part is to prevent reinfestation. For this reason every pet owner should know, in a general way, the life history of all of the common parasites.

External Parasites. THE FLEA: Those little elusive insects that jump so far and those big, brown, long-bodied insects that crawl about on our pets are fleas. The big ones are always females; the little jumpers may be either males or young females. Fleas are a serious threat to the health of

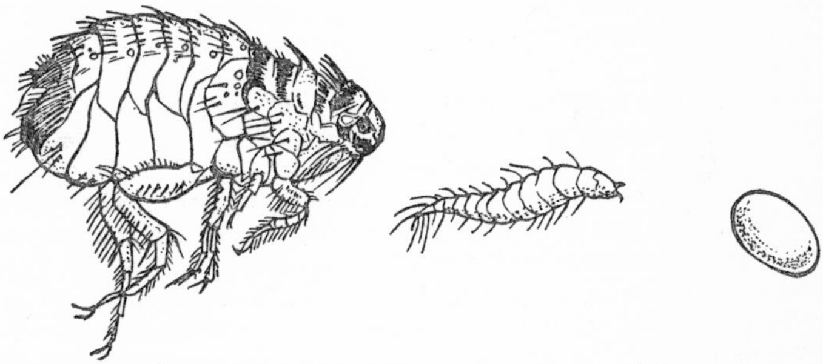

Stages of the flea, enlarged fifty times. Left, adult; center, newly hatched larva; right, egg.

animals. They carry and spread tapeworms, bubonic plague, and heartworm. They also help spread summer skin diseases, cause loss of weight and poor coats on their hosts.

There are four common types of fleas: the human flea, dog flea, cat flea, and the sticktight flea. The human flea may breed on dogs and cats as well as on humans. The dog flea and the cat flea infest either dogs or cats, but prefer their specific hosts. When they bite humans it is only because they lack a dog or cat to feed on. The sticktight flea is most often found infesting the rims of the ears of animals but may also be found attached to other parts of the body.

Fleas produce large numbers of eggs, which drop off the host. The eggs sometimes get into cracks in the floor, into a sandbox, or into the furniture where the pet sleeps, and lie there in a dormant state for many months before conditions become right for their development. Some hatch very soon after they are dropped. Moisture and heat are essential for hatching. The egg is deliquescent, absorbing water from the air, so that whenever the weather becomes warm and humid, flea eggs soon hatch. In excessively dry climates fleas are almost unknown.

Out of the egg comes a worm, the larva. The worm feeds on organic matter such as scales from dog skin. It grows quickly. When it reaches the size of a very small maggot, it spins a cocoon and pupates like the caterpillar. Out of these cocoons come males and females, and at this stage they look very much alike. They are able to jump prodigious distances and are remarkably well protected against pressure. If you roll one tightly between your fingers and let it go, it will jump about as well as it did before.

After they hatch, fleas crawl up anything vertical and wait there, about a foot from the ground or floor, for a host to pass. If your pet is taken out of your home during the summer, you may find after a few weeks that the fleas are attacking you instead. The fleas you find in the house have developed from eggs which were dropped from your pet, and since the original host has been removed, they use you as a substitute. Nor are the fleas confined to the house or kennel. You may easily be flea-bitten in the garden if your pet had the run of the grounds and eggs were dropped there.

Sticktight fleas do not move about or jump, but cling to the skin, often in large clusters. The female burrows into the skin and lays her eggs in the ulcers she produces. After the eggs hatch the larvae fall to the ground, where they complete their development in about four weeks, when conditions are right. This flea is more prevalent in warm climates than in cold. Not only dogs, cats, and other four-legged pets are infested by sticktight fleas, but birds as well. This is a good fact to know where sticktight fleas are a problem; it may help you keep your dog free of them.

In some sections ticks are called sticktights. This is a colloquialism. Actually they are not the same thing.

THE LOUSE: The louse lives all its life—embryonic and adult—on an animal or bird. All species of pets may be infested, and it is believed that no type of louse can live for more than three or four days off the animal or bird on whose body it depends for sustenance. There are two kinds of lice—sucking and biting—and each type is subclassified into several species. Some are red, some gray, some bluish, but in spite of obvious differences their life histories are very similar.

A louse hatches from its egg, called a nit, which the female has fastened to a hair. The little louse, if it is a sucking type, crawls onto the body of the animal, fastens its mouth in the skin, and sucks blood. A large number can suck so much blood and give off such a toxin that the host often becomes anemic and dies. The biting louse, on the other hand, feeds on skin scales and organic matter as well as on blood. The males and females copulate, the female's body fills with eggs, the female lets go of the skin and, crawling on the hairs, attaches to them tiny silvery eggs which are large enough to be seen. The eggs of the biting louse hatch in five to eight days; those of the sucking louse in ten to twelve days. The young mature two or three weeks after hatching. Lice do not drop off their hosts spontaneously. In general, infestation is spread by contact and by close association. Apparently lice move from one host to another of a different species quite easily. For example, dogs and cats kept in close proximity are usually infested equally.

Lice are frequently a cause of death for whole litters of puppies. When a bitch is infested with lice, the fact may be unknown to her owner; but, when she has puppies, the lice tend to leave her and gravitate to the puppies. Apparently the latter are more tender morsels. Before the owner knows it, the pups have developed a boardy feeling, fail to thrive, and die. Every litter of puppies should be watched constantly for the presence of lice.

Scratching by dogs is one of the means by which lice are spread.

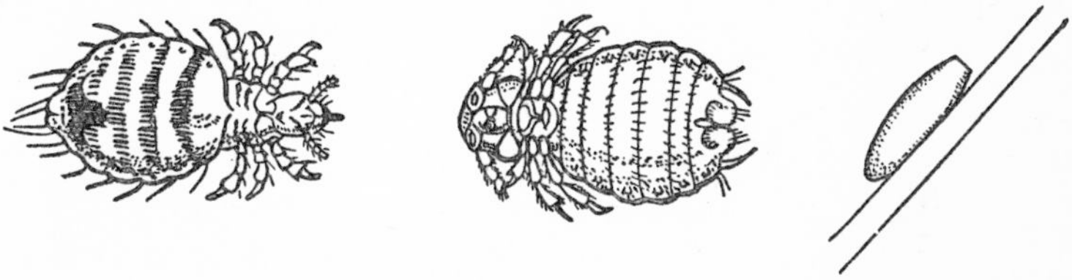

Lice and nits, enlarged twenty-five times. Left, blood-sucking louse; center, biting louse; right, nit glued to hairs.

Naturally the dog itches when infested, and his scratching can't help but remove a small number of the parasites. It is believed that this is one of the chief means of transferring lice from one dog to another, provided, of course, that the new dog comes along before three days. The same occurs in the case of hairs which the dog breaks off in scratching. If nits are attached to those hairs, they may lie around for a considerable period before hatching.

One type of human louse, *Pediculus capitis,* can live on dogs. In many cases, pets which have been treated for lice have become reinfested by lice from human beings. Fortunately, not all types of lice are able to infest both species.

THE TICK: Ticks are rapidly becoming a very great problem to dog owners and they are often a nuisance in the house, even in a home where no pet is kept. Ticks feed on many species of domestic animals as well as on wild ones, and some are found on birds. One characteristic of the most common ticks found on pets and man is the necessity for each to feed on blood at some stage of its life.

Dog ticks, wood ticks, spotted-fever ticks, Pacific Coast ticks, brown dog ticks, lone-star ticks, Gulf Coast ticks, blacklegged ticks—all are common names for the several kinds of ticks. Some kinds are known by several names. All of them are very much alike and all have similar life histories.

Ticks pass through four stages: egg, seed tick, nymph, and adult. The female lays enormous numbers of eggs in a mass on the ground or in a clump of grass. There may be as many as three thousand to six thousand eggs in one such mass. When the American dog tick hatches from the egg as a seed tick, it has six legs. It attaches itself to a rodent which carries it about for from two to twelve days and loses it after it has become

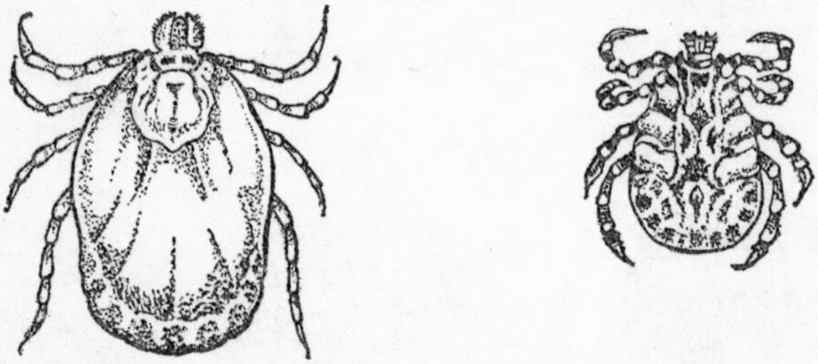

Dog ticks, enlarged six times. Left shows adult female before feeding; right, adult male.

engorged with blood. By this time the tick has eight legs, has molted, and is called a nymph. It again attaches itself to a rodent and for three to ten days rides and engorges blood, then drops off and molts again. It is now mature and, in order to attach itself to a larger animal, gravitates close to a path through the woods and climbs a bush, where it is rubbed off onto its new host. It is an interesting if unexpected fact that studies made of these pests show greater concentrations along paths than in the pathless woods.

After the female has attached herself to a host, the male crawls under her and mating occurs while the female is filling with blood. If you look under the big beanlike body of female ticks on an infested animal, you will almost invariably find a male—a small creature which does not grow nearly so large as his mate. The female engorges on the host for from five to thirteen days, then drops off, falls to the ground, and, being enormous and practically helpless, lays her eggs and dies.

Some ticks are not quite so discriminating as the American dog tick. Some spend their seed-tick and nympb stages on birds and even reptiles, and one, the Gulf Coast tick, spends its immature stages on birds which live on the ground, such as quail, turkeys, and pheasants. Still others feed on birds exclusively, notably *Argas reflexus,* whose host is the pigeon.

The brown dog tick, which is becoming the most widely distributed tick in the North, prefers to pass its early life inside dwellings. It is often found under picture moldings, behind baseboards, and in furniture. Even adults can be found in such hideaways. Fortunately they do not suck human blood as some other species do.

MITES: Mange on pets is caused by mange mites, which are so small that they cannot be identified without a microscope.

The *red mange mite* (*Demodex canis*) is also known as demodectic mange mite and follicular mange mite. When a dog shows a baldish area under the eyes, on the cheeks, on the forehead, or on the front legs, he may have red mange. If it is not checked early, it may soon have

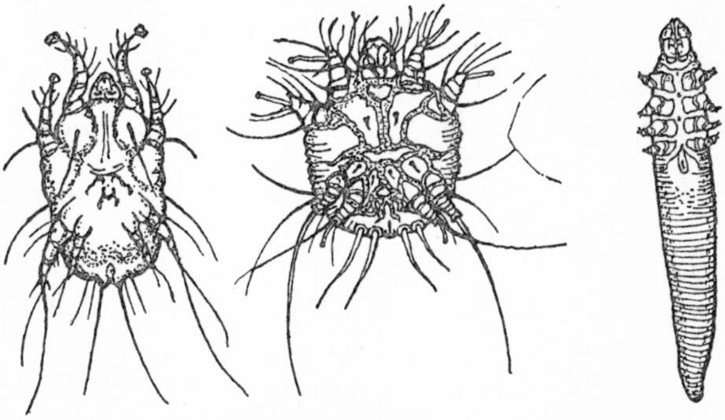

Mites which attack mammalian pets, all greatly enlarged. Left, ear mange mite; center, sarcoptic mange mite; right, demodectic mange mite, also called red and follicular mange mite.

serious consequences. One of these is the bacterial infection which often develops, causing pustules and intense reddening of the skin, with violent scratching from the irritation.

The young mites, as they hatch from the eggs, appear to be elongated globs, but they mature very quickly to look like minute eight-legged worms. They live in sebaceous glands and in hair follicles, so that when an animal has been infected the hair soon drops off the infected area. They reproduce prodigiously. In eight days a thousand female mites may have increased to twelve thousand. In eight more days these may have become 132,000.

Sarcoptic mange mites (*Sarcopters scabeii*) produce a disease called scabies. The mite is round, with four pairs of short legs. The female tunnels into the skin and lays from twenty to forty eggs, which hatch in three to seven days. One female can easily produce 1,500,000 descendants in three months. The newly hatched larvae have three pairs of legs, but they molt to become nymphs which molt still again before they become adults. This process requires two to three weeks for completion. Only the adult female burrows beneath the outside layers of skin; males and immature forms live on the surface under scabs or skin scales.

Because humans as well as dogs can become infested with scabies, a person who develops spots that itch persistently should consult a physician. Many veterinarians who have discovered sarcoptic mites on pets have also found that the pets' owners were infested. Human diagnosis is often difficult because it is necessary to scrape the skin quite deeply in order to uncover the burrowing females.

Ear mange mites (*Otodectes cynotis*) are round and have somewhat longer legs than the sarcoptic mites. They live in the ear canal, causing a crumbly wax which is quite distinctive from normal wax. Actually the substance found in the ear is composed more of scabs than wax, because the mites pierce the skin to suck plasma or lymph. The irritation causes animals to shake their heads sharply, which helps distribute the mites to other animals. Some dogs scratch their ears so vigorously that blood tumors develop between the layers of the ear flaps.

The life history of the ear mite is believed to be similar to that of the sarcoptic mite.

Sand flea (*Leptus irritans*) is also called chigger, harvest mite, chigga, chigre, jigger, red bug. Adult red bugs, which are quite large, do not bother humans or pets. Nor does the second, or nymph, stage. The larvae alone attack animals, and then only shortly after they have hatched. Like ticks, they suck blood and drop off to molt. After this molt the nymphs may even feed on plants, but not on mammals. The tiny larvae annoy pets a great deal. They often cause severe scratching and sometimes loss of weight, without the owner's understanding the cause. Birds are also troubled by this pest to such an extent that they have been known to die from the attacks. Red bugs are native to the southern United States and semitropical countries.

BEDBUGS belong to the family *Cimicidae,* of which *Cimex lectularius* is the most common. Because of their flattish shape, bedbugs can crawl into narrow places, as under baseboards, in cracks between boards, even in spaces in metal cages. Over a period of several days the female lays about one hundred eggs, which hatch in ten days. The emerging nymphs feed and digest their food while molting their skin. This is repeated five times over a period of forty days before the nymph becomes an adult.

When a bedbug feeds, usually at night, he gorges himself within ten minutes. He is able, however, to withstand prolonged periods of starvation, which is one of the reasons for the remarkable power of survival of bedbugs. Even nymphs can survive for more than two months without food, and adults are said to be able to live for a year without eating.

Internal Parasites. Many pets suffer from parasites which damage the inside of the body, in contrast to those we have previously considered, which attack from the outside.

ROUNDWORMS include all worms under the classification of nematodes, such as hookworms, whipworms, esophageal worms, heartworms, lungworms, and kidney worms, as well as the large round worms which most pet owners recognize. But as we use the term "roundworms" in this section, we shall limit it to the whitish or yellowish worm which grows up to five inches long in the stomach and intestines of pets, is pointed at both ends, and inclined, while alive, to curl up. When dead, it straightens out so that it may appear to be simply bowed at the ends.

Although there are several kinds of intestinal roundworms, their life histories are much the same. The eggs pass out of the animal with every bowel movement. In less than a week, if the temperature and moisture are propitious, a little worm forms in the egg. In other words, it has to incubate before it can hatch. Now this egg is in the infective stage and, as such, it will live for years, waiting to be picked up by a suitable host. It may enter the host in any one of dozens of ways. A cat may walk in a spot where feces have entirely disintegrated but where the eggs remain. They stick to her feet; she licks herself and becomes infested. A puppy may find the eggs on his mother's breasts, or a dog may drag a moist bone through an infested area. Or a raccoon may walk through its own feces as it paces back and forth in its pen, and subsequently lick itself clean.

The egg enters the stomach, and the shell, or coat, is digested, liberating the embryo. If it happens to be an egg of *Toxascaris leonina* the larva

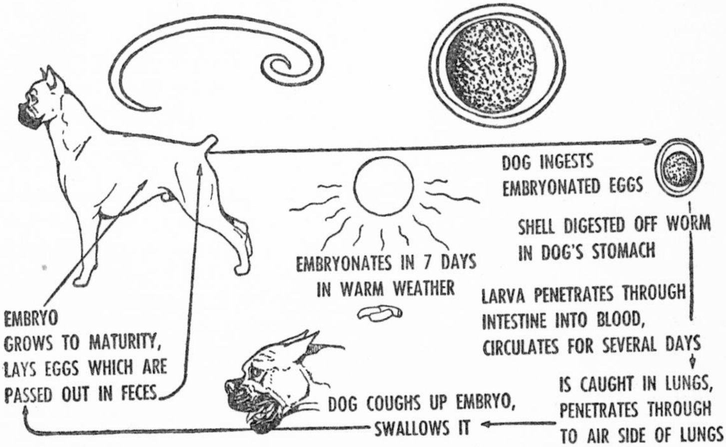
DOG INGESTS
EMBRYONATED EGGS
SHELL DIGESTED OFF WORM
IN DOG'S STOMACH
EMBRYONATES IN 7 DAYS
IN WARM WEATHER
LARVA PENETRATES THROUGH
INTESTINE INTO BLOOD,
CIRCULATES FOR SEVERAL DAYS
EMBRYO
GROWS TO MATURITY,
LAYS EGGS WHICH ARE
PASSED OUT IN FECES
IS CAUGHT IN LUNGS,
PENETRATES THROUGH
TO AIR SIDE OF LUNGS
DOG COUGHS UP EMBRYO,
SWALLOWS IT

Life history of a common roundworm. Above, left, mature worm; right, egg magnified four hundred times.

moves along into the intestine, where it penetrates into the lining, remains there for ten days, and grows. Finally it returns into the lumen, or hollow part of the intestine, and continues to grow to maturity, feeding on the animal's partially digested food.

If the roundworms are of the *Toxascaris canis* or *T. cati* varieties, they are much more harmful to their host. In the intestine the little larvae bore through the intestinal lining and enter the blood stream, where they grow. Many may be found in the liver and spleen while on their way to the lungs. In the lungs they penetrate through from the blood vessels into the air spaces and are moved on to the windpipe. Up this they move in mucous secretions until the irritation causes the animal to cough and gag as if clearing his throat. The small amount of mucus with the worms in it is swallowed. Down the gullet go the parasites, which from then on until old age overtakes them, or worm medicine kills them, live in the intestine, migrating up and down at will, copulating and laying thousands of eggs.

Not only do roundworms give off a toxin, but the migrations of the larvae in the body, especially in the lungs, frequently cause death. The pneumonia they cause is called verminous pneumonia.

Hookworms are minute leeches, living on blood which they suck from the intestine, to which they cling with a set of hooks or teeth about the mouth. Hookworms cause anemia and loss of condition. A heavy infestation causes death.

The animal hookworm is not the same worm which causes so much

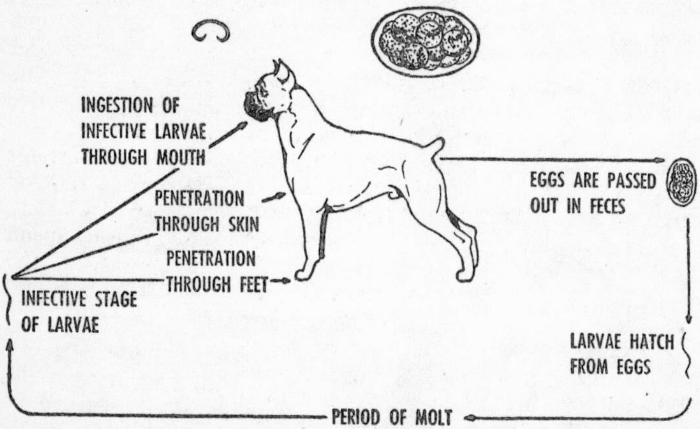

Life history of the hookworm. In the body, the larvae behave much like the roundworm larvae, spending their early days in the dog's blood and lungs. They are coughed up and swallowed. They then attach themselves to the small intestine by their hooks. Above, left, hookworm life size; right, egg enlarged four hundred times.

hookworm anemia in humans. No animal hookworm is over five eighths of an inch long for females and slightly less for males. Three types are found distributed in different sections. *Ancylostomum caninum* has a very wide distribution, while *A. braziliense* is more or less confined to the South and tropical regions. *Uncinaria stenocephala* is a northern hookworm found in wild foxes and dogs kept in northerly climates.

The life history of the hookworm is interesting. The eggs, passed out of the host in the feces, need warmth to develop. Therefore the warm months are the hookworm months in the North, whereas the whole year is hookworm time in the South. After the eggs have incubated from three to six days, larvae emerge. These are called the first-stage larvae. Three days later the larvae molt and become the second-stage larvae. Eight days later they molt again to become third-stage or infective larvae and then lie waiting for a host. Hookworms can bore through the skin to reach the blood stream. More often they are ingested through the mouth and are sometimes inhaled with dust kicked up in a place where stools have disintegrated and become mixed with soil.

If the larvae have reached the blood stream by boring through the skin or internal tissues, they eventually reach the lungs, bore into the air sacs, are finally coughed up, swallowed, reach the intestine, and molt two more times. By three weeks after they first entered the body as larvae, hookworms are large enough to lay eggs. Sometimes hundreds cling to an animal's intestinal lining. They are very debilitating. A hookworm can suck half a teaspoonful of blood in a week. A thousand can suck one and a half drinking glasses *in a day*. No wonder hookworms cause anemia!

With these facts in mind, two questions can now be answered:

How can mother animals lick their offspring clean of feces without becoming infested with intestinal parasites? The answer is that all the eggs of parasites have to undergo several days' incubation to be infective. The eggs which the mother cleans from her offspring pass through her digestive tract and lie in her feces, unharmed, to become infective later.

How can two-weeks-old puppies be passing eggs of hookworms, for instance, when about three weeks are required for the eggs to develop into worms old enough to lay eggs? The answer is that the puppies were infected while they were embryos. Since several species of parasites spend some time in the blood, these larvae manage to penetrate through the placenta and into the blood of the embryos, whence they find the intestinal tract.

Whipworms: Considering its small size, the whipworm is one of the most debilitating parasites that pets harbor. The whip handle or body of the worm is approximately half an inch long, but the whip part is about one and a half inches. This part is sewed into the lining of the intestine, but the pest can withdraw it to move. The worm is very thin; even the body is no thicker than the diameter of coarse sewing thread. Whipworms are usually found in the intestine, but in dogs they are found in greater numbers in the cecum—a blind gut—where so many can sometimes be

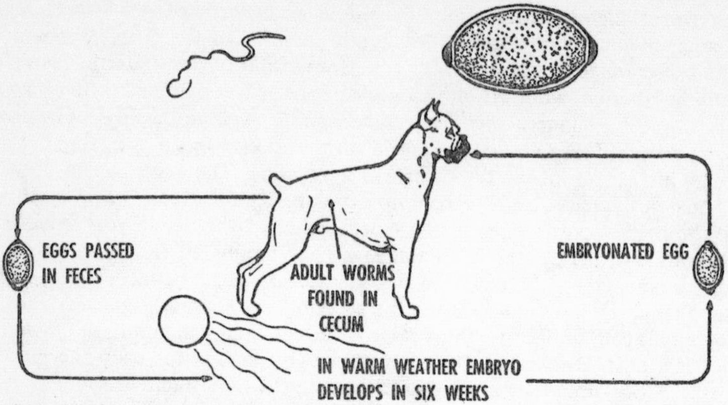

Life history of the whipworm. Above, left, whipworm, life size; right, egg, enlarged four hundred times.

seen on post-mortem that the lining of that organ appears white, especially at its upper end.

The females lay yellowish eggs of a lemon shape. Incubation in the soil requires about three weeks at a fairly high temperature before the embryos are infective. So far as is known, upon being ingested, the larvae are liberated and at once seek the protection of the dog's cecum or fasten themselves along the intestine, chiefly in the large bowel or colon.

Esophageal worms: Colonies of these small reddish worms live in gullet cysts in dogs. Dogs become infested with them by eating dung beetles, the intermediate hosts of the worms.

Heartworms (*Dirofilaria immitis*)*:* These parasites depend upon insects for transmission and cause death and weakness to large numbers of pets. Although fleas and lice have been implicated, mosquitoes are believed to be the chief vectors (carriers). Heartworms live in the side of the heart (right ventricle) which pumps blood directly to the lungs, and in the pulmonary artery—rarely anywhere else. The females are ten to twelve inches long and nearly one sixteenth inch in diameter; the males are half as large.

The females do not lay eggs, but produce larvae which float about in the blood. Microscopic blood studies reveal their presence as small worms which lash about among the red blood cells. Mosquitoes suck blood which contains larvae. Inside the mosquito, they molt and change to the infective stage. Blood from an infected dog can be transfused into another without danger of the larvae developing. But the life in the intermediate host makes them able, when placed by the mosquito in another dog's blood stream, to grow to maturity. How long this takes is not known, but it is a matter of months.

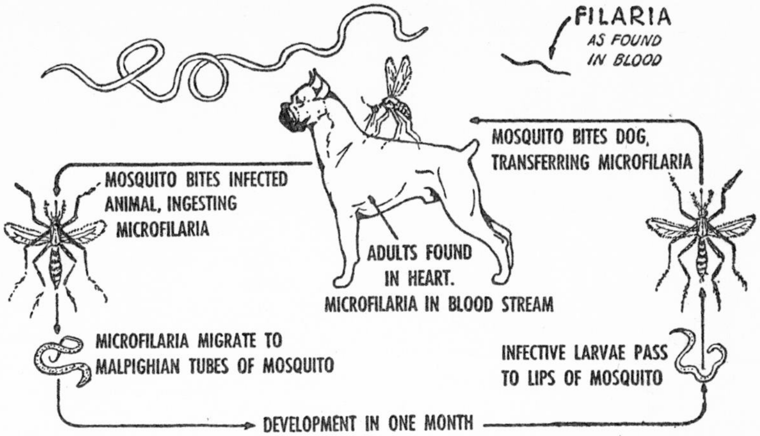
FILARIA
AS FOUND
IN BLOOD
MOSQUITO BITES DOG,
TRANSFERRING MICROFILARIA
MOSQUITO BITES INFECTED
ANIMAL, INGESTING
MICROFILARIA
ADULTS FOUND
IN HEART.
MICROFILARIA IN BLOOD STREAM
MICROFILARIA MIGRATE TO
MALPIGHIAN TUBES OF MOSQUITO
INFECTIVE LARVAE PASS
TO LIPS OF MOSQUITO
DEVELOPMENT IN ONE MONTH

Life history of the heartworm. Above left, heartworm, one-half life size; right, microfilaria, enlarged four hundred times.

Larvae in the blood may live for years after parent worms are dead. For this reason, and because newly infected dogs are often unsuspected, buying animals from heartworm areas is a gamble. It was usually believed that heartworms were present only in the warmer sections of the world, but this is no longer true. Heartworm infestations are reported even in Canada. Wherever there are mosquitoes, heartworms are being found more and more.

Badly infested animals have such large numbers of worms in the heart as to make one wonder how the animals can live at all. The blood flow is greatly restricted, and the animal becomes very sluggish and is unable to stand normal exercise.

Lungworms: Many species of animals seldom suspected of being infested harbor the lungworm parasite. However, their coughs, gagging, and general debilitation often make owners suspect them of having other parasites or diseases. City pets seldom harbor lungworms; in some sections rural pets are severe sufferers.

Almost no work has been done on the life history of lungworms, although pathologists know what their infestation means to pets. One of them—called the *capillarid lungworm* (*Capillaria acrophila*)—is similar to the whipworm. This one lives in the bronchial tubes. Another, *Filaroides osleri,* produces tumors of a wartlike nature in the bronchial tubes, sometimes in such numbers and of such size as to cause death through suffocation. Another, *Aeolurostrongylus abstrusus,* is found in the lung tissue and is believed to require a snail as the intermediate host.

All lungworms cause coughing and wheezing, but these symptoms are so common that they are not conclusive evidence of lungworm. The only positive diagnostic method is to find their eggs in a microscopic examination of the feces.

TAPEWORMS: It is comparatively easy to remove tapeworms from pets. The hardest part in their control is in the prevention of infestation. This requires a knowledge of tapeworm life history.

There are two general kinds of tapeworms—the armed and the unarmed. The armed have suckers and hooks with which they cling, while the unarmed are equipped with only a pair of grooves which hold to the intestinal lining. A large armed tapeworm has powerful devices which enable the worm to hold fast despite all of the pull exerted on it by the passing food. It seems almost impossible that the little head can hold all of the worm, yet that is what it does. Besides the host in which they spend most of their existence, all tapeworms require an intermediate host and, in some cases, two such hosts. All are composed of a head to which are added a series of flat segments, joined one to another.

The Flea-Host Tapeworm (*Dipylidium caninum*): This is the most common tapeworm of our pets and occurs in dogs, foxes, and cats. It is about a foot long. The head is smaller than a small pinhead and the segments close to the head are stretched to the thickness of a thread. This section is called the neck. As the worm grows, the segments become wider and shorter. The last few segments are again longer and contain eggs. When ripe, these segments are shed and passed out with the stool. If no stool is present, the segment is moved downward to the anus, where it may cling until it dries into a small, brownish, seedlike grain which drops from the pet.

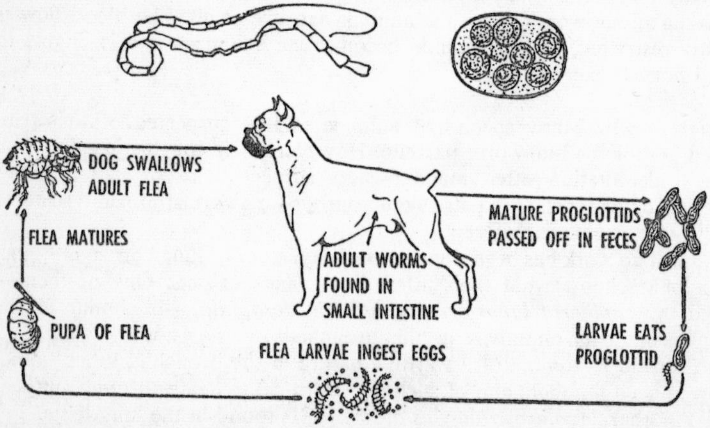

Life history of the flea-host tapeworm. Above, left, worm, life size. Often grows to be eighteen inches long. Right, capsule with eggs, enlarged one hundred and fifty times.

The eggs are not extruded without considerable pressure to the segment; then they appear in capsules and look, under a microscope, like bunches of grapes. When your veterinarian makes a fecal examination and tells you that your dog is free from worms, do not blame him for not detecting the presence of tapeworms. After you have seen a dozen segments, you may have an examination made and receive a negative report. Your veterinarian studies the stool for eggs, and if the tapeworm has laid no eggs before the examination, he won't find any. Finding segments is the only effective way to determine the presence of this worm.

Fleas and biting lice are the intermediate tapeworm hosts. When fleas are in their larval stage, they feed on tapeworm segments, among other foods. The eggs from these segments develop into tapeworm larvae as the flea matures. If an animal ingests the flea, the tapeworm larva is released and attaches itself to the intestinal wall, where it remains and grows.

The Rabbit-Host Tapeworm (*Taenia pisiformis*): This is a coarser worm than the flea-host tapeworm. Sometimes five to six feet long, its

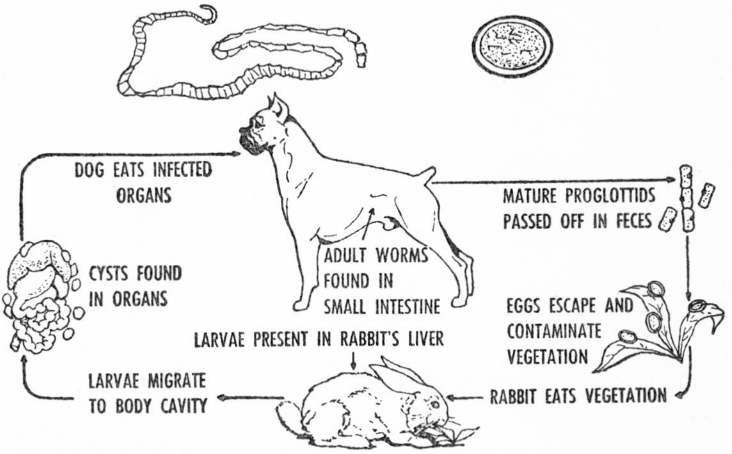

Life history of the rabbit-host tapeworm. Above, left, worm, life size. Often grows to be two or three feet long. Right, egg, enlarged four hundred times.

segments are larger and more active. The intermediate host is the rabbit or hare. This tapeworm lays many eggs which pass out of the dog in his stool and cling to vegetation. Rabbits eating the vegetation become infested. The larvae work into the liver of the rabbits to develop, and from there into the abdominal cavity, where they attach themselves to intestines in small cysts. When a dog eats an infested rabbit, it too soon becomes infested.

The Pork, Beef, and Sheep Tapeworms (*Taenia soleum, T, saginata, T. marginata, T. ovis*) have been reported as long as fifteen feet. It is rare to find these tapeworms in city pets. In country animals, which may feast on carcasses of dead animals, these infestations may occur. Hogs, cattle, or sheep which have fed in pastures where human excreta has been deposited can eat grass to which tapeworm eggs cling. The dog eats flesh from these animals and becomes infested from the cysts containing the tapeworm heads. In the North a tapeworm, *Taenia krabbei,* infests dogs which eat infested reindeer muscles.

The Sheep Brain Tapeworm: While some tapeworm larvae are found singly in cysts in different parts of the intermediate hosts' bodies, *Multiceps multiceps* is found in bladderlike cysts in the brains of sheep. The pressure may kill the sheep, and animals which eat the brain will become infested. *Multiceps* is the smallest of the common tapeworms, being only one fourth inch long and consisting of only a head and three segments.

The Rodent-Host Tapeworm (*Taenia taeniaformis*) is a widely distributed form which probably does its worst damage to cats. Rats, mice, squirrels, muskrats, and other rodents may act as intermediate hosts. The heads in the cysts develop in their livers and remain dormant until eaten by an animal. Cats are the most likely pets to suffer from this parasite, and indirectly spread it to dogs.

The Hydatid Tapeworm (*Echinococcus granulosis*)*:* This unique parasite, short like *multiceps,* is dangerous because it does damage to so many species of animals. It infests many pets which eat meat. As intermediate hosts, most animals, including man, can be infested if by any chance the eggs are ingested.

The embryos bore through the intestines to the blood stream and are transported to various organs where they become cysts which may measure three inches in diameter. The lining of the cyst produces numerous brood capsules in which heads are formed. A brood capsule may contain as many as forty heads six months after infestation. If a dog eats an organ infested with the hydatid he eats many heads, and in less than two months the worms which develop from the heads are laying more eggs to infest other animals which inadvertently consume them.

There are three unarmed tapeworms which are important to dog owners:

The Fish-Host Tapeworm (*Diphyllobothrium latum*) occurs in pets fed on fresh-water fish, generally within a few hundred miles of the Great Lakes in the United States. *D. mansoni* affects cats and dogs in Puerto Rico. *D. mansonides* has been reported in New York and Louisiana.

A human harboring the tapeworm passes out the eggs in feces which are dumped via sewers into the lake. Small crustaceans eat the eggs. In the first type, fish eat the crustaceans; in the latter two types, reptiles, such as frogs, or mammals which swallow the crustaceans can be the second hosts. Of course dogs which eat the fish or reptiles or infested mammals become infested in turn. Raw whitefish, trout, salmon, pike, perch have all been incriminated as passing the cysts of these huge worms to pets.

Some of these worms have three thousand to four thousand segments and at their widest may be half an inch or even more across.

Taenia serialis: This is an intermediate worm between two and three feet long which dogs and foxes frequently carry in their intestines, and which they contract by eating cysts and their inhabitants—the heads which may number a dozen or more—when they eat hares, rabbits, or squirrels. Some cysts may be an inch in diameter and cause the intermediate host great discomfort. The rabbits or squirrels become infested from eating grass, nuts, or other vegetation to which eggs of the worm are sticking.

It should be noted in passing that many pets which are only intermediate hosts can be made very sick by the cysts of tapeworms developing within their organs and muscles as well as in their intestines. Rabbits are notorious in this respect.

PROTOZOA

Besides these already mentioned, there is a different kind of organism which produces diseases of a very serious nature in pets. This organism is the protozoa, the lowest form of animal life. There are several forms, of which the sporozoite named *coccidia* are most important. These one-celled minute organisms live among the cells of the intestinal lining. Their life history is exceedingly complicated, and the damage they do is accounted for by the enormous numbers that develop before the body eventually overcomes them. Two other types, piroplasma and anaplasma, cause considerable damage as parasites of pets.

Coccidia: Each species of animal and bird is infested by specific types of coccidia, but some have more than one. Dogs and cats have three principal forms affecting both species. Rabbits, poultry, and even reptiles are afflicted. All types of coccidia are extremely prevalent, the year round in warm climates and in the summer in the North.

In size, coccidia are microscopic. The form found in the feces, the egg

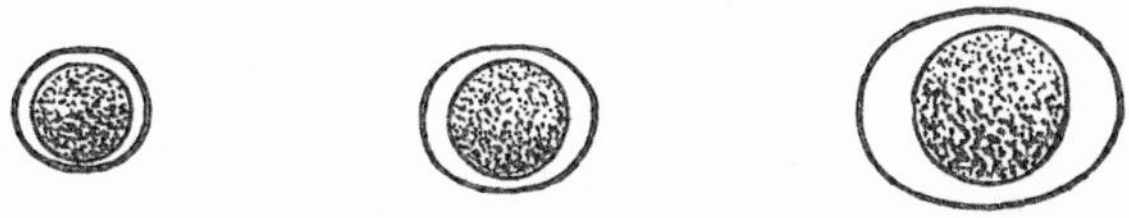

Coccidia. Three common types as they appear when enlarged through a microscope. Left, Isospora bigemina; *center,* Isospora rivolta; *right,* Isospora felis.

or oocyst, is roundish with a nucleus inside. Some oocysts show divided nuclei. The forms infesting dogs and cats are *Isospora rivolta, I. bigemina,* and *I. felis.* We are fortunate our dogs have only three principal forms. Birds may be host to at least a dozen species. Some are residents of the cecum and some are found in the intestine. Guinea pigs, rats, and squirrels each have specific types.

After it has been outside of the host for several days, the coccidia egg form develops into the infestive stage, provided conditions are favorable. Flies carry it to feeding pans or animals pick it up by licking their feet or by getting feces into their mouths. Inside the animal the coating of the egg form is digested and the infestive forms which have developed in the egg are released. These bore into the cells lining the intestine and develop until they divide into other bodies.

This division and growth damages or destroys the cells, but these new forms now enter other cells and repeat the cycle. This goes on through several divisions and attacking of new cells, until at length male and female forms are produced. The males fertilize the females and thus produce the egg form which is passed out with the feces and deposited with the loose stool to infest other animals or birds.

Coccidiosis is a disease of self-limiting character. Once over a specific species of coccidia, the animal can no longer be infested, but this does not apply to all other species of the disease. A dog recovered from *I. rivolta* can be infested with *I. felis* as readily as though he had never been infested at all.

Piroplasma and Anaplasma: These are carried by ticks. They are minute animals which live in the red blood cells and produce diseases called piroplasmosis and anaplasmosis. Of course the disease is due to the enormous numbers of piroplasma which develop, and to their effect on the efficiency of the red cells in transporting carbon dioxide and oxygen.

Two or three days after infestation the first symptoms appear. The number of red corpuscles is reduced and the white increased. The color from the broken-down red cells being thrown off by the body causes reddening of the urine. The parasites multiply by division. New ones attack other red cells.

An intermediate form does not develop in the vector of this parasite as in the case of tapeworms or heartworms; injections of infested blood into a susceptible animal will be all that is necessary to start the disease.

So far the disease has been confined to the warm climates where ticks are prevalent, but with the increase of ticks in the North, piroplasmosis may become a Northern problem as well.

TUMORS AND CANCER

That lump growing under the dog's skin which develops slowly, that rapidly growing tumor on the shoulder, that soft pliant swelling, that wart, those lumps in the breast of your pet—what are they? Will they cost his life? Should they be removed? Will they return if they are removed? The veterinarian hears scores of such questions. Many pet owners have misconceptions about growths.

A tumor is a growth of new, useless tissue growing independently of the surrounding tissue but not replacing it.

In medical terminology the term *malignant* means a virulent growth that tends to go from bad to worse.

A *benign* growth is only a relative term. Compared to a malignant tumor, it stays within itself and does not recur elsewhere. But what growth could really be benign? A wart? Even so small and seemingly innocuous a growth causes itching and sometimes pain. No tumor is really benign in the common sense of the word.

Cancer is a malignant tumor. The word comes from the Latin, meaning *crab*. This implies that it is a growth which invades other tissue by extending crablike tentacles. But this is an old definition, hardly acceptable in the light of newer knowledge. There is cancer which grows in a lump apparently as benign as any nonmalignant tumor. Then this lump in the lungs, let us say, sends off a bud or cell into the blood stream which is halted in the skin on the pet's back, where it grows. Careful microscopic examination of the lump after removal discloses that it is tissue characteristic of the lungs, even though it is growing in the skin. This is called a *metastasis*. Surely such a tumor is a cancer. Or a lump comes in a dog's neck. It shells out easily in the hands of a surgeon. It looks benign. But down the lymph chain, a month after the tumor's removal, another lump grows which is found to be a tumor with the same characteristics as the first. The first, then, was definitely malignant, even though it was not invasive in a crablike sense.

Dogs are subject to a great many forms of cancer, some serious, some practically harmless if discovered and treated in time.

Carcinomas arise in the skin, in the intestinal linings, and in all tissues which develop from the same original embryonic sources. *Sarcomas* are tumors made up of connective tissue—the part of the dog's body which binds it together and supports it.

Warts: Perhaps one, perhaps many small growths, with tiny fingerlike protrusions giving them a rough surface, appear in a dog. They usually remain less than a quarter of an inch in diameter. They often become raw, and remain that way from the dog's constant nibbling or scratching. Older dogs may have from fifty to a hundred. There is a definite family tendency to develop them after the age of eight. One cocker spaniel strain showed it so strongly that word spread about this objectionable feature and the breeder disposed of all of them because the public wouldn't buy them.

Warts are considered by most experts to be a virus disease. Vaccines have been prepared to be injected to induce the body to build up antibodies against them. With this treatment they often disappear.

Surgery, which removes the wart in its entirety, is successful with individual warts, and healing is quite rapid if the skin is sutured, but sometimes surgery has to be very extensive if all the warts are to be removed from extreme cases.

Under these two classes, carcinomas and sarcomas, fall the various kinds of tumors. If your veterinarian tells you your dog has a malignant melanotic sarcoma, you know it is a tumor of the connective tissue, that it gives off buds or invades the adjacent tissue, or both. Melanotic means black, so it is a darkly pigmented growth. A pigment cell must have gone wild.

What causes these growths? The causes of a few kinds are known. Some believe a virus is the initiating agent of certain forms, if not all. Irritation, such as the constant rubbing of a snag tooth on the lip, certain hormones, contact with irritating chemicals, inhalation of smoke—all are known to cause some types of growths; for others there is no explanation. Perhaps mutations or sudden changes in the characteristics of a cell are induced by irritation and, once started, simply grow out of control.

When a cut or abrasion occurs in an animal, the body heals it by the growth of surrounding cells. Something in the body applies a brake to this healing growth at the right time. If it didn't, every cut might grow out of all proportion. We are not sure what this brake is. The cancer cells have no brake applied by the body and grow by cell division on and on until they overwhelm the host.

This overpowering growth may kill a pet in several ways: (1) It gives off poisons. Lest this fact be doubted, one has only to remember the cases of dogs with even small tumors who became listless and prematurely old. When the tumors were removed, rejuvenation was effected. (2) It may exert pressure on vital organs which prevents their proper functioning. (3) It may create an obstruction, such as a growth within the intestines which prevents passage of food. (4) It may increase the size of a male dog's prostate gland so that pressure on the colon prevents passage of stools, or an enlargement within a gland, as when a tumor develops in the spleen and inhibits the free passage of blood through it.

Diagnosis of malignant growths is accomplished by removing a section of the growth and preparing it by an elaborate process of slicing and staining until it can be examined with a microscope by a pathologist who can classify it.

DEFICIENCY DISEASES

Negative as well as positive factors cause disease. Many pets have died from lack of oxygen. There are the obvious cases of suffocation; the carrying cage or shipping crate may be insufficiently ventilated, and when it is opened the pet is found dead. Fishes which stay at the surface of the water are short of oxygen because there are too many for the surface area of the water. Lack of oxygen, obvious as it is, constitutes a deficiency disease. There are many more subtle deficiencies.

Some deficiencies produce what should be called conditions, not diseases. A disease is a morbid process with characteristic symptoms. Thirst is neither a disease nor the result of disease. The symptoms of dehydration are cured by water consumption. Anemia is a disease in one sense, a condition in another. Millions of humans go about in an anemic condition. In general, deficiency diseases are quite easily cured, simply by furnishing the body with the missing elements.

Anemia is caused by a shortage of oxygen. We have considered the obvious form but not the symptoms. *When an animal suffocates, the pink color of the tissue turns blue.* A lack of oxygen in the tissues can be produced by many causes other than lack of air. The blood may simply be unable to carry it about the body. This, in turn, may result from a diminished supply of red cells in the blood. There may be too few, or the chemical composition of their components may be inadequate.

Hookworms are the most common cause of an inadequate supply of red cells. Their blood consumption strains the blood-building equipment, which cannot keep up with the loss. A hookworm-infested animal lacks animation and gets out of breath easily. He shows all the symptoms of anemia, as though blood had been drawn from his arteries or veins. Little puppies are frequently found to be anemic because of hookworm infestation. There is so little iron in milk that they cannot regain their losses despite deworming, and they frequently die because of their owner's ignorance of this fact.

Heavy infestations of sucking lice may also cause anemia. Some dogs harbor so many lice that they touch one another in places. The animal's gums reveal a sickly pallor; it can't stand cold and loses its appetite. The basic condition is probably aggravated by toxins from the lice. Animals are often seriously weakened by these parasites. Dogs have actually been known to die from lice infestation.

Blood diseases, rare in animals, produce an altered blood picture. Some ordinary diseases alter the proportion of red and white cells, not by reducing the number of red cells but by increasing the number of white cells. This is not anemia. Diseases which produce toxins or attack the blood-building apparatus of the body produce anemia by reducing the number of red cells.

A lack of iron or copper or both causes anemia. Insufficient iron is responsible for a shortage of hemoglobin, and though there may be a full quota of red cells, they can't pick up and transport oxygen. Copper deficiency also causes anemia. Copper is not part of hemoglobin, but is concerned with its formation.

Niacin deficiency, which causes black tongue, a shortage of vitamin-B-complex factors, pyridoxin deficiency, all cause anemia.

Rickets: After anemia, rickets is probably the most common deficiency disease. It is a result of a lack of one or more of these factors: vitamin D, calcium, or phosphorus.

Eclampsia is a disease of nursing mother animals, caused by an inadequate amount of calcium or an inadequacy in the parathyroid glands.

Black Tongue: This is a disease almost unheard of where dogs eat table scraps. A deficiency of niacin in the diet over a period of many weeks is at least one of the causes. The dog develops a general loss of condition and muscular inco-ordination. He slobbers constantly from the mouth, and his breath is obnoxious. His gums and tongue appear inflamed. Associated with the disease one finds a great proliferation of spirochetal bacteria, such as cause trench mouth. The term "black tongue" is misleading because that symptom is seen only in a dead dog. Soon after death the mouth, because of congestion in the tissues, turns deep purple. Injections of niacin (nicotinic acid) or the whole B complex will effect dramatic recovery.

Mineral Deficiencies: The only two minerals of great consequence to dogs are calcium and iron, but nevertheless, in passing we must recognize that the absence of others causes dire consequences. Iodine is essential. Its lack causes goiter in animals, and when pregnant females are iodine-starved they may produce abnormal young called cretins. Common salt is also essential. Since 99 per cent of the calcium in the body is found in the skeleton, obviously a calcium deficiency results in poor skeletal development, as we saw in the case of rickets. But calcium does more than develop bone. It is necessary to proper nerve function and acts almost like some vitamins as a catalyst or "marrying agent" between other minerals. Bad teeth may be traced to a fluorine deficiency. Cobalt and boron, though needed in minute quantities, produce sickness through their absence. Potassium deficiency causes paralysis, and so forth.

Vitamin Deficiencies: The subject of vitamins has been covered in Chapter 3.

A number of deficiency diseases of an odd nature are due to what are known as inactivators. For example, a substance in raw fish destroys vitamin B, causing a deficiency, which in turn produces a paralysis known as Chastek. Cooking destroys the inactivator, which is, of course, why we recommend that fish be cooked for our pets. In raw eggs there is an inactivator, avertin, which inactivates biotin (one of the B-complex vitamins) and prevents egg-white digestion. Cooking destroys avertin also and prevents biotin deficiency.

5. Drugs and Their Uses

NOT long ago a dog with even a small spot of red mange was practically doomed. Pneumonia was a killer; leptospirosis, streptococci, and meningitic diseases progressed unhindered; intestinal infections often proved fatal. Today we are able to treat all of these diseases with confidence. We have developed new uses and better methods of administering many of the older drugs. The discovery of the sulfas and such antibiotics as penicillin, streptomycin, and aureomycin has made it possible to cope with many of the most devastating diseases. We have developed new insect destroyers of great potency and seem to be on the verge of perfecting others in the near future. Equipped with a vastly improved arsenal of drugs and aided by an enormously expanded knowledge of the actions of those drugs, veterinary medicine has made astonishing progress in the last decade.

The value of these life-saving drugs is too often taken for granted by the dog owner. All of them are actually of the greatest importance to him, for in a very real sense it is they that have made it possible for him to own pets and keep them healthy and vigorous. If the owner is to be able to take full advantage of this new science of health, he must know some of the fundamental facts about drugs and their actions so that he can use them more intelligently and more effectively. Obviously there is no need for him to understand the pharmaceutical intricacies of the various medicinal preparations, but he should certainly know the characteristics of the several general types of drugs and be familiar with their common uses.

With a very few exceptions, there is no reason why your veterinarian should not tell you exactly what he has prescribed for your pet. Your understanding of what is being given and why will make for more intelligent home care. And there is no reason why you should not be able to understand what your veterinarian tells you and what he has prescribed. There is a small revolution coming to pass in prescription writing. Latin names of drugs are being dropped and the metric system is being used instead of the old avoirdupois with its minims, drams, scruples, et cetera. The U. S. Federal Food and Drug Administration insists that the simplest names or the exact chemical names be used on labels. A few years ago you might have found a label with *adeps* and *terebinthina* among its elements. Today you would find *lard* and *turpentine*.

In order to understand the uses of drugs, you must first understand that drugs work in several different ways. Some drugs do not kill germs outside of the body as well as they do in the blood stream; working in combination with the bacteria-destroying white cells in the blood, they are highly efficient. Without the white cells the drugs are of little value, and the cells without the drugs are helpless. This might be called a synergistic action. Phenols (such as creosol, thymol, tars), and mercurial salts, such as bichloride, kill by causing the protoplasm of the cells to precipitate. Other drugs, such as arsenic, prevent the multiplication of bacteria. Still others combine chemically with some constituent of the protoplasm of the organism. Some have oxidizing properties and some interfere with the functioning within the bacteria themselves. There are drugs that may not be given together, being spoken of as *incompatibles*. Those likely to be given from the home medicine chest are few and will be indicated in the course of the discussion. There are other drugs that are incompatible with species; for example, phenol for cats. Still others produce odd effects; for instance, morphine when given to a cat.

The success of all drugs depends on their being used in proper concentration. They must be strong enough to kill bacteria, yet weak enough to cause no harm to the tissues of the animal. The required strengths for the various drugs have been worked out by long study and testing, and your veterinarian's instructions should be followed explicitly. When he gives you pills or tablets with instructions to give them at certain intervals, he is usually calculating how fast the drug is eliminated, in order to be sure that your pet always has enough in his system to accomplish results. If you cannot give the prescribed doses at the precribed intervals, it is better to leave the pet with the veterinarian, where the drugs will be given as they should be.

Which brings us to the question of body repair. Always remember that the body of a pet is composed of many delicate organs. Its potential length of life is more or less determined at conception. With good care and nonexposure to some diseases against which it may not be resistant, the pet should live its normal life span. But when it becomes sick there is no certainty that, with the jab of a needle and a dose of medicine, it will recover. Life isn't like that. Recovery takes care—and time. Think how long it takes for a cut on one's hand to heal. Cells slowly grow together, scar tissue forms and shrinks, and several weeks may pass before the area looks normal. Yet, too often, we expect pets to recover in a day or two from diseases more telling and debilitating than influenza is to humans. Drugs can and do have marvelous properties but they can't abolish the element of time.

Great care must be taken not to overdose, a common tendency on the part of laymen. If a teaspoonful cures, then three teaspoonfuls should cure in a third the time, he often reasons. Sometimes it kills. Doses have been worked out by pharmacologists with great care. The animal's size and the effect desired determine the dose. Overdoses are wasteful even when not dangerous. One most interesting fact is that the larger the animal, the less drug is needed proportionately. Doses are proportional to surface area rather than to weight, but weight is easier to measure. Whereas one might think that a smaller animal was tenderer and should have less than his proportional weight might indicate, the opposite is true.

GENERAL ANESTHETICS AND SEDATIVES

The drugs which allay pain and make surgery possible for pets include: those which are administered as a vapor, inhaled into the lungs, absorbed by the blood, and carried to the brain, where they temporarily deaden the sense of feeling and consciousness; those which are injected in liquid form; and those given by stomach.

Ether and **chloroform** are commonly employed in veterinary practice. Animals anesthetized with ether first experience an irritation to the nasal passages, then a moment of great excitement or stimulation, and finally a gradual loss of consciousness and inability to feel pain. The ether is lost from the body as it was gained, by being carried back to the lungs and exhaled until the blood is purified.

Ether is dangerous because it is explosive. All flames must be kept away. It is safer as an anesthetic than some others because an overdose will cause breathing to stop first and heart action last. Thus, if an animal stops breathing, artificial respiration often saves his life.

Chloroform, obtainable by laymen without a prescription, has been used widely for euthanasia. As such, it is a crude method, definitely inferior to the ether, chloral, or injectables which any veterinarian can give.

Among the general anesthetics used in small animal veterinary practice are those of a group usually injected into a vein, the abdominal cavity, or given by mouth. These are *chloral hydrate, phenobarbital, pentobarbital* (Nembutal), and *pentothal.*

Chloral hydrate is most dangerous because the margin of safety is less than that of the others. A very little more than the amount required for anesthesia will produce death.

Phenobarbital, well known to laymen under the trade name Luminal, is one of the oldest barbiturates from the standpoint of use. Its introduction followed that of the first barbiturate, Barbital. Given in both tablet and liquid form, it is one of the longest-acting of this class of drugs.

Barbiturates, of which phenobarbital is a good example, are composed basically of urea and malonic acid and have the following general actions:

Depressant. The size of the dose determines the degree of depression.

Sedative. Results are quickly accomplished, usually within an hour.

Analgesic. Barbiturates relieve pain without causing unconsciousness.

Anticonvulsant. Occasionally almost anesthetic doses must be given to animals convulsing severely, but they are effective even against the convulsions of strychnine poisoning. For this purpose, injectable barbiturates like Nembutal (pentobarbital) are preferable.

Anesthetic. Phenobarbital is seldom used for this purpose. When overdoses are given, the blood pressure falls and breathing becomes slowed.

Pentobarbital is the anesthetic most generally used for pets today—even more frequently than ether. It produces a deep sleep, which starts even before the hypodermic needle is out of the vein and lasts for several hours. The anesthetic dose is one c.c. of solution (one grain) for each five pounds of body weight. If the animal is kept quiet and in the dark, he may sleep until the last of the drug has been destroyed by the body, mostly by the liver. The pet may get up, stretch, drink, and show no ill effects. He has been unconscious long enough for a numbness to have set in around incisions and for all trace of surgical shock in minor operations to pass.

If your veterinarian is planning to use a barbiturate for an anesthetic, there are several things he should be told about your dog, if you know them. If your pet has had an increased thirst, it may suggest kidney disease. Animals with kidney diseases require much smaller amounts of barbiturates given by any route of administration. They are partially poisoned by the wastes in their systems. Liver disease and general debility also make a pet a poor subject for barbiturate anesthesia.

Animals terrified by thunderstorms, explosions from fireworks or blasting, or auto riding can be given small doses of pentobarbital with safety for partial sedation and to produce a temporary loss of fear and memory.

Pentothal is a short-acting general anesthetic which has many virtues but some disadvantages. Your veterinarian may offer you your choice of this or pentobarbital. Don't say, "You're the doctor," but consider the advantages of each. Suppose you want to wait until an operation is over and carry your pet home with you. This often happens in my practice. Do you want to wait for perhaps half an hour and take home an almost completely conscious pet, or would you prefer to take a completely anesthetized one which will lie perfectly quiet? Are you willing to keep him quiet? No radio, no moving about, nothing to disturb his deep slumber. If he rouses, you must realize that he may try to get up, try to walk, act for all the world as if he were intoxicated. He may lie making his legs go as if he were running, or he may moan, cry, even bark. (People do strange things, too, as they come out of anesthesia.) If pentothal were used, your dog would be all over the anesthesia an hour or two after the operation, but his incision would pain him more. Pentothal is quite safe because, like ether, it first depresses the respiration.

Amytal is sometimes used, and its action is similar to that of pentobarbital.

Ethyl Alcohol. Clients are forever telephoning their veterinarians to say that they have just given their dogs a dose of brandy or whisky as a stimulant. Somewhere the layman has picked up the idea that alcohol is a great animal saver. Actually it has so few warranted uses in veterinary medicine that it need be mentioned only to emphasize the fact that it is actually a depressant, rather than the excellent stimulant which most people believe it to be. It stimulates neither the respiration, the heart and blood system, nor the muscles.

Alcohol irritates the skin, injures the cells, has an astringent action, and shrinks tissues; it causes irritation and inflammation to mucous membranes. When injected into tissue, it acts as an anesthetic, but may permanently destroy nerve tissue. Alcohol anesthesia lasts longer than ether or chloroform, but if given in large enough doses to anesthetize, it is too near the fatal dose for safety.

Alcohol has very little germ-killing power, and only at 70 per cent by weight—a percentage difficult to approximate—is it worth using for this purpose.

Never give alcohol to "warm" a pet. All it does is lower his temperature by bringing the blood to the stomach and producing a false sensation of warmth. Nor should it be given as an aphrodisiac. I have known clients to use it in an effort to get shy breeding males to attempt copulation. They have found it often makes them worse.

LOCAL ANESTHETICS

These drugs, which can be injected to cause loss of pain in a given area, are a great boon to animals, doctors, and pet owners. They may be injected over a main nerve trunk, around the area to be anesthetized—for example, around a bad gash which needs to be sutured, or around a tumor which requires removal.

Cocaine is not made from opium, as so many think, but from leaves of trees which grow in Peru and Bolivia. It is dangerous to humans because of addiction, but animals cannot develop addictions without human help. Used locally, it blocks off nervous conduction. Much higher concentrations are needed for main nerve trunks than for terminal branches.

Procaine (also called Novocaine), **butyn,** and **nupercaine** are being more and more widely used. The first is used more widely than the others in veterinary practice. Butyn is frequently used in the eyes to relieve soreness.

When adrenalin (epinephrine) is combined with any of the above, the capillaries of the anesthetized area shrink and bleeding is greatly reduced. It is well to remember this if you take home a pet that has been operated on or sutured under a local anesthetic of procaine and adrenalin. When you start for home from the doctor's, there may be no bleeding, but as the effects of the adrenalin wear off, considerable bleeding may ensue, so be prepared. It is nearly always better to leave an animal that has been operated on in a hospital for twelve to twenty-four hours, but so many veterinarians maintain only offices and operating rooms with no facilities for keeping pets that it is often necessary to look after your own pet at home.

Some doctors prefer combinations of local anesthetics, and there are many new ones coming along. **Urea-and-quinine** is a favorite where very long-lasting anesthesia is desired. Its effects may last for several weeks.

TOPICAL ANESTHETICS

Several of the drugs we have mentioned are also used to deaden pain simply by allowing them to soak through tissues. In addition to butyn, *procaine, quinine,* a coal-tar derivative called *phenol,* and *benzyl alcohol* are often used as topicals. Such anesthetics stop itching when they are incorporated in salve applied by being rubbed in, and relieve pain when they are ingredients of ointments used in cuts, sores, anal ills, or ear canker.

In using them it is essential to keep them in contact with the tissue. If the dog persists in licking or rubbing them off, they must be replaced. If you also have a cat to treat, never use phenol on it. The same applies to foxes.

Benzyl alcohol is a useful local anesthetic for surface application. It will dissolve in water one part to twenty-five. Its pain-quieting power is of short duration. When first applied there is often a stinging sensation, followed by numbness. It is used in ointments to quiet skin irritation, in ear remedies to reduce the itching, and in salves applied to cuts or sores. Four per cent solutions are strong enough. It must not be used full strength.

PAINKILLERS

Acetylsalicylic Acid (Aspirin). "Doctor, how about an aspirin for my dog?" How many times I have heard these words over the telephone! The client sometimes goes on to tell me that she has already given Fifi three and the little thing still seems to have a pain. Fifi is a twelve-pound Pekinese.

The derivatives of salicylic acid, a synthetic drug made from coal tar, are numerous, but only acetylsalicylic acid (aspirin) is of much interest to pet owners. The salicylates act to reduce fever slightly. No effect on heat production is noticed, but the heat loss is heightened by bringing the blood to the body surface where, in short-haired animals, it tends to dissipate.

We can judge the effect of aspirin as a painkiller only by questioning human subjects. Students assure us it does not relieve sore throat, or toothache, or pain in the intestines. It does afford relief from neuralgia, rheumatic and headache pains. In canine encephalitis, when dogs seem to have headaches, aspirin may be effective. Salicylates do not exert germ-killing power in the blood, so should not be given to cure disease.

The dose for an adult human is five to fifteen grains (the usual aspirin tablet contains five grains). It is evident from this what a huge dose even one five-grain tablet is to a cocker spaniel, for instance, or to twelve-pound Fifi. If the cocker weighs twenty-five pounds, he weighs one sixth as much as a human being. One tablet for him is equivalent to giving a person six tablets—obviously an overdose, especially when given four or five times a day. One half tablet is enough for a twenty-five-pound dog, while a grown St. Bernard can be given three with safety.

Acetanilid (Antifebrine) and **Acetophenetidin (Phenacetine).** These coal-tar derivatives belong to still another group of painkillers. Neither is as safe or as valuable as the salicylates, but both cause a lowering of a fever temperature as well as some relief from pain. A twenty-five-pound pet needs no more than half a five-grain tablet.

Aminopyrene and **Antipyrene** are drugs similar in action to those above. We used to hear about them frequently, but today they are little used because of their inferiority to the salicylates.

Bromine. Bromides are used in medicine as depressants of the nervous system. They are prescribed less frequently today than formerly. However, many drugstore remedies sold to pet owners as sedatives are bromides. Whether they are *sodium, potassium, calcium,* or *ammonium* bromide makes little difference; the bromine does the work. Sodium bromide is probably the safest and ammonium bromide the least desirable. Since no prescription is required, it is sometimes advisable to resort to bromides when no veterinarian can be reached.

Their action is to cause a general quieting which results in drowsiness and sleep; overdoses and continual dosing may even produce coma. When given in just the right amounts, the animal calms but remains alert to his surroundings. The principal use of bromides recently has been in the prevention of convulsions. But in this respect they are inferior to phenobarbital. Since too large doses often cause vomiting, they are considered fairly safe drugs. When it is desired to give large doses, they had best be given with or after meals. The bromides give longer sedation than other drugs used for the purpose but produce "hangovers" far more severe, and their sedation to prevent fits and epilepsy in animals is only a fraction of that produced by other drugs.

Laymen almost always give too large a dose of bromide. When we realize that five grams a day is a maximum human dose, then one gram is a safe dose for a forty-pound dog. One gram is fifteen grains, so that one five-grain tablet every eight hours is enough. Yet I have seen dog owners give forty-five grains a day and wonder why the dog became sicker. Bromine poisoning may be worse than the condition for which the bromine was given.

Dilantin is one of the newer drugs used as an anticonvulsant and to lessen convulsions. Equivalent doses are far more efficient than bromides or phenobarbital. Doses of one grain daily for a forty-pound dog, or even as high as one and a half grains, produce excellent results. A St. Bernard needs only three or four grains. One has to try dilantin in slightly varying amounts on each pet to determine the proper dose.

Morphine and the **Opiates** (Morphine, Paregoric, and Codeine). Since many veterinarians no longer care to use opiates, feeling that other drugs fill the bill as well or better, morphine is being used less than formerly. There are others, however, who still believe that it stands at the top of the list of all drugs as a painkiller. Derived from the poppy, morphine, camphorated tincture of opium (paregoric), and codeine in cough syrups are used in veterinary work.

Morphine kills pain and brings sleep, produces constipation.

Paregoric is used to induce similar effects, but the concentration of the opiate is so slight that there is less danger in its use. In general, paregoric produces a quieting effect, at the same time relieving pain. Like morphine, it produces constipation. All these drugs cause the pupils of the eyes to contract to smaller than normal, varying with the size of the dose given. Paregoric, which causes the mobility of the intestine to decrease, will produce a definite sleepiness in dogs but causes cats to become restless.

Paregoric with 0.4 per cent of opium is given in fairly large doses. When a forty-pound dog has been poisoned and is hemorrhaging bloody diarrhea, a drastic dose of a teaspoonful three times a day may be necessary. A giant dog with diarrhea can manage two teaspoonfuls. For small puppies with diarrhea, from six drops in a little water up to one fourth teaspoonful in a six-weeks-old collie puppy has proved successful. Your veterinarian will tell you the safest dose for your particular pet.

Codeine is used considerably to check coughing. Opium or any of its derivatives accomplishes this result. It is frequently combined with terpin hydrate. Whether its use is sensible therapeutics depends on the kind of cough. If phlegm has accumulated in the air passages, coughing helps to remove it. Then why should anyone want to stop the cough, except because it annoys the pet's owner? Better to place the animal where he won't be heard and let him cough. But if the cough is a dry, useless, hacking spasm, opiates or any antitussives are definitely indicated.

STIMULANTS

Caffeine. Besides having a slight stimulating effect on the peristalsis in the intestine, caffeine is useful because it (1) stimulates the general circulation by accelerating the heart, increasing its force and raising the blood pressure. It affects the heart muscle directly. Overdoses cause such rapid heartbeat that blood pressure drops. (2) It increases the rapidity and depth of respiration. (3) It stimulates the nervous system. (4) It increases muscular strength and power. (5) It stimulates the production of urine by heightening the activity of the kidneys without irritating them. Thus it is a *diuretic.*

Caffeine can be given in pill form as caffeine citrate, as an injection in the form of caffeine sodiobenzoate, or as ordinary coffee. If an old dog can be taught to take coffee, it may be a lifesaver. Sugar and cream with it are not harmful. Very little coffee is required as a good-size dose for a dog. The error most people make is in giving their pets too much. In proportion to the human dose, when used as a stimulant, a cocker, weighing twenty-five pounds, needs only one third to one half a cup, while a cup is enough for a great Dane. Yet an owner will often mistakenly give two cups to a small dog if the dog is hungry for it.

As a stimulant to counteract a narcotic or barbiturate poisoning, fairly large amounts of coffee should be given, but great care is necessary to prevent some from running into the lungs of the anesthetized animals. It is safer to give it via a stomach tube, or let your veterinarian inject caffeine sodiobenzoate. If coffee is not handy, strong tea is an excellent substitute. A cup of tea contains almost as much caffeine as a cup of coffee. Cocoa contains theobromine, whose action is similar to that of caffeine.

Ammonia. Aromatic spirits are often given to dogs and other pets to sniff, or by mouth as a stimulant. A cocker can stand one half c.c. in water, but very often large doses are given mistakenly. Ammonia has also been given to stimulate kidney action, and to help the animal to raise phlegm from the windpipe, but for these purposes it is inferior to other drugs for pets. Best to forget it.

Camphor. Many laymen apparently believe that camphor, by its odor alone, has some extraordinary power to avert disease. Often veterinarians also find that the owner has hung a wad of cloth soaked in camphorated oil about his dog's neck, in the expectation that the camphor would somehow stimulate him. Contrary to the earlier belief that camphor was one of the heart stimulants, studies show that its value is so small as to be inconsequential.

Strychnine. The seeds of a small tree called quaker-button, growing naturally in the East Indies, yield a drug called *nux vomica.* From this in turn are isolated strychnine and brucine. The former is available to laymen at drugstores in some states. They need only sign in a book as receipt for the poison and it is theirs. Safe doses of strychnine do not stimulate respiration, as many people think, nor has it value as a heart or intestinal stimulant, or to strengthen muscles, though it is often given for these purposes. Despite all you may have heard about its value, the best place for strychnine is in the drugstore, where it cannot poison some person or animal who might inadvertently swallow it.

DIURETICS

Agents which increase the flow of urine are diuretics. We have noted earlier the action of several drugs which incidentally increase urine flow, although they are used primarily for some other purpose. In addition to these, certain drugs, such as salines, by increasing thirst, cause the blood to absorb a surplus of water which later escapes through the kidneys.

Diuretics are occasionally useful to flush some circulatory poison from the blood or to pull dropsical fluid from the abdomen and relieve pressure on the heart and lungs without resorting to tapping. Sometimes when animals have bladder infections, copious urine formation and elimination helps wash that reservoir clean. There are also times when abundant urine helps prevent formation of urine crystals and flushes out those which have formed.

It need hardly be said that while you are trying to eliminate part of the dropsical fluid by diuresis without tapping the abdomen, you must prevent the dog from drinking more water. You are trying to make him soak this surplus fluid back into his blood vessels. To do that you cause him to urinate copiously, which reduces the water content of the blood, which in turn causes him to replenish it from his abdomen.

Water. The basis of diuresis centers about water. Reducing the percentage in the blood is one thing that is striven for. This in turn creates thirst; more water is drunk, more eliminated. So your veterinarian may inject water with added salt to make a "physiological solution." Or he can inject a small amount of common salt in solution, or even give it by mouth so that the pet will drink copiously.

Urea, in its pure chemical form, is coming more and more to be used. It is not necessary to administer it as an injection, but it may be given mixed with fluids such as meat broths. It is not advisable to give it to an animal with kidney disease. Your veterinarian will suggest the proper dose, if any is needed.

Sugar. Either glucose or cane sugar, or both, may be given, but in such large amounts that the pet can't utilize it all. It must be given by vein, and when so given, especially in poison cases, helps detoxify some poisons and hence is worthy of use for several reasons. A 50 per cent solution is generally used, a forty-pound dog requiring about 12 c.c.s.

Cane sugar is used intravenously in double the dose of glucose and in some ways is preferable.

There are also proprietary drugs and mixtures, such as *calomel, squill,* and *digitalis,* which your veterinarian may favor, or he may tell you to use coffee for its caffeine.

When dogs are known to have infected or defective kidneys, your veterinarian may prescribe some mercurial drug. One dose in combination with, say theophylline, either injected or used as a suppository, may keep up its good work for nearly a day and reduce the dropsy and edema considerably.

HEART STIMULANTS

Digitalis. Of the drugs whose action is specifically on the heart, digitalis stands first. The dried leaves of the lovely garden flower, foxglove, are the source of this remarkable drug. Several other plants produce the so-called digitalis principles: squill, a sea onion; strophanthus, a tree whose seeds are used; and even the bulb of the lily-of-the-valley.

Digitalis directly affects the muscle of the heart, whose force of contraction it greatly increases. The rate is also slowed. It is useful in many disturbances which result from heart failure—and heart weakness is heart failure. Dropsy and edema of the tissues may be due both to heart and kidney failure. Digitalis gives relief in some cases. It is not, however, the universal remedy some people think. Digitalis is not a useful stimulant when a quick one is needed, because it takes too long to establish the desired effects. It is almost useless in some forms of heart trouble, in pneumonia, in shock. The dose is such a tricky matter it should be left to your veterinarian.

Epinephrine (Adrenalin). When your veterinarian injects a small dose of epinephrine into your dog, to treat him for shock after an accident or severe intestinal bleeding, he does so because of certain life-saving properties which this drug, produced by the adrenal glands, has demonstrated. Of its many effects, those he desires are contraction of the capillaries and arterioles sufficiently so that a clot may form without being washed off from the injured tissue or organ, so that some increase in blood pressure may occur to help the animal recover from shock, and so that breathing may be easier and oxygen-absorption promoted. Its effects are of short duration—only a matter of minutes—but those minutes usually are all that are required to save the pet's life. This wonderful drug can be relied upon to produce all these effects; it is the perfect antidote for shock.

Suppose sometime in the past your dog was given a dose of anti-tetanus serum. Again he receives a puncture wound filled with filth difficult to remove. You rush to the nearest veterinarian and forget to explain (or don't know that it is necessary) that the dog had had horse serum previously. Another dose of tetanus serum is injected. Shock! Anaphylaxis! Adrenalin may save your pet.

Mixed with procaine and used as a local anesthetic in surgery, epinephrine helps prevent capillary bleeding. In cases of heart failure or stoppage, adrenalin, injected directly into the heart, may sometimes cause it to beat again. In acute bronchial asthma it brings relief. The dose is very small. Your veterinarian usually uses a 1:1000 solution and injects fractions of a cubic centimeter.

Ephedrine. Another drug, this one of plant origin, has similar properties. Unlike epinephrine, it has the advantage of being absorbed from the digestive tract; it need not be injected unless quick action is required. Moreover, it has much longer effects. Practically everything said regarding epinephrine applies to ephedrine, except that it is sometimes harmful when used in shock treatment. In pet medicine it finds a wonderful use in emphysema in old, wheezy animals. Animals which cough constantly, apparently trying to raise phlegm from the lungs, are often benefited by a little ephedrine. A mixture with atropine sometimes works wonders.

Your veterinarian will advise you on its use and dosage, but it must be remembered that the smallest human doses obtainable from drugstores are enough for large dogs and should be divided to make the proper amount for smaller pets.

SECRETORY GLAND DEPRESSANTS

Belladonna. All the old veterinary books had much to say about the wonders of belladonna. It was a favorite remedy used by all sorts of people. The old horse "jockeys" used to give mixtures of it with arsenical preparations to give temporary relief to horses with heaves, so that they could trade them to some unsuspecting victim.

Today belladonna is seldom used by small animal practitioners, but one of its derivatives, *atropine,* finds many uses. Atropine does almost everything that the parent product will do. Other drugs with the same effects, such as *metropine,* are also used. All are given principally to cause dilation of the pupils, as in eye examinations, to dry secretions, because they inhibit glandular secretions with remarkable efficacy, to aid in preventing car sickness, and to counteract overdoses of drugs such as arecolene or Lentin, as well as poisoning by such drugs.

If a dog has been eating plants in a garden where there is deadly nightshade (a rich source of belladonna), and you see him bumping into objects, trying to get into a dark spot; if you open his mouth and find it dry; if his temperature is high, heart very rapid, pulse weak, and gait abnormal; if he is restless and excited—call your veterinarian. He can flush out the offending herbage, inject arecolene, pilocarpine, or Lentin repeatedly until the pet's mouth shows moisture, and thus save him.

DRUGS ACTING ON THE ORGANS OF REPRODUCTION

Nearly every pet owner has wondered what drug he could use in some particular phase of his pet's reproduction cycle. Could males be made to stay home if certain drugs were fed to them? Could other drugs cause a bitch to dry up? Could a female hunting dog have her heat period postponed by injections? Could anything be used to stop the undesirable results of a mismating? In these matters the up-to-date veterinarian can often be of the greatest assistance.

The Female. Starting with preparation for breeding, we know that certain vitamins are essential for reproduction. Chief of these is vitamin A. Vitamin E is essential for rats; despite the testimonials you may have seen to the contrary, it has not been demonstrated as necessary for other species. These facts are covered in the chapters on feeding, since vitamins are not drugs, but food. Here we need only repeat that no supplementary vitamins or drugs are apt to have beneficial effects on reproduction, provided the animal has been fed a complete diet.

What can you do if your bitch is bred by accident to an undesirable male? If she has been bred during the very first part of the acceptance period, breed her at once to the desired male. Then breed her every other day as long as she will accept him. The chances are good that her pups will be sired by the proper male.

But if she is bred too late to do anything, then have your veterinarian inject her with heavy doses of estrin, which will prevent the ova (eggs) from nesting in the uterus. You may douche her, but that can be risky, and the estrin treatment is preferable. Pressure douches are needed. Nearly always laymen fail to hold the tube in long enough to get the douche fluid up to the uterus through the Fallopian tubes, and in to the ovarian capsules. There is also danger of overdoing it if the pressure is sustained too long, for then the fluid may spill into the abdomen, where it can cause trouble.

How can a pregnant female animal be helped at the time for parturition? Is she sluggish? Your veterinarian can inject an extract made from the posterior pituitary gland. It may be one of the many put out by drug houses. Pituitrin is of great value. Pitocin has been of even greater worth because it has its principal effect on the uterus and less nausea accompanies its use. Any of these drugs should be injected only by your veterinarian. None of them should be given to an animal with a constricted pelvis. If a puppy is too large for passage through the pelvis, it would be cruelty to inject the mother. What she needs is a Caesarean operation.

At weaning time should we rub the mother's breasts with camphorated oil or other substances? No, let them cake naturally and they will soon stop secreting. Drugs are unnecessary.

Very old bitches often resorb their partially developed fetuses. How can the veterinarian help them carry to full term? He may give small amounts of stilbestrol, the female sex hormone, at regular intervals. I treated one famous fourteen-year-old, forty-pound bitch by giving one milligram every three days during her pregnancy and she whelped two puppies, though she had resorbed both of her previous litters.

The Male. Male animals have had all manner of drugs fed them and injected into them to make them eager to mate and fertile if they do. Some drugs make matters worse. There was a vogue for using testosterone until it became apparent that it was making animals sterile instead of fertile.

Puppies whose testicles are not descended are often rendered normal by A-P-L (anterior-pituitary-like) injections. And this synthetic hormone may have some effect on sexual vigor in mature animals. In either case it is worth a try, but you must be prepared for a series of treatments.

ABORTIFACIENTS

Pet owners have repeatedly attempted to cause abortion in their pregnant charges by using drugs which they think cause human abortion. Most of these drugs do not accomplish the desired result, and many cause sickness in pets just as their misuse does in humans.

The safe abortifacients, testosterone and a so-called gonadotropic pituitary hormone, are known to your veterinarian. For obvious reasons they may not be circulated to the public. If any drugs should be "kept under lock and key," these are among that group.

DRUGS TO KILL INTERNAL PARASITES

The drugs which are used to eradicate the worms which infest pets (the helminths) are called anthelmintics. Some are flat worms (platyhelminths) and some are round (nemahelminths). This class of drugs is of vital importance to us all, since the most prevalent group of diseases to which pets fall heir is caused by worms and external parasite infestation, with the consequent symptoms. The life histories of all of the common parasites have been considered in an earlier chapter. Here we will discuss only the drugs used in their elimination.

Male Fern. One of the oldest worm expellers is the dried root of a common fern (*Aspidium*) or extractions from it. It has been used since ancient times and is still in use where people do not know of more efficient drugs. However, with the greatly improved anthelmintics available, there is little reason to use male fern today.

Arecolene Hydrobromide. We have few more efficient expellers of tapeworms than this drug with its unique properties. Since it not only causes the tapeworms to let go, but also has a vigorous flushing action on the intestine, it performs the feat of expelling tapeworms in as little as twenty to sixty minutes. But it may produce griping pains. Fifteen to twenty hours' fasting should precede the dose. The dose is about one tenth grain for each fifteen pounds of weight.

If possible, animals given arecolene should be exercised about half an hour after dosing. Dogs may be taken for walks. Exercise, such as walking, tends to prevent griping.

Arecolene comes in sugar-coated pills in a variety of sizes, from one sixtieth grain to one half. It is cumulative, so that when a normal dose causes vomiting, it may be given in three or four split doses about seven minutes apart and will do its work admirably. The dose for small animals is necessarily larger in proportion than that for large. Study the graph and dose accordingly.

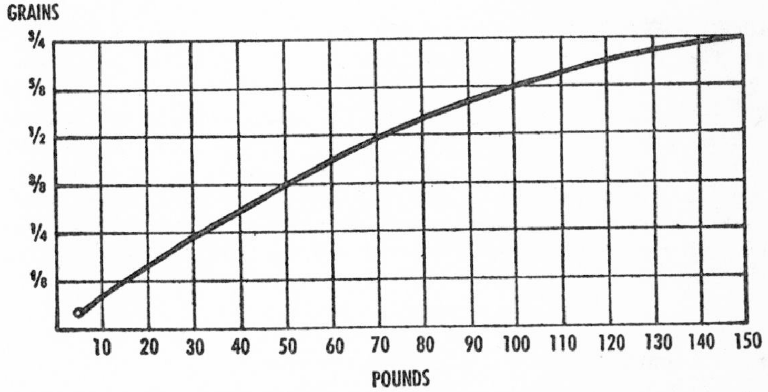

Safe doses of arecolene hydrobromide. Find the weight of your dog. Follow the line vertically until it intersects the heavy black line, then follow to the left to read the dose. Doses are given in multiples of one-eighth because the drug is most often sold in one-eighth-grain pills. In some cases you may have to cut pills in halves, thirds, or quarters.

Nemural is a proprietary drug whose characteristics are similar to arecolene. The manufacturers advise no more than twelve hours fasting before dosing. The recommended dose is one pill for each eight pounds of body weight, given in a little food. In using Nemural, we have also found that larger dogs need less in proportion. It seems especially useful for cats. The drug is dispensed only through the veterinary profession.

Di-phenthane. At present this drug, too, is sold only through the the veterinary profession under the name of Teniathane, but since it is a chemical available to anyone, it may come into common use and become available at drugstores. Di-phenthane has the unique property of killing tapeworms, which are then partially or wholly digested. It is fed with food. Its disadvantage is that the pet's owner does not see the worms and so is never sure that they have been eliminated.

Hydrogen Peroxide. This household drug immediately kills every worm it touches. The difficulty lies in getting it to the worms. Since it is such a remarkably effective emetic, oral dosage seldom gets beyond the stomach and so destroys worms only up to that point. It must be given rectally under very slight pressure, so that as it turns to oxygen and water the gas can precede the solution upward and not form pockets where the gas pressure may balloon the intestines and cause irritation. The pet may have blood in the stools for several days if this occurs. The solution itself is harmless to the tissues.

A 1½ per cent solution, half the drugstore strength, is strong enough. This will give off five times its volume of oxygen. The solution generally requires from two to five minutes to travel up the intestinal tract to the stomach. When it reaches the stomach, the animal will belch.

Excellent results are claimed for hydrogen peroxide in ridding dogs of whipworms which are difficult to reach in the cecum. Given rectally, the fluid reaches into the cecum quickly. In fact, an enema tube can be inserted almost to the mouth of the cecum.

Wormseed Oil. This is another very old anthelmintic and was discovered by the Indians of North America. It is a peroxide. Because of the newer and more efficient drugs that have supplanted it, most pet owners and veterinarians no longer find it useful. It is irritating, especially toxic to puppies, and dangerous to give when there is any intestinal damage.

Santonin. This drug was discovered as long ago as male fern and, like the fern, has been supplanted by newer and more efficient drugs. It was used for roundworms and tapeworms, and later to eliminate whipworms.

Carbon Tetrachloride. In many sections of the world this is still the drug most often used, but it is slowly giving place to tetrachlorethylene, for obvious reasons. If a dog bites a capsule of carbon tetrachloride, the animal often dies from inhaling the fumes, which are highly toxic.

Tetrachlorethylene. This is a common drug of commerce. As an anthelmintic it is safe provided there is no fat in the digestive tract of the animal. Because of its affinity for fat, it quickly combines with it. The fat is absorbed and carries the drug through the intestinal wall into the circulation, where it proves poisonous, as evidenced by the staggering gait and even comatose condition of its victim. Some veterinarians refuse to give it for home use because of the tragic incidents of carelessness they can cite.

However, if you could be absolutely sure that your dog had been completely starved for twenty-four hours before dosing, you could give several times the recommended amount without harm. It may be given to very young puppies safely, even at the rate of one tenth c.c. for each twelve ounces of weight. But for grown dogs, if one c.c. is given for each ten pounds it proves highly effective, killing roundworms, hookworms, and whipworms which are not in the cecum. Very large dogs need somewhat less in proportion. The graph shows the safe dosage if the pet is empty.

It should be followed in an hour to two hours by a saline physic, such as milk of magnesia or Epsom salts or arecolene hydrobromide. Giving arecolene after tetrachlorethylene is a reliable way of expelling several kinds of worms at once.

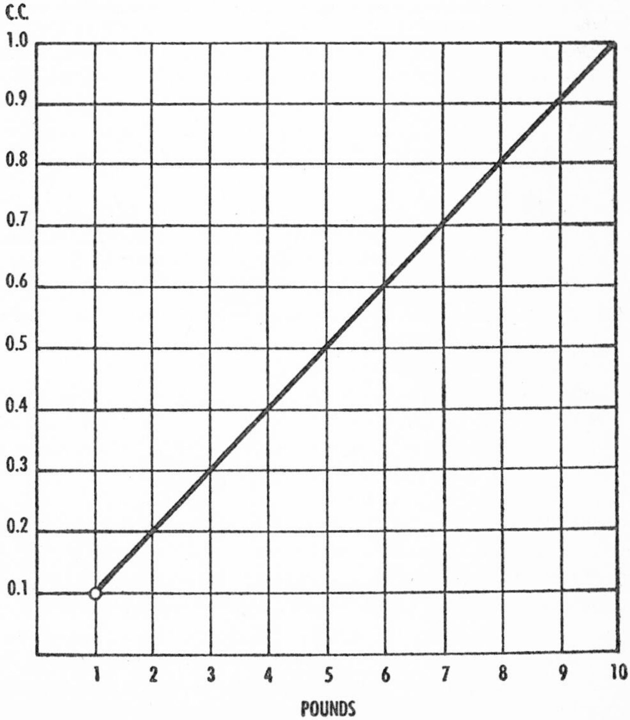

Safe doses of tetrachlorethylene for robust, empty puppies. Find the weight of your puppy. Follow the line vertically until it intersects the heavy black line, then follow to the left to read the dose. Doses are given in multiples of one-tenth c.c. because the drug is often sold in two-tenths-cc. (three minim) size capsules. You may have to prick the capsule with a pin and squeeze some of the drug out to make the proper amount.

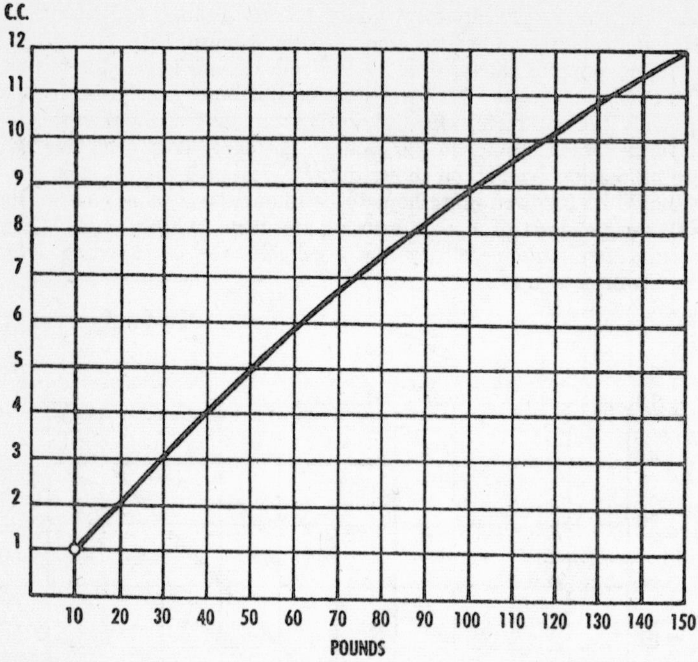

Safe doses of tetrachlorethylene for robust, empty dogs. Find the weight of your dog. Follow the line vertically until it intersects the heavy black line, then follow to the left to read the dose. Doses are given in c.c.s.

Normal Butyl Chloride. While tetrachlorethylene was hitherto the drug usually sold in drugstores for the home deworming of pets, N butyl chloride has now largely replaced it. This is not because it is any more efficient, but because it is safer if the pet has been fed by mistake. It is more toxic to little puppies than the former, and I personally prefer the tetrachlorethylene for every purpose except deworming for whipworms.

Very large doses of N butyl chloride may be given without danger, and these work into the cecum and kill whipworms. Such large doses are extremely nauseating, however. Dogs generally vomit the drug, so it is almost imperative that an anti-emetic be given first, and when it has taken effect, the N butyl chloride capsule can be administered. Pentobarbital at about one third the anesthetic dose makes an excellent anti-emetic. But it also produces sleepiness and giddiness—a condition which the pet appears to enjoy but which often causes panic in the owner. Forewarned is forearmed!

An even better and more efficient method of eradicating whipworms is to starve the dog twenty-four hours, then give the hookworm dose. Repeat

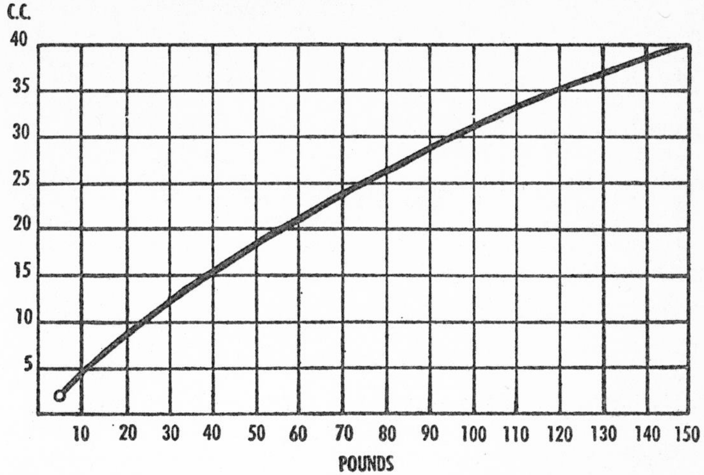

Safe doses of normal butyl chloride for robust, empty dogs in the treatment of whipworms. Find the weight of your dog. Follow the line vertically until it intersects the heavy black line, then follow to the left to read the dose. Doses are given in c.c.s.

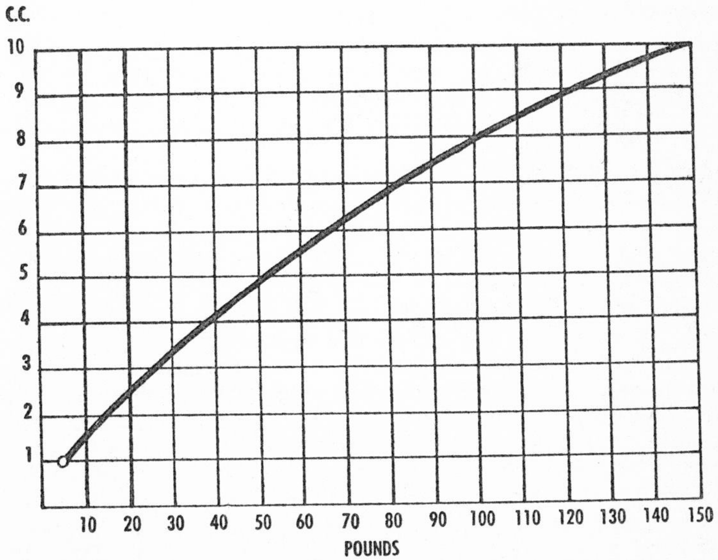

Safe doses of normal butyl chloride for robust, empty dogs in the treatment of roundworms and hookworms.

with the same dose every hour and feed the dog two hours after the fourth dose. Give no physic. The results from this method have been uniformly satisfactory.

DRUGS TO KILL EXTERNAL PARASITES

Dozens of drugs can be used to kill insects, but most of them will kill mammals and humans too. There are four modern drugs which are quite safe if used with reasonable care, and new ones are appearing and being tested annually.

Rotenone. This drug (and related resins) is obtained from the roots of tropical plants, notably derris in the East Indies, cube in South and Central America; it is one of the most potent insect killers known. It kills animals by paralyzing their respiratory tracts. Pets can eat it in small amounts usually with no ill effects. It is more poisonous if inhaled, and is especially so if it gets into fresh open cuts.

Rotenone also kills fish. If you use it, don't allow rotenone to blow onto the water in a fishpond. And don't allow a dog dusted against flea infestation to swim in such a pool.

Probably rotenone in dusts, diluted to 1 per cent, is as safe for flea and louse powders as anything one could ask. No dog should be put in a closed box and dusted, since it is then forced to breathe the dust. It is hard to believe that pets could be so mistreated, but they often are—by people who want to keep the powder off their clothes.

Incidentally, with some people—not all—rotenone causes numbness of the lips and tongue tip. The sensation soon passes. If you are sensitive, dust the pet in the open where the breeze blows the dust away from you.

Rotenone is an ingredient of some of our best dips and rinses. A one per cent solution in pine oil to which an emulsifier has been added kills all insects except ticks.

Pyrethrum. Chrysanthemums contribute pyrethrum to our store of drugs. In pure form, the chemical agents made from it are called pyrethrins. They are mentioned here because they are so often ingredients of flea powder, but the fact that they are included here is not an endorsement, since they merely stun the insects. The early powders were sold with the advice that you dust the animal, brush the fleas and lice onto a newspaper, and burn the paper. You burned it because the insects usually refused to "stay dead" and manufacturers knew it.

Pyrethrum has a wonderful psychological effect on the pet's owner. When it is used as an ingredient of a powder or rinse, the insects appear to die instantly. They drop off, and that is what the owners love to see. Mix in some rotenone and the bugs not only drop off but they stay dead! The combination of the two drugs makes a fine treatment for the owner as well as for the pet.

DDT. This is also called by the simple (to a chemist) name of diphenyldichlorotrichloroethane. It really kills insects and lasts for weeks without decomposing and losing its potency. It finds uses in fly sprays, mists, dusts, rinses, and all vehicles for spreading bug death. When it is used in liquid-soap shampoos at a low concentration of 2 per cent, the effect will last in the animal's coat for a week or more, killing any insect that gets on the fur.

Chlordane is another potent insecticide. You will find it as the principal killing agent in flea and tick destroyers. It is relatively safe and extremely lethal to all forms of insects which torment dogs.

Benzine hexachloride, also called *Sixide* and *cyclochlorohexane,* is the newest of the lethal products to date, and it kills ticks as well as other insects. It is probably one of the safest for pets, since it may be used in powders at a dilution of 1 per cent. This is relatively non-toxic to pets in the amounts that would be used to kill fleas or ticks. Lindane, the *gamma isomer,* is the most toxic to insects and animals too. Like DDT, this drug has a long-lasting effect. It is used in a very wide variety of ways, even for killing mange mites.

Phenothiazine. This drug, used in farm animal practice to kill several forms of intestinal parasites, is not effective against the dog forms. In addition, it is toxic to pets if given internally. However, it has been found to be one of the more potent mange remedies. The drug is available to the public.

Because of its toxicity, it cannot be safely used if it must be applied on areas which a pet can reach to lick. If an Elizabethan collar is applied, the drug is safe, and one or two applications usually destroy the mites.

DRUGS APPLIED TO THE SKIN

Possibly because vanishing and other creams are thought by many to be essential aids to beautify the human skin, many pet owners have come to the mistaken conclusion that there must be skin lotions necessary for animals' skins. Some think there are miracle drugs or vitamins which may be given to make an animal's skin and coat shine and his eyes sparkle. There are no such lotions, nor does a healthy animal need any.

What we are going to consider here are the vehicles, skin remedies, drugs used in burn treatments, antiseptics for cuts and scratches, and liniments.

Vehicles for Drugs Applied to the Skin. WOOL FAT, also called lanolin, forms an excellent vehicle because it holds most drugs and, when it is absorbed into the skin, carries the drugs with it. It is coherent, sticking even to surfaces which are moist. Wool fat of the ordinary variety contains about 25 per cent water. It can also be obtained in an anhydrous form (without water).

PETROLATUM is available as a liquid (mineral oil), or as a jelly (vaseline). When used as a vehicle, it is not absorbed, and drugs used with it remain more or less outside of the skin. Depending upon whether a liquid or solid non-absorbable is desired, one or the other form is used.

LARD is still a standard base, as is *suet*. Everyone knows that it is usually advisable to mix some pleasant odor with them when they are used in medication.

GLYCERINE. This thick, sweet, syrupy material is mixed with innumerable drugs for skin application where liquids are used. But glycerine absorbs water from the tissues. Because it finds so many uses in human medicine, one would expect more in veterinary practice, but pets often lick the sweet substance and may be sickened by the accompanying drugs unless they are repellent.

Skin Disease Remedies. Almost every veterinarian has his favorite remedy for skin diseases. Some smell so unpleasant that the cure is almost worse than the disease. Some require such frequent application that treatment becomes a great bore. Some irritate. It is unfortunate that one general remedy cannot be given which will cure all such diseases, but since some are caused by mites, which require special drugs, others by fungi, and probably still others by bacteria and viruses—not to mention occasional cases resulting from some food idiosyncrasy—no one remedy can be suggested. Here are the common effective drugs and chemicals used today:

SULPHUR. This is one of the oldest and still one of the most reliable of skin remedies. Sulphur should not be used alone—as such it is useless. But when oxygen in the air combines with sulphur it forms sulphur dioxide, a gas deadly to fungus diseases and to some insects. It is this constant gas formation which cures. Sulphur, to be of value, must therefore be kept in position by some base which holds it in place and yet does not cover it to such an extent that air cannot reach it. The old lard-and-sulphur or axle-grease-and-sulphur treatments had some virtues, but they cured very slowly because the grease coated the sulphur particles.

The fineness of the sulphur particles, too, makes a great difference. Coarse sulphur crystals are not so effective as the sulphur which is close to the colloidal state. Colloidal materials are so fine they will stay in suspension as if they were in solution and never settle out. It is possible to obtain colloidal sulphur, but it is expensive and its results are not enough better than those obtained by the finest air-floated mechanically ground product to warrant the additional cost.

Sulphur mixed with vegetable oils produces better results than that mixed with heavy greases, but other drugs can be added which help materially, as we shall see.

TAR. This is a product greatly prized by the old farriers. It is much too irritating to be used full strength, and is diluted in various ways. Pine tar, juniper tar (also called oil of cade), coal tar, and oil of tar are all available.

Pine tar has a turpentiny taste and a typical pine odor. Its medicinal agents are chiefly creosotelike chemicals. Oil of tar is a distillation product made from tar. Many veterinarians use it as the principal ingredient of skin remedies. If you can stand the odor, it has some advantages. To my mind its disadvantages far outnumber them—the way it discolors coats, the fact that, used injudiciously, it may burn, and the odor.

OIL OF TURPENTINE. Many skin preparations employ gum turpentine. It was and still is used widely for horses, but for pets this product finds small usage. Besides its use in skin remedies, some is incorporated in liniments, where it has some value.

In curing skin diseases and relieving soreness, a veterinarian depends upon bringing blood to the skin—practically producing a mild inflammation. Turpentine in full strength would burn, but dilutions are often of value. When it is used, the proportion is small—not over 10 or 15 per cent when mixed with oils, and even less when mixed with other irritating products. Turpentine has a mild antiseptic effect.

One should be very sure not to use it on old dogs, especially those with kidney diseases. It has a strong diuretic effect, and even the amounts absorbed may damage kidneys irreparably. Occasionally we see blood in the urine of dogs when turpentine has been applied to the skin and absorbed through it. Turpentine as an ingredient of skin lotions should be used prudently.

CALAMINE LOTION. Some mild forms of skin disease are cured by this white liquid, which needs shaking each time before application. Calamine itself is a 98 per cent zinc-oxide preparation with a little iron rust mixed with it. Calamine lotion contains 8 per cent calamine. It is effective in certain cases where only the surface layers of the skin are attacked. The ear is part of the skin, and quite good results have been obtained by pouring the ear canal full of calamine lotion and allowing as much to stay as possible after the pet has shaken his head. But it had best not be used when the eardrum is broken, since it may cake around the delicate mechanism of the middle ear.

BORIC ACID. The medical profession has prescribed boric acid for so many years for so many millions of people that the first thing the layman thinks of to cure almost anything is boric acid or boracic acid. Boric acid and boracic acid are the same thing. In skin disease its value is questionable. It does not kill germs, but does retard their growth.

SALICYLIC ACID. One of the reasons salicylic acid is useful in skin remedies is that it destroys the outer layers of skin but does not destroy the growing layers. Who hasn't used corn removers, most of which contain salicylic acid and collodium? When applied, the skin swells, becomes soft, and the outer layers slough off. Like boric acid, its action on bacteria is to slow their growth but not to kill them. Salicylic acid is seldom used stronger than 10 per cent of any solution or ointment.

POTASSIUM PERMANGANATE. A favorite water solution, this useful drug is more valuable in human skin treatment than for animals. In humans, dressings can be applied and allowed to stay in place; animals often tear them off. Laymen often apply too strong solutions. One part to one hundred parts of water is as strong as should be used when applied uncovered. If a wet dressing is used, a solution of 1:10,000 is strong enough. And don't forget that it leaves a purple discoloration.

GENTIAN VIOLET. Speaking of stains, gentian violet, a dye, will really leave its mark. Used at 1:500 parts water when applied to the skin uncovered, it kills many kinds of germs. Even a 1:1,000,000 solution will kill some. If a pet licks it off, no harm is done, since it is safe enough to use in internal medicine. It may be applied many times to skin sores with no harm to the pet. The 1:1,000 strength usually proves practicable. Its one great disadvantage is its color. Few people want great purple patches on their pets.

TANNIC ACID. This is an astringent—an agent which causes shrinking and stops discharges. Considerable difference of opinion exists among veterinarians as to whether it is preferable to apply an astringent, and dry up an area affected with dermatitis, or to inflame it with some substance like turpentine and, with the aid of the inflammation, to cure it with other drugs.

In a 5 or 10 per cent solution, tannic acid is effective over raw areas such as those eroded by disease organisms or sore from constant scratching, since it causes a film protective protein to form. But there is a question whether, except in the case of burns, this is always desirable. Dogs may bite and scratch the film off as fast as it forms.

PHENOL (Carbolic Acid). This is a coal-tar derivative. Again let me remind you never to use it or any of its relatives on cats or foxes. A few drops will kill a kitten; a few drops will make any cat sick. And it can be absorbed through the skin. Phenol dog remedies are safe only on dogs.

Phenol is the standard by which other germicides are compared. We speak of Phenol Coefficient of 5, meaning that a comparison of germ-killing power of a certain dilution has been made with a given dilution of phenol.

Only weak solutions should be used, as phenol is a poison. It precipitates proteins. When applied to the skin, it first produces a whitened area which later turns brown and sloughs. As we have seen, it is a topical anesthetic, for which reason it is often incorporated in skin preparations by those who do not object to its odor. But it is always used in extremely small amounts. If half a teaspoonful will kill a dog, one can easily see how foolish it is to bathe him in a solution made by pouring phenol or one of its relatives indiscriminately into a bucket of water.

True, it will kill fleas and lice and mange mites outside the skin. But it is too harsh to be recommended for use on pets. As for skin disease, it cannot be relied upon to cure many forms, and the odor will advertise the treatment to every visitor for days.

ICHTHYOL was once widely employed as an ointment, but today it is used to a lesser extent. It is a dark gummy substance made by distilling the bituminous remains of fossil fishes. Some think it is because of its 15 per cent sulphur content that it exerts a curative property. In my experience it is inferior to many other skin remedies.

IODINE. This old stand-by of a generation ago is slowly being replaced as a skin remedy, as it is as an antiseptic. For ringworm in animals, it is used in the proportion of 50 per cent of the tincture with an equal amount of glycerine.

SPERGON. Since so many skin diseases are of fungus origin, a search is now under way for fungicides harmless to pets but deadly to fungi. One of these which offers much hope is Spergon (tetrachlorobenzoquinone). Mixed with flea powder, it has proved an effective preventive against some skin diseases and has even cured some.

Burn Remedies. When an animal is burned either by fire, scalding, or corrosion, by acids, caustics, or other chemicals, the capillaries of the skin become dilated in all the burned area. You will remember that any skin burn seeps a moist material. This seepage goes on and on until, in cases of large burned areas, so much plasma escapes that the animal's blood-volume loss is extremely serious. That is point one to remember. The second point is that all of this area affords an excellent growing medium for bacteria, whose toxic by-products may cause death to the burned victim. The third is that supportive treatment for the animal is essential because one often finds a temporary improvement followed by prostration, due to shock. What drugs can you use for burns?

TANNIC ACID is now the first thought of many doctors. When a fresh 10 per cent solution is used, a thick scab forms over the burn and to a large extent prevents the loss of plasma, although under the scab the tissue may remain moist.

To prevent growth of bacteria, some veterinarians use *gentian violet*, *acriflavin*, or *brilliant green*. Others prefer application of *powdered sulfa drugs* or solutions of *penicillin* or *streptomycin*. Still others use *tannic acid and dilute silver nitrate* with excellent results. Some favor salves embodying combinations of drugs, but spreading salves over painful burned areas adds to the pain. In first aid, however, it's a case of any port in a storm, and salves may be the only available remedy besides tea, which may be used for its tannic-acid content.

After the burn itself has been treated, supportive treatment is often necessary. If the pet seems to be in shock, an infusion with saline solution and glucose often saves its life. Clients often want their veterinarians to give sedatives in such cases, thinking it is the pain causing the shock. If they are given, the dose must be small or the drug may cause death.

Drugs for Cuts and Scratches. Does it sound unprofessional to say that any ordinary cut or scratch or scraped area which the pet can reach to lick is just as well off left untreated? If it is so small or unimportant that it does not need suturing, it does not need medication—if Dr. Dog can reach it. The scales on our pets' tongues can clean a wound beautifully, and clean wounds heal well. There are, however, many wounds in places our pets cannot reach, such as those on the head, neck, and shoulders, abscess formations under the skin, and wounds under long hair. These should be cared for by the owner. The variety of drugs available for treatment is wide, and the list is growing. Here we need discuss only the most important ones.

Disinfectants, germicides, antiseptics, bacteriostatics, fungicides, bactericides—what are these things? Disinfectants free areas of infection by destroying bacteria, fungus organisms, viruses—all kinds of infective organisms. Antiseptics inhibit the growth of bacteria or other infecting agents, but do not necessarily kill them. Germicides and bactericides are agents that kill germs. Contrary to what you may have thought, there are not very many which will kill germs and not injure tissues too. Bacteriostatics arrest the growth of bacteria. A viricide is an agent which kills viruses. Fungicides are agents which destroy fungi.

TINCTURE OF IODINE. One of the mainstays of veterinarians of a few years ago, as it was in the average household, tincture of iodine still has its uses. It is germicidal against all bacteria and many fungi and viruses, regardless of their race, creed, or color. It is twice as potent as phenol as a germ killer. Since a number of applications to the same area may result in burning, when several treatments are indicated it is better to use the tincture diluted by an equal amount of water. Iodine discolors, and animal hair once discolored with it may retain the stain for months. This, plus the fact that the treated area burns and smarts when it is applied, makes its use of limited value for pets.

PHENOL and its derivatives have already been discussed. Their chief drawback is the odor. Phenol kills flies and insects as well as bacteria.

CREOSOTE is bactericidal, but it, too, is objectionable because of its odor.

THYMOL, one of the related drugs, is more bacteriostatic than phenol against some germs and not so much so against others. Its chief drawbacks are its odor and the fact that, unlike phenol, it draws flies.

HEXYLRESORCINOL is a remarkable product in that even in dilutions of one to one thousand it is highly bactericidal. The drugstore product may be obtained in a glycerine solution. If pets lick it off, it does no harm. Its disadvantage is that, like iodine, repeated applications irritate tissues.

CHLORAMINE is one of the antiseptics that kill by the liberation of chlorine. It is excellent when used on wounds which are covered, and its effects are quite long-lasting. When it is applied to dressing in dilutions of one to one thousand, healing progresses nicely.

HYDROGEN PEROXIDE. When you apply this product to raw tissue there is a strong fizzing, and a white foam appears. This means that the peroxide is decomposing into water and oxygen. And only while this decomposition is progressing is the treated area being disinfected. But this fizzing helps wonderfully at times to loosen debris in wounds. As a germ killer, it is less efficient than many others. Phenol is about one hundred times as potent. In wound and external treatment it is best employed to cleanse wounds and to flush out the sheaths of male dogs when they become infected. The drugstore strength is 3 per cent, which has been found best for all such tasks.

POTASSIUM PERMANGANATE. There are many veterinarians who use this chemical for wound treatments, though it is now used less than formerly because we have so many better antiseptics. It is a brownish crystalline substance, generally used in concentrations of about one to five thousand parts of water.

MERCURIC COMPOUNDS. Our first thought is bichloride when we think of mercury. The large coffin-shaped blue tablets are synonymous with poison in the minds of many and are dangerous to have around for humans or pets. Best forget bichloride.

But there are many other useful mercuric compounds. What household does not have Tincture of Metaphen, or Mercurochrome, or Merthiolate? Recently much publicity has been given to the failure of these mercury compounds to kill germs. The inference is that they are worthless. Actually, at the "drugstore" dilutions, they are bacteriostatic, and to some extent bactericidal. To my knowledge, that is all the manufacturers ever claimed for them. If bacteria or their spores cannot grow in the presence of these drugs, then they serve a useful purpose. The red dye used gives the pet owner satisfaction in applying them and shows where the product has been used. As an application to sutured incisions, they prevent infection, but used under bandages, they may cause irritation.

SILVER. In veterinary medicine, silver is used as silver nitrate, silver oxide, and in colloidal form. Silver nitrate will kill bacteria, but it is a caustic and astringent. Except in burns (in dilute solutions) and in wart removal, it has few uses. Silver oxide is used in ear-canker unguents. Colloidal silver is greatly prized by some. It is not caustic or astringent and can be used safely, but the field of use is restricted, since many bacteria are not killed by it. Moreover, it stains hair black and stains clothes as well.

THE DYES. Acriflavin, a yellow dye, methylene blue, gentian violet, methyl violet, crystal violet are in use—one can judge how often by the number of vividly stained areas he sees on pets. Unfortunately these dyes are effective against a limited field of infectious organisms.

Liniments. The real value of a liniment is that it makes the one applying it massage the lame part of his pet. Because veterinary medicine has only so recently graduated from farriery, where the emphasis was on horses, for which liniments were regarded as a necessity, there are still those who use them and call for them, though seldom in my experience have they been of value for pets. Racing greyhound owners sometimes favor liniments.

Oily or alcoholic substances generally are the bases; some slippery or soapy substance is added along with pungent aromatic drugs and irritants. Some contain chloral hydrate, chloroform, or belladonna; many include turpentine, ammonia, or capsicum well diluted. The purpose is to cause a mild irritative effect which friction heightens. This draws blood to the part, and with increased circulation, it is hoped that lameness or stiffness will disappear.

Blisters—mixtures of irritating drugs, applied to the skin to actually cause blistering—are greatly prized for horses, so some owners often want a mild blister for pets, a cross between a blister and a liniment. Improperly used, they may burn the skin and do no good. In my opinion they are cruel and unnecessary.

THE SULFA DRUGS

The person who did not own pets B.S.D. (Before Sulfa Drugs) can possibly appreciate what their discovery has meant to pet owners. True, some are already outdated, and all are being replaced for some purposes by the antibiotics, but veterinary medicine is now a far happier profession because of them.

The first to be discovered was sulfanilamide. Shortly thereafter unfounded claims were made for it as a cure-all; it was said to be a specific for coccidiosis, viruses, including distemper in dogs, all kinds of bacteria. But genuine study showed that its field was very narrow—that it killed only a limited number of bacteria and was ineffectual against viruses, coccidiosis, warts, bad disposition, or ingrowing toenails!

Laymen cannot obtain sulfa drugs without prescriptions. Let your veterinarian tell you why he prescribes the sulfa drug he prefers for your pet. Here, in general, are a few things you should know about them, which will save his time in instructions and explain why he tells you to use them as he does.

Some of the sulfas do not kill certain bacteria. Some are more toxic than others. Some are much more soluble. Sulfathiazole and sulfadiazine accomplish approximately the same germ-killing effects, but the sulfadiazine, being more soluble, is a better bladder and kidney disinfectant. Some sulfas are but slightly absorbed from the digestive tract. Sulfathalidine disinfects the colon principally; sulfaguanidine, the whole tract. Some leave such acid residues that it is wise to prescribe bicarbonate of soda with them. Some do their best work when injected, some when taken orally.

In spite of all their wonderful effects, no sulfa drug and no combination of them has yet been found which will kill all the bacteria, and none affects viruses.

One of the most important facts to remember when you use the sulfas, which are absorbed, is that many of them are excreted via the kidneys quite soon after they are administered. Others, sulfamethazine, for example, need be injected only once a day. If your veterinarian says "give every six hours," don't stretch the interval to eight hours. For some, his instructions may be every four hours. The reason for giving them frequently is that sulfa drugs will not kill germs when their concentration in the blood drops to below one to fifty thousand. Your veterinarian may prescribe one grain, split in four doses, to each pound of body weight of your pet. When the drug is first absorbed, the concentration may be 1:25,000, but after a few hours it will have left the blood and the concentration may fall so low it can no longer kill germs in the body, so they grow again unimpeded. It pays to follow your veterinarian's instructions.

Powdered sulfa drugs are often sifted into surgical incisions and wounds, where they are of great help. Now they are being used in solutions, as in propylene glycol, and poured into inaccessible wounds where they often prove to be true miracle drugs and lifesavers.

THE ANTIBIOTICS

When researchers learned that some bacteria and molds give off substances toxic to others, a new branch of bacteriology was born. When further research demonstrated that these substances would kill bacteria and not poison animals, a lifesaving blessing of inestimable value was bestowed upon both us and our pets. And we are told that wonderful as penicillin, streptomycin, and aureomycin are, they are but heralds of far more wonderful drugs to come. Several which are still in the experimental stages, including aureomycin, have a specificity for certain types of bacteria. As yet none has been found specific for viruses, except aureomycin in the case of human virus pneumonia and possibly for ornithosis.

The antibiotics, like sulfas, are prescription drugs. At first they were given in quickly absorbed doses, mostly intramuscularly and at very frequent intervals. Later a way was found of combining them in a wax-and-oil solution from which they are slowly absorbed, so that injections once in twenty-four hours now suffice to furnish a high enough concentration in the blood to destroy effectively the germs against which they are being used. Aureomycin is eliminated so slowly that one dose a day, given orally, is sufficient.

NUTRITIONAL DEFICIENCY REMEDIES

These are principally minerals and vitamins, and they are discussed in the chapters on nutrition and specific nutritive problems under each species.

EMETICS

Hydrogen Peroxide. Used at half the ordinary drugstore strength, which is 3 per cent, this drug probably is the best emetic yet discovered for dogs. Mix equal amounts of peroxide and water and either make the animal swallow it or administer it with a stomach tube. Vomiting occurs in about two minutes and is repeated at intervals of about thirty seconds for several minutes thereafter.

Apomorphine is a prescription drug. It can be injected, or it can be given by dropping in the eye, from which it is absorbed. Your veterinarian usually uses a solution and gives about one milligram to a forty-pound dog. The animal becomes restless and may shake. Sometimes a severe depression follows its use.

Copper Sulfate. When neither of the above is available, copper sulfate, given at the rate of one grain in a little water for a forty-pound dog, often proves effective. A grain is about as large as a grain of wheat. It leaves no depression.

Mustard. This is difficult to administer orally and had best be given via stomach tube. One teaspoonful will cause vomiting fairly effectively for a forty-pound dog. Larger doses may continue the vomiting for too long a time.

Ipecac. Although many laymen try to use ipecac to make pets vomit, it is about the slowest-acting emetic of any and therefore of small use in emergencies. Drugstores carry syrup of ipecac. The dose is generally half a teaspoonful for a forty-pound dog.

Salt. Common table salt may be used, but it is hard to give. A strong solution is administered, so that the animal—our forty-pound dog—receives a teaspoonful of salt.

Lentin. This is an injectable drug which causes very rapid vomiting and also acts as a violent physic. It must not be used where only vomiting is desirable.

CATHARTICS

These drugs, which promote defecation, may be classified in a variety of ways; according to their severity (mild, medium, violent); according to their natures (oils, salines, metals, glandular stimulants, et cetera); according to their action (lubricants, bile-flow stimulants, et cetera); and so on. I shall simply list the most easily available cathartics and a few of those prescription drugs which your veterinarian uses or prescribes, and tell you why. The order of their listing is no indication of their value.

Castor oil is a fairly quick-acting cathartic. Dogs defecate about two hours after dosing. The stool is not fluid but only slightly softer than normal, unless overdoses are administered. Castor oil should be given on an empty stomach for the best results. The dose for a forty-pound dog is one half to one teaspoonful. Remember that in giving castor oil you are not trying to lubricate the intestinal contents, but that an irritant acid is causing a speed-up of evacuation. Racinic acid does the physicking; the oil is partly digested.

Mineral oil. In contrast to castor oil, the oral dose of mineral oil is almost all deposited with the feces. It is a lubricant. Larger doses may be given, but overdoses are inadvisable because they run out, and dogs sometimes will lick themselves and thus take feces into their stomachs. Overdosing is common. I have known clients to give a puppy a tablespoonful, which would be equivalent to the owner taking more than a glassful.

The chief danger in using oils is that inadvertently some—even a little—may be poured into the windpipe and cause pneumonia. However, some dogs will often lap mineral oil out of a dish. They may not refuse it if it is thoroughly mixed with their food. There is little difference in the cathartic effect of the light and heavy mineral oils. Two teaspoonfuls is the dose for a forty-pound dog.

Long-continued use of oil is not advantageous, since it dissolves the fat-soluble vitamins out of the food, preventing their absorption.

Milk of magnesia is magnesium hydroxide, one of the mildest of cathartics. Less than 10 per cent of milk of magnesia is hydroxide. It is therefore a moderate, harmless laxative. Doses of a teaspoonful produce laxation in a forty-pound dog in about six hours. Overdoses do little harm but do retard digestion because of their reduction of stomach acidity. In pets, the pill form is seldom satisfactory.

Epsom Salts. This would be the perfect cathartic for dogs were it not so intensely disliked, even in solution, because of the bitter taste. Several theories have been advanced as to how the salts accomplish their results. Probably they do it by drawing large amounts of water from the intestine (osmosis) and, by thus filling the intestine, soften the contents and mechanically stimulate its action.

The dose for a forty-pound dog is a teaspoonful, usually partially dissolved in water. Its action is fairly rapid, and evacuation occurs in two to four hours after dosing.

Phenolphthalein. For those who want a mild laxative for pets, phenolphthalein is among the best and deserves much wider use. It is combined with chocolate to form some of the more common human laxatives. It has a slightly irritating effect on the intestine, but, interestingly enough, exerts its principal action on the colon. Generally five or six hours elapse before the pet wants to defecate. The dose is one fifteenth to one twentieth of a grain for a forty-pound dog.

An excellent home remedy consists in dissolving one grain of phenolphthalein in two ounces of mineral oil. The dose is one teaspoonful of the mixture.

Arecolene Hydrobromide and **Lentin.** Few cathartics have been found to act more rapidly than these. Arecolene can be given in tablet form or injected; Lentin must be injected. Their action is to cause a profuse outpouring of the glandular secretions, which loads the intestines with fluid, and they, in turn, stimulated by the presence of the fluid, work to eliminate it. Lentin first causes prompt vomiting. Hence it is almost the perfect treatment for poisoning. Defecation occurs in a matter of minutes. Arecolene requires twenty to forty-five minutes for drastic doses and longer than that when milder doses are given.

The dose of arecolene is one tenth grain to each fifteen pounds of body weight. Lentin in a 1:1000 dilution is injected hypodermically at the rate of one drop for a five-pound dog, five drops for a forty-pound dog, ten drops for a one-hundred-pound dog.

VACCINES AND SERUMS

Antiserum. If your veterinarian tells you there is only one hope for your dog—antiserum, or "serum" for short—he means that he feels the dog should be given, by injection, the liquid part of the blood of an animal which has recovered from the disease the dog has. This is *homologous* serum. If it is produced in another species it is called *heterologous*. Great care must be exercised in a second injection of the latter type if more than a week elapses after the first injection.

There are several different types of serum, depending on their source. *Convalescent* serum comes from the blood of an animal just recovered from a disease. *Immune* serum is that which has been produced from an animal immune to the disease in question. *Hyperimmune* serum is made from animals which have been hyperimmunized against the disease, that is, by subjecting an already immune animal to massive doses of the virus. All these types are in common use in veterinary medicine.

Serum, having been made from the blood of recovered animals, is full of antibodies. When we inject it we simply add these antibodies against the disease to the blood of the animal we want to protect or try to cure. This addition does not in any way cause the body to produce more antibodies, and after a few days they are lost and the body is no longer protected. When serum is used as protection against disease it must be given repeatedly at not more than two-week intervals.

Vaccines are biologics for preventive inoculation. They may be bacterial or virus, and induce the body to produce antibodies against the disease-producing agents.

Vaccine may consist of several different materials. It may be bacteria, live or dead; virus, live, dead, or attenuated. If we are vaccinating against a bacterial disease we sometimes use live bacteria of some strain that does not produce a disease of much intensity. This is done to vaccinate against undulant fever. The animal is given the real disease, but of a strain which has proved from long study to produce mild symptoms. The animal actually becomes sick, recovers, and is henceforth immune. *Autogenous* vaccine is made from the very organism affecting an animal and then used against the disease.

Dead bacteria in suspension form a common type of vaccine which is used for several diseases of pets—always as a preventive. Sometimes several species of bacteria are mixed in one vaccine in order to immunize our pets at one time against all the diseases these bacteria cause.

Virus vaccines may be of *live virus,* so the animal actually is given the disease. *Attenuated virus* vaccines are those which have been either attenuated (weakened) by passage through a different species or by chemicals. Everybody has heard how smallpox, if given a calf, produces cowpox, and how if we are given that disease it immunizes us against cowpox *and* smallpox. Dog distemper virus passed through ferrets is weakened and when given back to dogs makes them slightly sick, but thereafter they are protected against distemper.

The dog distemper vaccine most commonly used is made by grinding up spleens of dogs removed while they are at the height of the disease, diluting the material with water and salt, and then attenuating the virus with formalin. When this virus, though attenuated and possibly dead, is injected under the skin of dogs it is absorbed into the blood stream and the dog's body goes to work building up immunity by destroying the attenuated or dead virus and proliferating antibodies. The dog is henceforth immune, as though he had actually had the disease.

Rabies vaccination lasts but a year or so, distemper seems to last a lifetime, and other vaccinations last for varying lengths of time. In the early days of vaccines it was thought that in order to establish a high antibody content of the blood and cells (titer) it was necessary to give several small doses of vaccine. Newer research indicates that best results may be attained by the injection of one large jarring dose which shocks the body into building up huge antibody content. Moreover, the practice of giving the same amount of vaccine to all animals regardless of size is slowly being replaced by the grading of the dose to the size of the animal. Surely it has been wrong to give the same dose to a Pomeranian as to a St. Bernard, thirty times as large, yet for years this has been the accepted procedure, with the result that so many of our dogs of large breeds have not been properly protected.

Part Two

6. What You Should Know about Restraint and First Aid

ADEQUATE care and intelligent handling are usually sufficient to keep a dog in good health. But even a healthy animal—like a healthy child—cannot be perfectly guarded against every eventuality. Accidents do happen; emergencies arise in spite of every precaution. The most conscientious owner cannot know that his dog will surprise a porcupine on a particular country path; he cannot prevent his dog from killing and eating a poisoned rabbit that wanders across his back yard.

Two things the owner *can* do. By exercising reasonable and humane precautions, he can avoid the accidents resulting from carelessness. He can learn how to cope with emergencies when they do arise.

Every year thousands of pets are lost needlessly simply because their owners have never taken the time to familiarize themselves with a few simple principles of first aid and emergency treatment. The owner who has never learned how to handle the common emergency situations becomes panicky and does nothing to help his injured pet—or does worse than nothing, the wrong thing. The person who has no understanding of the normal recuperative processes or powers of animals too quickly assumes that the best he can do for an animal that has been hurt is to put it out of the reach of pain and so destroys his pet when it might have recovered easily and completely.

Too many pet owners feel that since they prefer to have their veterinarian prescribe for all serious pet problems, there is no necessity for them to be able to handle difficult or unpleasant situations themselves. Such owners should remember, however, that emergencies have a way of happening at inconvenient moments. Even in metropolitan areas there are often times when a veterinarian is not immediately available, and in most sections of the country it may well take several hours to reach a veterinarian when he is needed. So long as that is true, the owner who doesn't take the trouble to find out what he can do to help his pet in an emergency is risking the animal's life foolishly.

Any owner can be and should be prepared to administer first aid to an injured pet. He should know how to restrain an animal that is frightened or in pain so that it will not harm itself or others. He should know how to stop the flow of blood from a wound, how to relieve the pain as much as possible, how to protect the pet until the veterinarian reaches it. He should know *what not to do*. The skills and techniques are not difficult to learn or to apply. They are available to everyone—the cheapest and best insurance a person can get against the loss of his pet.

HOW TO RESTRAIN A DOG

Before you can attempt any sort of treatment for an injured dog, you must know how to protect yourself and how to prevent the patient from doing damage to himself or escaping before you have taken care of him properly. Restraint of some sort is usually necessary to administer first aid and always necessary when surgery of any sort is involved. With some unruly pets it is even necessary when the animal is being groomed.

Your dog's defenses consist of biting and clawing. He must be held so that he cannot reach the handler. His head must be covered or his mouth must be tied closed. An injured pet is often a panic-stricken animal. Under such circumstances even the most gentle animal may bite and scratch when you attempt to help him. Don't blame him, and *don't destroy him as vicious*. Remember that biting is a normal reaction of a frightened or injured animal. Remember, too, that his pain may have subsided for the moment and that in handling him you may have caused it to recur with terrible intensity. Don't expect the animal to respond as he usually does. Expect him to act like what he is—an animal in pain.

What can you do when you see a dog that has been struck by a car lying in the street—probably surrounded by a crowd of sympathetic but helpless people? For one thing, you can move him out of the street. He has dragged himself ten feet. He can move his tail, so you know his back is not broken. His pelvis has probably been crushed. Approach the dog from the side, with his head at your left. Put a hand near his head. If he makes no attempt to bite, with your left hand grasp as large a handful of loose skin as possible, high up on the neck, and hold tight. So long as you hold fast he can't bite because he can neither shake himself loose nor turn his head far enough to reach you.

The dog can be lifted by this grip until he is high enough so that your right hand can reach under his chest just between the front legs, thus encircling his body. The dog will not try to bite your clothing. He cannot reach your hand. He is held too low to be able to bite your face. By holding him in this position, you can lift and carry even a large dog without much difficulty. Let us suppose you want to carry him into your home to his bed, or that you want to put him into your automobile. Just push your right arm forward and place him gently where he will rest, pulling your hand backward from under him as he reclines. I have even handled setters, collies, and hounds in this manner and have never been bitten doing it.

But suppose that dog, when you put a hand near him, snaps viciously at it. What then? That is when a simple piece of cloth, three feet long and three or four inches wide, does the trick. Cross the ends and start to tie a knot, but instead of drawing it taut, let a large loop hang down, while you hold an end of the tape in each hand. The dog is now approached from the front. Your hands are far enough apart so that he cannot reach either one. Slip the loose loop over his nose, about one and a half inches from the tip, draw it tight, and tie a knot. To prevent his scratching it off his nose, tie another single knot under his chin and then bring both ends around his neck, tying them in a bowknot behind his ears. When you have done this you can safely lift him as described above.

But suppose again that he is badly lacerated about the face and chest, and savage. It would be cruel to place a tie around his muzzle. What can you do then? Obtain a blanket and spread it on the ground beside him. Then make a slip lasso, toss it around his neck, and drag him gently onto the blanket so that two men can pull the four corners taut and make a stretcher of it.

The blanket may be used in another way: fold it to the smallest size that will cover the dog's chest and head with enough extra to extend several inches in front of his nose. This will probably be eight thicknesses, and even if a large dog should bite through it, he can inflict very little damage. The folded blanket is dropped squarely over his head and shoulders and he is grasped firmly from behind, with one hand in back of each shoulder. With this grip the dog can be lifted with the blanket wrapped around him and held securely in front of the handler.

When the injured dog is safely in the car or in the home, he may be restrained by the mouth tie for examination of broken bones, gashes, bruises, internal bleeding, or any other injuries that may be indicated.

Suppose you are handling a dog dazed from a head injury inflicted by a glancing blow of an automobile bumper. You have cornered him, tied his mouth, and started to carry him. Everything goes well until he wriggles out of your grip. Then you remember that you neglected to snap a leash to his collar. When you have caught the dog and fastened the leash, remember to take the time to tighten his collar. In his struggling he will probably slip the collar over his head unless it is drawn tighter than usual.

If he is too large to carry and won't be led, run the leash backward, encircle his chest behind his front legs, and loop the leash through as if he were in a giant knot. You can then pull forward with a lifting force. It will usually make him walk, even when he is not leash-broken. By grasping the surcingle just above the dog's back, you can move him along almost as you would carry a suitcase.

A large dog that is vicious can be restrained only under a foot or between the knees of a strong man. Even a very strong dog can't get away when he is clamped in a knee hold. Back the dog into a corner, holding him by the collar, and at the same time squeeze him with the knees. This is a potent hold, a sort of "full nelson" with which a man can strangle a dog. Fortunately such rigid handling is seldom necessary. There are times, however, when you can tie a dog's mouth in no other way without being bitten.

The double-lasso method is effective for powerful animals which can inflict damage if not restrained. Two lassos are thrown over the head and around the neck and pulled in opposite directions until the dog is thoroughly subdued. The pullers must be careful or they may strangle the dog.

The dog warden's loop on a pole, or through a pipe, is excellent for bad actors, because the dog can't escape and can be held at a distance.

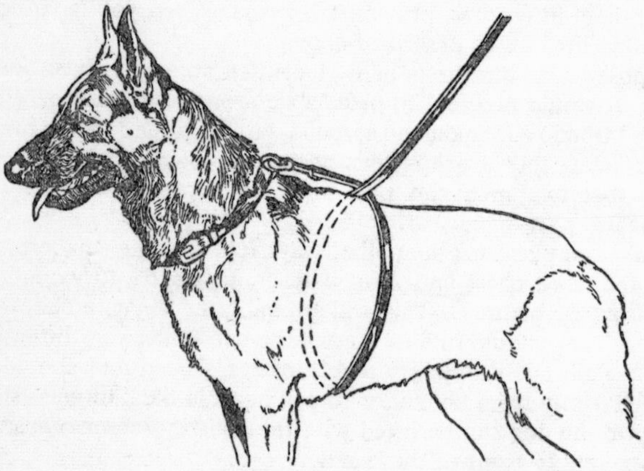

A useful hitch for a stubborn dog.

Household pets are ordinarily affectionate and gentle, but there are emergencies when even the mildest of them must be dealt with firmly and even severely. I remember once seeing a small bull terrier attacking another dog ferociously. As I approached, the terrier growled but still held fast to the other dog. People stood about the fence, the owner of the attacked dog was screaming, a policeman was ready to shoot, and the bulldog's owner was pleading with him not to shoot. I grabbed the bulldog by the tail close to the body. He let go of the other dog and tried to attack me. There was only one thing to do—swing him around and slam him down on the grass plot until he was stunned. This had to be done three times before I could get a foot on his neck and pin him to the ground. The policeman held his back legs and rolled him on his side. He was controlled. No one was bitten. We tied his mouth and let his owner take over. A person can hold a strong dog with his foot if he uses it correctly in conjunction with his hands.

HOW TO STOP A DOGFIGHT

There are times when you may find your dog engaged in one of those occasional natural affairs which some dogs seem to enjoy—a dogfight. Your dog may be the aggressor or he may be the victim of a bully. In either event you will want to stop the fight or the mutilation. *Don't reach for the collar of either dog!* You are almost certain to be bitten. Quickly catch hold of a hind leg or the tail of the more aggressive dog and pull. If you are strong enough, lift him off the ground and throw him as far as you can and then use your voice and scold. It must be a severe loud tone or the dog will pay no attention to you. Get between the dogs and hold the weaker behind you until help arrives.

FIRST AID

The principles of first aid which the dog owner needs to master are simple and relatively few, but they are of vital importance in handling emergencies. Whether an animal that has been injured is to recover quickly or slowly, whether it is to be completely restored or marked or scarred—indeed, whether the animal is to survive at all—often depends upon the treatment it gets immediately after it is hurt. The balance of this chapter is intended to give the dog owner the general information he needs and at the same time to provide him with a reference manual in which he may quickly find the specific way to handle any emergency that may arise with his pet.

Shock. Any severe injury—a burn, a struggle, a fight, or even a severe fright—may bring on this condition. The animal usually seems to be prostrated in a semi-oblivious state, yet apparently anxious. The nervous system is in depression, sometimes so severe as to cause complete immobility. On the other hand, an occasional animal may suffer the opposite effect, so that it seems to be in a state of nervous excitement. The pulse is slow and weak, the breathing shallow. Often, as the animal recovers, the pulse becomes too rapid and the temperature may rise well above normal. (See page 165 for normal temperatures.)

First aid consists in covering the patient so his temperature will rise to normal. High artificial heat is not necessary if the animal is at home in familiar surroundings. Administer a stimulant, such as coffee, then let him rest. Occasional fondling is often reassuring and helpful. Recovery may sometimes take an hour or more.

Heat Strokes. Of all pets, dogs are most subject to heat strokes. Bulldogs and fat dogs are the most frequent victims. Dogs with heavy coats of fine fur suffer most, of course, and, for their protection and comfort, should be clipped in the summer.

We are all conscious of the refreshing sensation of a breeze in hot weather. This is due to evaporation of moisture from our bodies and the consequent cooling of the surface of the body. The bodies of animals are cooled by the same process, which is aided by evaporation in the throat and mouth when the pet becomes overheated and pants. Dogs have few sweat glands in the skin compared to humans and horses, but they do have some. When an animal is sufficiently cooled by bodily evaporation, he stops panting.

In itself, panting is a normal method of reducing body temperature. It may sometimes be an indication of thirst. A hot, panting dog is obviously evaporating an abnormal amount of moisture from his body and needs to replenish the loss.

In a heat stroke, however, the panting is sharp and continuous. The dog seems to be "burning up," his tongue turns purple, and he finds it difficult to catch his breath. You know he has been exposed to great heat, possibly to excitement. What should you do until the veterinarian arrives?

Remember the principle of cooling we have just discussed: the evaporation of water reduces body temperature. Lay the dog on a flat surface and pour cold water over him until he is thoroughly soaked. Set up an electric fan a few feet away, turn its blast directly on him, and keep on adding water as it evaporates. Take the dog's temperature occasionally. Usually his fever will drop in less than half an hour from about 108° to 101°. When it has come down to normal or nearly so, dry the dog with a towel and keep him out of the heat.

If an electric fan is not available, a cold-water enema is advisable. If this is impossible, immersion in cold water is a satisfactory method of reducing the temperature quickly. A great many animals have been saved in this manner.

Dogs are frequently afflicted by heat stroke in cars. If this should happen, stop for water and lay your patient on the floor in front. As soon as you have got the water, drive on with the cowl ventilator open so that the draft will blow directly on him. Pour on the water, keeping him wet, and before many miles his temperature will have dropped to normal.

Anyone who takes a dog on a long trip in very hot weather should be aware of the danger of a heat stroke and be careful to avoid it. He should carry a pan and water for the pet. The animal that is losing an unusual amount of water by evaporation needs to replace it by drinking frequently. If he has enough water, he is much less likely to succumb to the heat.

Accidents. The most common cause of accidents among pets is the automobile. So common is it that companies which insure dogs' lives often exempt death by automobile from policies. Dogs will dash across the street to get to another dog. Even dogs which are so well trained that they will wait for a car to pass will walk across the street behind it only to be struck by a car coming the opposite way. The brightest have not learned to look both ways, to anticipate so far into the future.

When a pet is struck by an automobile, you must first restrain him and then treat him for shock. Look at his gums to see if he is losing blood too rapidly. If his gums appear gray or white, he probably has suffered an organic injury and is bleeding internally. Roll up long strips of bandage—an old sheet may be torn in strips for the purpose. Have an assistant stretch the pet out and hold his front and hind legs. Then wrap the bandage around his body tightly, corset-fashion. Keep on wrapping it until you have made a good firm support. Be sure that it will not pull together in a narrow roll around his abdomen when he moves. It must form a long tube, which holds the animal's organs relatively immobile, so that a clot can form and remain in place. Without this firmness and pressure, the organs can move freely and break the blood clot loose. Do all you can to keep the animal quiet. The veterinarian, when he comes, will administer a drug to check bleeding and may decide upon a transfusion if he feels that the transfused blood will not run into the abdomen and be wasted. Whatever you do, do *not* move him far after an accident if there are indications of internal bleeding. He can bleed to death very quickly. He may be saved if you keep him quiet.

If an animal does bleed internally, what becomes of the blood which runs into the abdomen? When a clot forms, it is composed of red and white cells, plasma, and fibrinogen, which causes coagulation. As it forms, the clot squeezes out a fluid or serum. This serum can be, and is, soaked up by the peritoneum (the lining of the abdomen and covering of the organs). Obviously the serum gets back into the circulation and thus helps to increase the blood volume. Many of the red cells which transport oxygen through the body are in the clot. This clot does not persist permanently as a liverlike lump. Instead a process called lysis occurs. The cells simply dissolve into the fluid in the abdomen. Their covering disintegrates and releases the contents. The fluid is now circulated, but only a small amount is utilized by the body; most of it, including the red pigment, is passed out of the body through the urine as waste. When you see your weak but mending patient urinating what appears to be blood, don't presume he is passing blood from his kidneys and bladder; it is probably blood-coloring matter. Indeed, anticipate his doing this. This fact is sometimes used as a diagnostic means of demonstrating internal hemorrhage which occurred several days before the red color is seen.

Mad Dog. The cry of "mad dog" is no longer heard in America as it used to be, or as history tells us it was in Europe. Nevertheless, it *does* occur. An animal which manifests *any* symptoms of rabies is suspect. Rabies is discussed in detail in a later chapter, and here we need only concern ourselves with the problems of first aid—first aid to the dog and to the animals or humans he has bitten—and the subsequent management of the incident.

For the suspected mad dog, isolation must be provided. Shut him in a yard or room and call your veterinarian immediately. Keep people and animals away from him. Your veterinarian and the health authorities will diagnose his condition, using a mouse test if advisable. Either the local authorities or veterinarian will provide isolation until the diagnosis is clearly established. If an animal *is* infected, the local authorities will determine its disposition. Frequently they prefer to let the disease progress until Negri bodies have developed in the brain.

Any pet that has been bitten by a rabid animal should be quarantined. Since a high proportion of all animals—75 per cent of all dogs, for example—are susceptible to rabies, no other course is safe. The period of isolation is long. An exposed dog must be confined for six months. Will it pay to maintain the dog so long at possibly a dollar a day? Will he still know you when he is returned? Will you ever have complete confidence in him? Rabies is such a horrible disease that it is advisable that all rabid animals be destroyed.

Needless to say, if a human is bitten, call a doctor immediately. Only a physician is qualified to decide on the treatment or prophylaxis for the humans involved.

Cuts. Dogs hustling through barbed-wire fences, stepping on broken bottles, scratching in ash piles, and stepping on concealed metal scraps come home gashed, bleeding, and torn. They seldom bleed to death.

Most of the cuts which occur on animal skins are triangular tears. Some, of course, are clean, straight cuts. In either case only a limited kind of first aid should be administered. In animal saliva there is an enzyme which digests germs. The surface of an animal's tongue is made up of small, tough scales so strong that he can wear flesh away if he wants to. There is no better way of cleaning a cut than allowing him to do it. He will lick away all dead flesh or debris and kill germs as he does so. He will heal his own wounds.

First aid consists not of strapping the cut together with adhesive tape, nor of binding up the wound, unless it is bleeding badly, but of allowing the patient to clean his wounds and then having the veterinarian treat them. So there need be no hurry in rushing your pet to the doctor. When you do he will cut away any dead edges on the flap and suture it in place, so that when it has healed no ugly scar will remain.

There are cuts which dogs cannot reach to lick, however. In long-haired dogs these may be covered with hair, which should be trimmed off about the area. Or they may be on areas of the body, such as the neck, head, face, and shoulders, which the dog cannot reach. In such a case, clean the cuts yourself (peroxide is excellent for this purpose) and take him to the hospital as soon as possible.

Cuts deep in the feet usually cause profuse bleeding, since this area is filled with blood vessels. A cut of this sort should always be examined to see if a long sliver has remained in it. After this examination it is necessary to stop the bleeding. A plug of cotton pressed against the opening and a pressure bandage which holds it there will quickly check the bleeding. If the cut should hemorrhage, apply a tourniquet immediately above or below the wrist joint. It must be loosened and reapplied every ten minutes. On the trip to the veterinarian take along some cloths to absorb blood which may stain the car or clothes.

The most dangerous cuts are those made by filthy objects. These cuts may heal or mat over with hair which becomes part of a scab, and tetanus (lockjaw) germs frequently infect such wounds. Since they can develop only in a cut or puncture wound which the air cannot reach, cuts of this sort must be opened, cleansed, and kept open until they have been disinfected and sutured. There are some wounds which are best left unsutured for a considerable length of time. These must be flushed daily while they heal from the bottom out, and they are sutured to avoid unsightly scars only when the healing process has reached the surface layers of the skin.

Bites. Animal bites and poisonous snake or insect bites need very different treatment, so we shall consider them separately.

ANIMAL BITES. It is sometimes important to determine the kind of bite to be treated. The bite of a dog, cat, and even that of a rat, can usually be distinguished by the number of teeth marks. When a large dog attacks an animal, if one tooth mark is found, three others can nearly always be located. The distance between these skin punctures, as well as their size, gives some idea of the size of the attacker. Little dogs sometimes open their mouths wide and leave impressions of their upper and lower canine teeth perhaps four inches apart, but the distance between the two upper canines will still be small. Large dogs may happen to get hold with only a small nip, but the distance between their upper canines may be as much as three inches in some breeds.

Because of their size and strength, large dogs inflict greater damage than do small dogs. Ordinarily, a dog attacking another animal does not simply attack, hold on, and squeeze; he shakes his head and thus drives his fangs deeper. These teeth wounds can be cleaned by shaving the hair away and filling them with antiseptic from an inserted medicine dropper. The attacker may have pulled the skin loose from the underlying connective tissue over a large area. In such cases your veterinarian will flush this area clean and bind it down. It usually heals in a few days.

Cat bites on dogs often become seriously infected. The skin should not be allowed to heal quickly over them. First aid often consists in hurrying the animal to the doctor. If infected, the punctures become large abscesses which burst, carrying with them large areas of skin which has been killed in the process of abscess formation. A bite that has been allowed to abscess takes much longer to heal than does a properly treated bite, and the new skin which eventually covers the sore spot will never have hair.

Some bites result in jagged tears which may require suturing. If you know how, you may be able to do a good job, but whether you or your veterinarian do it, don't wait until the skin has shrunken.

SNAKE BITES. First aid in snake bites is extremely important. When you suspect a rapidly increasing swelling to be the result of a rattlesnake, copperhead, or water-moccasin bite, there is usually sufficient time to reach a veterinarian. If you can't reach him, try your family doctor. Many physicians have saved animal lives in emergencies. If neither a veterinarian nor a doctor is available, buy some potassium-permanganate solution which a druggist will prepare for you. Make a deep X-shaped cut right over the fang marks, remembering that they are pushed in at an angle and not straight. This cut induces bleeding. Drop the potassium permanganate into the cut and hold it there for a moment. Apply a tourniquet above the bite, if it is on the leg or foot. If the swelling ascends the leg and reaches the body, you may lose the animal.

SPIDER BITES. The only dangerous spider bites are those of the black widow. This spider has a predilection for old bones. Spiders are often found inside old skulls of horses and cattle that have died and been left

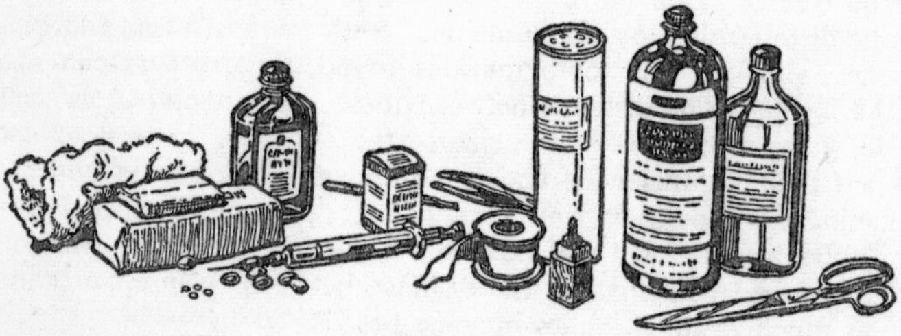

First aid accessories: cotton, bandage (3- and 6-inch widths), calamine lotion, arecolene pills, N butyl chloride capsules, 10 cc. hypodermic syringe, eye ointment, thermometer, forceps, adhesive tape, ear canker remedy, flea powder (preferably containing a fungicide), peroxide of hydrogen, skin remedy, scissors.

unburied. Dogs, too, enjoy such things, and so are often bitten by these poisonous insects. The bites are usually on the lips or face. Swelling occurs and increases proportionately with the amount of venom the spider injects. One bite may kill a dog, although it is unlikely. Very little can be done at home. If you know where the spider that bit your pet lives, a fine opportunity is offered to do some spraying and exterminate the spider and possibly all of her young, thus saving other pets and humans from being bitten.

Foreign Bodies. No first-aid discussion could be complete without suggestions as to the removal of foreign bodies.

IN THE MOUTH: Dogs sometimes overestimate their ability to manipulate certain bones. It is common to find such bones caught in various positions: wedged across the roof of the mouth between the back teeth; driven down into the gum beside a tooth; driven through the soft tissue below the lower jaw; stuck between two teeth; stuck on top of a molar tooth; or covering several teeth.

A T bone from a lamb chop is sometimes caught across a dog's mouth between the back teeth, with its sharp point sticking into the throat. The dog paws desperately at his mouth, and the owner often thinks that the end has surely come. Dogs sometimes chew two- or three-inch shank bones from lamb so that the rounded bone slips down over their teeth and they can't close their mouths without forcing the sharp edges of the bone farther down against the gums. These dogs become frantic.

Many other kinds of foreign bodies become wedged in the teeth or stuck in the mouth. Any dog may have such accidents. The mouth must be opened and the object pulled out. Whenever possible, it is wise to rush the pet to the veterinarian, who has the instruments to remove the obstruction without difficulty.

IN THE STOMACH: If you do not actually see a dog eat a foreign object, you can never be sure that the dog does have it in his stomach. You may have seen him eat gravel or sand, or chew on an old doll. But circumstantial evidence is usually all that is necessary. If a small item the dog was playing with is missing and the dog begins to show evidence of stomach pain, it is time for action.

Suppose you suspect that your small dog has swallowed one of your child's iron jacks, the crisscross gadget the child picks up when he bounces a ball. The dog will probably show some evidence of stomach pain, and you should act at once. Mix about an ounce of peroxide with an ounce of water and pour it down the dog's throat. Use more if he is a large dog. Vomiting will occur very soon. When it begins, lift the pup by his back legs so that his forepaws are touching the ground and his head is down. In almost every case the jack will be regurgitated the first time.

You may be surprised sometime to pick up your dog and hear stones rattling together in his stomach. Actually you shouldn't be too astonished, for this is a fairly common occurrence. And it shouldn't worry you very much. Stones can always be recovered with the peroxide treatment. Puppies with gravel impactions in their stomach can be relieved by the same means. Mineral oil should be given fifteen minutes after the peroxide, to help move along the gravel which has entered the intestine.

Remedies of this sort for the removal of foreign bodies are properly classified as first aid. More difficult cases should be left to the veterinarian. With X ray he can locate bullets, needles, pins, spark plugs, and any of the hundreds of other odd and dangerous objects that dogs have been known to swallow.

IN THE RECTUM: If your dog squats, strains, cries, and possibly exudes a little blood from his anus, the likelihood is that he has a foreign body in the rectum. If a constipated mass is considered a foreign body, he surely has. Not infrequently the stoppage is caused by sharp bone splinters which were not properly softened and digested in his stomach.

Poultry, pork, and lamb bones are the most likely to cause such difficulties. Since any movement of the sharp bones is extremely painful, the dog refrains from defecating. In time the fecal material piles up behind them and soon a solid, dry mass with sharp bones sticking out of it precludes all passage.

First aid consists of enemas to soften the mass, though they often are not sufficiently effective to allow passage of the material. Humane considerations indicate a prompt visit to the doctor, who will probably first soften the mass and then gently reach in with an instrument and crush it into small particles. Occasionally an oily enema is sufficiently lubricating to permit the stool to be passed without great difficulty or pain. In difficult cases the veterinarian may have to pull out the sharp pieces with his instrument to avoid cutting.

Needles are frequently found in the rectums of dogs. Often a thread hanging from the anus is a good indication of the cause of the pain. If the needle is just inside and can be felt, an ingenious person with a small wire cutter such as electricians use can snip the needle in half and remove the halves separately. Generally, however, this job is best left to the doctor, who will use anesthesia and a speculum to see clearly what he is doing.

IN THE SKIN: Foreign bodies in the skin or feet are usually splinters or bullets, although other objects, such as pitchfork tines, glass chips, and porcupine quills, are not so uncommon as most people think. Common sense dictates the quick removal of such objects, whenever possible, in order to relieve the animal. It also dictates the injection of an antiseptic into the wound. If a bullet has come to rest against a rib and it can be seen through the hole, you should—for once—do what your first impulse tells you: pull it out with the family tweezers and cleanse the wound.

Children often put elastic bands around the neck, leg, tail, ear, or even the penis of their pets. The hair covers the band and it goes unnoticed by adults until swelling starts. By that time it may have cut through the skin. There is little the owner himself can do after he has removed the band. If the skin gap's too wide, have the veterinarian suture it to prevent formation of a hairless scar. Ropes and small chains may also cut deeply through the skin. Most people have seen at least one animal with a hairless band of skin around the neck—mute evidence that some negligent owner left a rope or chain on until it cut the animal's neck. Having callously injured the animal, he failed even to have the gaping skin sutured.

PORCUPINE QUILLINGS: In many states in the United States, and in all parts of Canada, porcupines are common. They tempt courageous dogs to attack them, and when they do, the unfortunate dogs find their mouths and bodies full of quills. A quill, which is only a modified hair lightly attached to the porcupine's skin, has small reverse barbs protruding from the shaft for a quarter of an inch down from the sharp point. Under a microscope the barbs look like the prickles on a thistle, with one scale overlapping the next. When a quill penetrates the skin, every muscle movement of the victim draws it inward, since the angle at which the barbs are set prevents its moving outward.

When attacked, porcupines often inflict severely painful and dangerous injuries. Strong dogs may pick up the porcupine and shake it from side to side, driving hundreds of quills into themselves on each side. For good measure, the porcupine thrashes his quill-filled tail from side to side and up and down, swatting the dog's legs and body. The tail quills leave a pattern, because they are small and black and usually half studded with barbs. To cap the climax, the poor dog, now feeling the pain, rolls and paws at the quills, driving them in farther.

So many nonsensical ideas still persist about porcupines' shooting quills that we must emphasize this fact: the porcupine does *not* shoot quills; his quills are loosely attached to his skin, and when they become fastened into the flesh of his attacker they are pulled loose. The porcupine does not fight with dogs, but only defends himself.

If a dog were to attack a porcupine directly in front of a veterinarian's office, quill removal would be simple. The doctor would quickly administer an injectable anesthetic and pull the quills. It has never been my good fortune to have a dog quilled within miles of any place where they could be pulled surgically. I have pulled thousands and thousands of quills from hunting dogs with electrician's pliers when I've been far off in the woods without surgical equipment.

When they have no pliers, some old hunters just take out their jackknives, cut the quills off, and lead the dog home. They say a cut-off quill is not particularly dangerous and does not work in. Perhaps not so much as whole quills, but I have seen a dog blinded by a cut-off quill.

No one should take his dog into the woods where there are known to be porcupines without carrying a pair of pliers which have carefully machined jaws and tips. When a dog has been quilled, there is no time to take him to a doctor. Chain him firmly. Get right to work with the pliers from the car if no others are available. With no halfway measure, *pull quills,* blood or no blood. Here is a place where heroic methods are necessary.

If your dog is quilled in the woods, let him stand up while you pull the quills from the side on which you are going to lay him. Then pull the quills out of his mouth. Grab a handful of dirt from the forest floor and get hold of his tongue with it, covering your hand so the tongue won't slip. Pull the tongue out and remove the quills which have stuck into it. If the quills in his lips have worked through far enough to feel the points on the other side, pulling them point first through the lips is less painful for the dog. Tie his mouth to prevent his nuzzling the quills and driving them in farther. Remove quills from around his eyes. Then go to work on his body, first behind his shoulders, where quills may work into vital organs. When quills break off, feel sorry, but go to work on others.

On many occasions I have extracted quills from dogs surgically while they were in shock from the severity of the quillings. Anesthetics must be administered cautiously during shock. When they are used, the progress of any quill is stopped.

If quills are allowed to work in out of sight, they will continue to move about the body. Those which entered the front legs or shoulders generally move upward, and by the following morning the needle-sharp points of some can be felt emerging from the skin above the shoulder blades, whence their progress has been guided by the broad bones. Putting dozens or even hundreds of gashes over a dog's shoulders and legs is less satisfactory then letting the quills move themselves to a point where the tips can be felt through the skin. If the point doesn't emerge, nick the skin and pull it, thus removing a fresh crop every day, until they are all out. Feeling for quills is the only efficient method of locating them. X ray is useless.

Maggots. It is hard to believe that every summer hundreds of dogs are killed by flies. And yet dogs are lost everywhere in the United States from being eaten alive by the larvae of flies—maggots. In the North only long-haired dogs are attacked. But in the South, where the screw worm as well as the more common maggot is found, any wound which the animal cannot reach to lick may become infested.

Somewhere under the long bushy coat of a collie, or on the matted hair of an old English sheep dog, for example, an abrasion occurs. Perhaps it is a small patch of skin disease. Flies are attracted by the serum which the body has exuded and lay eggs on or in the wound. Maggots hatch and live on the moist tissue which they kill by the toxins they secrete. The hair prevents the dog from chewing and licking off these enemies. The maggots continue to grow and spread in the area. Finally some migrate to other moist spots and begin to feed. More flies are attracted and soon the dog is a mass of maggots.

Even a badly infested dog can be saved by prompt action, but many dogs have died for the want of adequate and timely attention. The coat should be clipped, the holes, which may be an inch deep, washed clean of the pests, and antiseptic dressings applied. Often the first sign to the owner will be prostration of the dog, for the maggots give off a powerful toxin. If you don't discover the worms until that stage has been reached, get the animal to your veterinarian at once. Infusions may save his life.

Screw worms will attack any sore on an animal and eat live tissue. Their damage is like that of the maggots just mentioned. Treatment is the same.

Skunk Spraying. Skunk odor has chemically a rather simple formula —a mercaptan, a sort of alcohol-sulfur combination. It is a volatile substance. Volatile chemicals usually turn into gas with heat and maintain their liquid character in cold. The way to dissipate skunk odor, therefore, is to get clothes hot; not to bury them. Hang them in the sun in the summertime, or in a garage attic—anywhere that is dry and hot. The odor leaves quite quickly. A hot bath with lots of soap will usually remove most of the odor from a dog—or from an owner, for that matter. Several baths certainly will. If the dog is left where it is hot, the odor more quickly evaporates to a point where it loses its unpleasantness. After all, it was once used as a basis for fancy perfumes. Washing the pet in tomato is said to be most efficacious in removing the odor. The amount used depends on the size of the animal.

Drowning. If a dog can be pulled out of the water while his heart is still beating, he can almost always be saved. Slow, steady artificial respiration does the trick. Not as you may have been taught to work on a human. Place the animal on his side and push with the flat of the hand on his ribs. Then pull your weight up quickly. Repeat at regular intervals about once in two seconds. He'll usually start to breathe very shallowly, and gradually breathe more deeply. Even when the heartbeat is faint, there is hope. It pays to try.

Electric Shock. Since animals' bodies are such excellent conductors of electricity, the shock of 110 volts—which ordinarily merely jolts a human—may kill them. When shocked, they sometimes stiffen so rigidly that they appear to leap into the air. There is a great temptation for a dog to chew a dangling electric cord, and many have been badly injured when they tried it. One such experience is sufficient to teach a dog's owner the hazard of loose electric wires—often at the cost of his pet's life. If the shock has not killed the animal, artificial respiration should be administered immediately. If he cannot let go of the wire, be careful when you pick him up. He may have urinated; you may step in the urine and, in touching him, the current may pass through you. It is always safer to pull out the plug first or take hold of the wire with a wad of dry cloth and jerk it out of his mouth. Call the veterinarian immediately. He will probably administer a drug to stimulate the heart and breathing when he gets to the animal.

Burns. If you are called upon to treat a burned animal, clean off all the hair which can mat down on the burned area. Then apply a solution of one part tannic acid to one hundred parts of water (strong, strained tea may be substituted). Then cover gently with vaseline. Your druggist will furnish his best burn remedy and help in an emergency.

Your veterinarian should be called on for all except very minor burns. The anesthetic and treatment he can administer may save your dog. Burns scab over and heal under the scabs, if left alone; but sometimes infections grow under the scabs. Tannic acid promotes healthy healing.

If half of an animal's skin is destroyed by fire, steam, acid, or any agency of burning, it is kindest to put him permanently to sleep. Burned areas usually fail to grow hair, and the period of healing is protracted and painful. Even the duration of shock that usually follows severe burns is long. The owner of any animal that has been badly burned must always decide quickly, "Is it worth it?"

Fits. The various kinds of fits, their causes, and the means of preventing them are discussed in later chapters of this book. They should be read carefully. Here we are concerned only with the first aid the owner should be prepared to administer.

The handling of a fit depends upon where it happens and also upon its nature. If a large dog has a running fit, he may tear through a house, upsetting tables, knickknacks, and chairs, and perhaps end up urinating and defecating on the floor behind the sofa.

You can't stop the fit, but you can reduce the amount of damage the animal may do. He probably won't bite you unless you get in his way. If you can guide him into a room where he can't do serious damage, by all means do it and close the door. Small dogs can be laid in a bathtub for the duration of the fit.

Many people, witnessing one of these fits for the first time, feel more terror than the dog. They have visions of being bitten by a mad dog. If you will realize that mad dogs don't have fits from which they recover, but a steady downhill progressive deterioration, it will set your mind at ease if your pet ever has a fit. German shepherds have been known to attack persons in the room with them when the fits came on. But most dogs seem fearful of even their masters and will bite only if you try to catch or hold them. Dogs that take fits in the street generally run into yards or under porches, apparently seeking a place to hide.

Let your dog alone until he has recovered from the fit and then look for the cause. Prevention of future attacks is the best first aid. Your veterinarian will help you to locate the cause and provide the cure.

A cat should not be handled while it is having a fit. Some leap up in a corner, others run for the darkest spot they can find. Let them be, and wait for the fit to be well over before you touch them.

Bruises. It requires a hard, glancing blow to bruise a dog. Even those dogs which have been skidded along on a road until the hair was scraped off and the skin left bloody seldom swell as do some other species. Probably the looseness of the skin over the dog's body is one of its prime protections. When uninfected swellings are found they need only cleansing. They soon subside without further treatment.

If the hair is rubbed off but the skin not cut through, the chances are the healed skin will not be hairless.

Broken Bones. You may find, when you examine an injured pet, that he has a broken bone. To treat a fracture properly you should understand the principles of bone growth and healing discussed in Chapter 2. You will also need to be familiar with certain first-aid techniques to prevent additional damage to the pet.

A broken leg is the most common animal fracture, and requires immediate attention. Its care involves straightening the leg and immobilizing it. Sometimes this takes courage. A splint is needed. A barrel stave, a tine from a bamboo rake, a yardstick may serve as an improvised splint. The leg should be tied to the splint below and above the break and wrapped with anything suitable to hold it securely in place until you can get the pet to the veterinarian.

A splint should be applied at once. If the broken bone slashes about the flesh, it can easily cut a major vein or artery and then the area around the break will become a large pocket filled with blood, greatly complicating the task of setting. It is just as important to splint a greenstick fracture, because movement or a fall may break it further.

If ribs are broken, keep the animal quiet. It is possible for ribs to puncture lungs, so lay him down with the broken ribs up and keep him as calm as possible until the veterinarian arrives.

A fractured pelvis heals slowly. Little can be done to repair pelvic breaks or to hasten the natural process of reconstruction. Occasionally only one side is broken and the dog can continue to walk on three legs. More often the pelvis is fractured in such a way as to preclude walking until the usual numbness develops and anesthetizes the area. For several days after the break the animal may be unable to raise himself without help. Gradually he takes a few unstable steps and soon is waddling about. Don't expect him to run for at least a month after the break. Even after the healing is well started it may be necessary to help him up, carry him outside, and sometimes hold him in a position to defecate. Some animals learn why they are taken outside surprisingly soon, and, as quickly as they are placed in position, will void. Standing the animal up and putting pressure on the bladder from both sides usually causes urination, and it is not uncommon to have a dog so co-operative that just touching his sides is suggestion enough for him to urinate.

Not all broken backs are hopeless. Many backs are set and wired so that the dogs can live normally again. Palpation will usually determine where the tips of the vertebrae are out of line. Get your pet to the veterinarian as quickly as possible with as little jolting as you can. The spinal cord is a delicate structure. If the animal is to survive, the nerve-fiber damage must be held at a minimum.

One of the most usual back breaks comes at the point inside the body where the tail vertebrae start. The tail in such a fracture hangs limp and lifeless. It is often soiled with feces because the animal cannot raise it to defecate. Sometimes there is enough muscular strength left to move it slightly. If it is not set, it may retain its life; more often the tail loses all its feeling and dries up with dry gangrene. In this case your veterinarian will have to open the skin over the break and remove the useless appendage.

Bee Stings. It is not uncommon to hear of pets being stung to death by bees. Dogs will frequently swell from single stings and more often come home drooling with mouths partly open from pain and swelling occasioned by snapping up a stinging insect—wasp, hornet, or bee.

The painful stings, the poisonous effect of the toxin, and, worst of all, the sensitivity to the foreign material developed by having been previously stung may produce a severe shock.

Treatment may be intravenous calcium gluconate, fifteen or twenty c.c.s of a 25 per cent solution for a forty-pound dog. Nembutal, one grain to each fifteen pounds, or paregoric in fairly large doses, say a teaspoonful for a forty-pound dog, will help ease intense pain. If nothing better is available, aspirin may be given.

Poisoning. Pain, trembling, panting, vomiting, convulsions, coma, slimy mouths are all symptoms of poisoning. Any of these, except a caustically burned mouth, may also be a symptom of another malady. But if your dog should manifest any of these symptoms, you should investigate immediately to see if he has been poisoned.

Animals are very seldom deliberately poisoned. Usually they are poisoned either by chewing plants which have been sprayed, by gnawing at a piece of wood which has some paint pigment on it, by catching a ground mole which has been poisoned with cyanide, by consuming poison put out for other animals or insects, or by eating infected garbage. Since none of the poisons is easily traced, you ought to know the procedure to follow *in case* your pet may have been poisoned.

An emetic *must be administered immediately*. The loss of a few minutes may give the poison time to do irremediable damage. Mix equal parts of hydrogen peroxide and water. Force your pet to take one and a half tablespoonfuls of this mixture for each ten pounds. A pup needs less than one tablespoonful, a large dog seven to eight tablespoonfuls. In two or three minutes the contents of his stomach will have been regurgitated.

Either mustard or a strong salt solution can be used as an emetic, but hydrogen peroxide has proved to be most effective.

Following the administration of this emetic, call your veterinarian. If you know the source of the poisoning and can look at the package it came from, you will find the antidote on the label. If you don't know the poison to which your pet has been exposed, your veterinarian will probably identify it from its symptoms and give further appropriate treatment.

If there is any chance that poison can be the cause of intestinal trouble, it is imperative that all traces of the poison be eliminated before giving the animal drugs which will stop bowel movement and allow the intestines to become quiescent—paregoric, for instance. But if the intestines are badly corroded, it is dangerous to give violent physics. I have been able to save more poisoned animals by using two simple drugs than by any other method I have ever heard of. The drugs are hydrogen peroxide and Lentin. The Lentin is used in all cases where the animal is known to have ingested the poison recently. Since it produces both emesis and purgation, it seems the ideal drug to use, and its swift action, coupled with the fact that it causes prolific outpouring of gastro-intestinal secretions, eliminates the entire stomach and intestinal contents before too great harm is done.

The dose is a matter of drops of the 1:1000 solution. Once the offending material is removed, our job is to give such common home remedies as milk of bismuth, paregoric, strong tea for its tannic-acid content. Strangely enough, some cases are benefited by castor oil, which removes the cause and tends to be followed by constipation. Veterinarians can prescribe sulfaguanidine and sulfathaladine and other prescription drugs.

The same drugs which are useful in human care can be employed. Today a variety of mixtures embodying kaolin, bismuth, pectin are available, and your veterinarian will advise you on their use.

Table IV—Household Antidotes for Common Poisons

POISON	ANTIDOTE
Acids (Hydrochloric; nitric; acetic)	Bicarbonate of soda; eggshells; crushed plaster (tablespoonful)
Alkalies (Sink cleansers; cleaning agent)	Vinegar or lemon juice (several tablespoonfuls)
Arsenic (Lead arsenate; calcium arsenate; white arsenic; Paris green)	Epsom salts (1 teaspoonful in water)
Hydrocyanic Acid (Wild cherry; laurel leaves)	Glucose (2 tablespoonfuls dextrose or corn syrup)
Lead (Lead arsenic; paint pigments)	Epsom salts (1 teaspoonful in water)
Phosphorus (Rat poison)	Peroxide of hydrogen. (Peroxide and water in equal parts, 1 oz. to each 10 pounds of weight of animal)
Mercury (Bichloride of mercury)	Eggs and milk
Theobromine (Cooking chocolate)	Pentobarbital, phenobarbital
Thallium (Bug poisons)	Table salt (1 teaspoonful in water)
Food Poisoning (Bacteria from garbage or decomposed food)	Peroxide of hydrogen. Give enema after stomach has emptied
Strychnine (Strychnine sulfate in rodent and animal poisons)	Sedatives such as phenobarbital, Nembutal (1 grain to 7 pounds of dog)
Sedatives (Overdoses in medicating)	Strong coffee (1 cupful for a 40-pound dog)
DDT (Flea powders; bug poisons)	Peroxide of hydrogen and enema. No antidote known

GENERAL ADVICE IN TREATING POISONING. Immediate action is essential. Some poisons are absorbed at once. If you can get Lentin in 1:1000 strength, inject one drop to each ten pounds of dog.

7. Minor Operations and Home Surgery

First aid and minor surgery are closely allied and at times almost indistinguishable. Adequate first aid for an injured animal sometimes involves more than merely moving him to a place of safety and preventing additional harm until the veterinarian arrives. Emergency surgery may be necessary to save his life. Hardly a week passes that I do not hear of several animals that were needlessly killed when the simplest kind of surgical treatment might have saved their lives. Not long ago I was told of a fine farm shepherd that was lost when a horse kicked him and ripped open his abdomen with a calk of his shoe. When the dog's intestines worked out through the rent and became covered with dirt, the owner decided that the only humane thing to do was to relieve the dog of his pain—by having him shot. That valuable dog, like thousands of other pets which are killed after they have been injured, could easily have been saved by an owner who had even a sketchy knowledge of emergency surgery.

This chapter is intended to acquaint the owner with the basic skills and techniques which he will have occasion to use in any operation he may undertake.

PREPARING A DOG FOR SURGERY

Surgical restraint is nothing more than an adaptation of the restraint used in first aid. It must, however, be dependable and certain. During surgery, the animal must often be held securely in a supine position, perhaps on its side or on its back. When a local anesthetic is used, sometimes only a hitch to the collar is enough and the operation can be performed with the pet sitting or standing on the table, but it is usually safer to use a few ties on the legs. If the operation is in the abdominal area, a kitchen table top can be used for the emergency operating table, with a cord running from each table leg to one of the dog's legs. If the operation is on the side, one tie can run from both front legs, one from both hind legs, one from the collar, and another from a loop about the flank just in front of the hind legs.

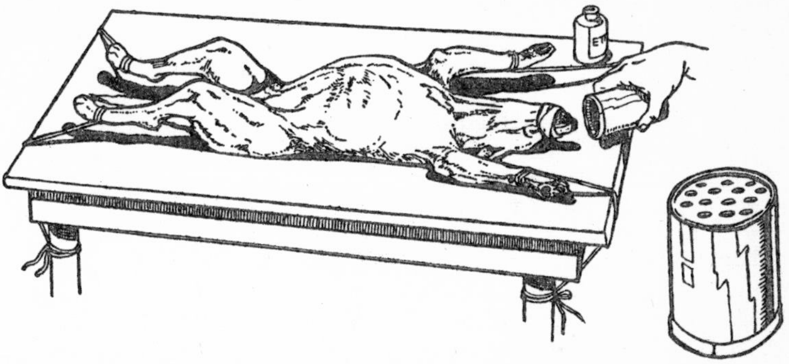

An emergency operating table. "Ether cone" is made by perforating the closed end of a tin can and placing gauze inside to hold the ether.

Anesthesia. Ether is probably the safest general anesthesia for the home veterinarian to use. It can be administered through a tin can with one end removed, the sharp edges covered with adhesive tape and the other end perforated with nail holes and an inch of gauze stuffed into the bottom. As much ether is poured on the gauze as it will absorb. A cloth is wrapped about the patient's face covering the eyes, and the can placed over it. Air is drawn through the gauze, which evaporates the ether and as vapor it is inhaled and absorbed by the blood from the lungs, carried to the brain, and brings unconsciousness. Before complete anesthesia, a period of excitement and struggling occurs. Sometimes two persons are needed to hold the patient until this initial struggling ceases.

It is imperative not to overanesthetize. A limpness which occurs in all the muscles is indication that a state of anesthesia exists. It you can touch the patient's eyelashes with a finger tip without causing any blinking, you can be sure that the animal is anesthetized. The ether container must be removed and the patient watched by the anesthetist to make sure that it is breathing regularly and that there is no evidence of pain. If the breathing becomes shallow and quick, too much anesthetic has been given. Watch out for a complete cessation of respiration and be ready for artificial respiration. If a very large overdose has been administered, the heart, too, will stop, and revival is then usually impossible. The person giving the ether has a task which requires his complete attention, and he must not allow his interest to be diverted to the surgery.

If the home veterinarian is sufficiently competent to use an injectable anesthetic, pentobarbital sodium (Nembutal) is excellent in the proportion of one grain to five pounds of body weight (one c.c. of solution to five pounds). This is a prescription drug and you must first find a doctor willing to give it to you. This type of intravenous injection is most easily given with a 23-gauge needle. A tourniquet of heavy elastic is affixed tightly about the leg above the point to be injected. The vein swells. It is held between the finger tips, which circle the leg from underneath, and the bone forms a base to prevent the vein from slipping out of the way. The needle is inserted through the skin and up the vein. The plunger is drawn back to ascertain that the needle is in the vein and then the tourniquet is removed. The syringe is emptied slowly while an assistant helps hold the patient's leg to prevent its being pulled away. If there is any question that the needle may have slipped out, it must be withdrawn and the clot of blood in it pushed out (if there is one) and the injection finished on the other leg. Even the most expert surgeons occasionally have difficulty finding the veins. Too often the tourniquet loosens, or the vein may be small and the patient jerky and nervous. In such cases the injection is made directly into the abdomen—all the way, not under the skin or into the muscles. In such a case, however, there is a long wait for profound anesthesia.

CAUTION: Pentobarbital should not be given to a dog in shock, nor to an old one with kidney or liver disease.

Local anesthetic applied with a hypodermic syringe can employ procaine (Novocaine), or a mixture of it with adrenalin (epinephrine), available in most drugstores. A 23-gauge needle is large enough. Without knowledge of nerve pathways, the home surgeon will inject a c.c. here and there about the area to be anesthetized. Remember that each layer of tissue must be anesthetized separately. If a deep rent is to be sutured, anesthetic in the skin is not sufficient to deaden the area underneath. The skin is first treated and incised, and then the next layer similarly anesthetized.

WOUND CLEANING

Soap and water clean the skin fairly satisfactorily; a razor can be used to shave the area to be opened; if a gash needs suturing, scissors can be used to trim away the hair. Ragged tissue is removed because if it has no blood supply it may become gangrenous. Blood clots, dirt, gravel, and any other foreign bodies, including hair, which retard healing, should be meticulously removed with tweezers. The area is flushed out with pure water and a gauze swab—cotton leaves lint. When it looks clean, hydrogen peroxide may be used to further cleanse it, or any household antiseptic in weak dilution, according to directions on the bottle. Powdered sulfa drugs, if you can get them, may be sprinkled in and the wound closed.

If there is no infection, the dog will usually leave any sutured wound alone. When he can smell pus, however, he will try to open the incision to lick the pus out.

TISSUE JOINING

You already know that the deepest layer of the skin is the growing layer. Hence it is the layer to be joined with its opposite. The amateur often folds the skin inward, suturing the outer layers together, and then wonders why it refuses to heal. The peritoneum, which covers the intestines and such organs as the bladder, stomach, kidneys, and uterus, must be joined if an incision through the abdominal wall is to be sutured. It heals together in a day or two. Making sure that peritoneum is joined to peritoneum, thin though it may be, is absolutely essential. Even the tissues it covers will often heal cleanly if the peritoneum is well joined.

Suturing muscle tissue is accomplished by sewing together the covering of the muscles (fascia). If this is joined, the muscle within heals more quickly. This layer is fairly tough too.

The periosteum (the skin around the bones) should be drawn together where possible. The capsule around the joints, when ruptured, should also be joined.

If, in an emergency, you can only remember to join like tissue to like tissue, your chances of success are good, provided reasonable care is taken with cleanliness.

SUTURING MATERIALS

Absorbable material, such as catgut, is generally used where the new tissue itself will be strong enough after healing. In hernias and in emergencies when nothing else is available, silk can be buried provided the knots are left without dangling ends. Linen sutures are preferred by many. Horsehair has been used in some emergencies—hair pulled from a horse's tail or mane—and many disfigurements have been prevented by its use.

Kinds of Sutures. Only a few of the surgeons' stitches need be remembered or will be useful in home emergency operations. What is of great

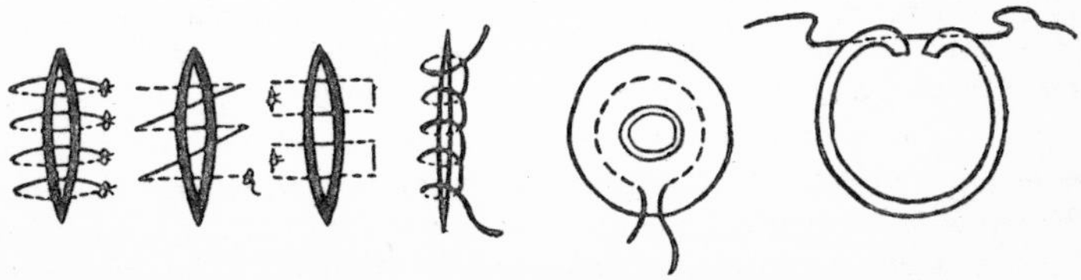

Common surgical sutures. Left to right: interrupted; continuous; Halsted; mattress; purse-string; Lembert.

importance is the kind of knot. Granny knots may loosen; square knots will not. If nylon sutures are used, at least three knots must be made or they will work open.

If tissue tends to pull apart as it is sutured, the surgeon's knot is used. Two twists instead of one are made of one thread about the other, followed by a one-twist ordinary square knot, to hold it securely.

Two correct surgical knots and an improper one. Left to right: square and surgeon's knots, both approved; granny knot, disapproved.

STOPPING HEMORRHAGE

In Red Cross work thousands of volunteer workers were instructed in hemorrhage control by temporary methods, such as by pressure bandages, tourniquets, and finger pressure on arteries and large veins. The same principles apply to pets, but with animals there is more that can be done.

Pressure bandages must be applied with real pressure. A wad of cloth is made and placed on top of the spot from which blood is gushing. A bandage is wrapped tightly about it and the dog is hurried to the veterinarian. For some reason the amateur is invariably unwilling to bind a wound firmly. In not one case of a badly cut foot have I ever seen a bandage applied by a client which was any more than a sop for the blood. Don't be afraid to bind it tightly. A good bandage will help the formation of a blood clot, and when the bandage is removed the clot itself will prevent more hemorrhage.

Tying Off Vessels. By locating the bleeding artery or vein, a stitch may be taken with thread and needle circling the vessel, and a surgeon's knot then tied tightly. In open wounds tying off is the safest assurance.

Stretching Arteries. If a little artery spurting blood is located, it may be grasped with forceps, pulled out, twisted, and then released. The flow is generally stopped effectively. Arteries are quite tough. In puppy castrations, most veterinarians rely on this method. The blood vessels are stretched until they part and no hemorrhage results.

DEVICES TO PREVENT SELF-INJURY

After any operation, or even to prevent a pet from chewing or scratching at an area of skin infection, it may be necessary to apply one of several devices designed to permit healing without interference.

Boxing Gloves. If scratching is the difficulty, the pet may have "boxing gloves" put on the feet. These are applied by first placing a wad of cotton around the foot, winding gauze over it, and then covering the whole pad with adhesive tape. The tape should be started an inch above the gauze in order to fasten it to the hair and prevent it from slipping off. Batting itself with such soft devices often entirely discourages a pet from scratching.

Tying the Legs. Where a dog refuses to let his face alone but insists on scratching with his front paws, and if only a day or two of prevention is required, the front legs may be crossed and taped together at the wrists. The tape is, of course, removed while the owner takes the dog on a leash for his outdoor duties.

Elizabethan Collars. These may be purchased as inflatable rubber collars which are slipped over the neck and then blown up. They may also be made, easily enough, by using two pieces of thin plywood or heavy stiff cardboard, which are put together and held with shoelace or cord ties.

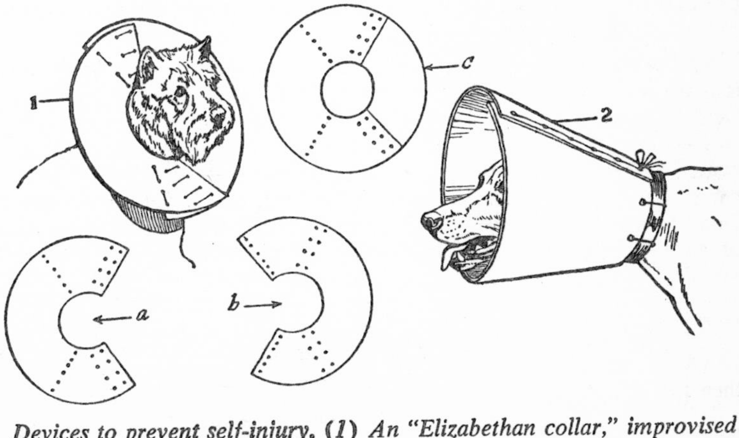

Devices to prevent self-injury. (*1*) *An "Elizabethan collar," improvised from thin plywood or extra-strong cardboard, is helpful in preventing an animal from chewing on cuts or sores or removing bandages.* a., b., *and* c. *show how collar is made and put together.* (*2*) *Head funnel of plastic or heavy cardboard prevents an animal from scratching sores or irritations on its head or ears.*

The Cone Collar. A piece of flat, flexible plastic is cut to make a partial cone. The edges are punched and the device is brought together around the head. The small end of the cone may either be fastened to the collar or left free; the larger end of the cone (the base) is a little beyond the dog's nose. See illustration.

MINOR OPERATIONS

Tapping. IN DROPSY. For the relief of a dog whose abdomen is filled with dropsical fluid so breathing is difficult, when there is not time to wait for absorption and excretion of the fluid, use a sharp 14-gauge hypodermic needle. Plunge it through the abdominal wall halfway between the ribs and pelvis and allow the fluid to drain into a pan. There is no appreciable amount of pain to the pet.

IN BLOAT. When the stomach of a dog has filled with gas under pressure, the tension may be relieved by passing a stomach tube. If this is unsuccessful, insert a 14- or 16-gauge needle directly into the stomach just behind the ribs and high up on the body and allow the gas to escape. A stylet may be needed from time to time to unplug the needle.

Liberating Fluids. FROM ABSCESSES. If an abscess has developed, shave off the hair over it and incise the skin with a razor blade or sharp knife. Let the pus escape and flush the cavity. Make the cut long enough so that it won't heal too quickly. Keep the skin separated by daily flushing until it has healed from the bottom.

CAUTION: Don't push a blade through an abscess. It is walled off by the body, and the bacteria must not be pushed through the wall into the circulation.

FROM CYSTS. After the area has been shaved, incise the skin and allow the fluid to escape. Make a long enough incision and retard skin healing by daily opening and flushing until the pocket has shrunk to normal size. Cysts, especially cysts of the salivary glands, occasionally have developed linings which are of a secretory nature and cannot be healed without dissection of the entire lining. This is a delicate task even for a skilled veterinarian. Dogs may develop cysts under the tongue (ranulas). Let the veterinarian remove them, as they should be done under general anesthesia, for there is danger of pneumonia if the pet inspires some of the viscous fluid with which the ranula is filled.

FROM FISTULAS. A fistula is an opening or passage between two parts of the body, such as from the larynx out through the skin of the neck. A fistula may result from a gunshot wound. A sharp stick or a splinter may remain in the pet's body unknown to the owner. The passage, an unhealing ulcer, in time becomes filled with fluid. The condition may be remedied by liberating the fluid and removing the foreign body. If this does not effect a cure, your veterinarian will have to resort to surgery.

FROM SERUM POCKETS. After accidents, great pouches of fluid often develop under areas of skin which have been loosened. Sometimes they fill with blood which clots and from which the plasma is absorbed back into circulation. If the injury was serious enough, bacteria may have gained access to the pocket. After the skin is shaved, an incision at the lowest part of the pocket should be made and the fluid and clots squeezed out. The area may be flushed with peroxide or sulfa-drug solutions and the body bound to press the skin against the underlying layers to promote rapid healing.

FROM EAR HEMATOMAS. Hematomas are pockets of blood between layers of the skin. The most common location is in the ear. Dogs with ear mites bruise the ears by constant scratching. Dogs shaking their heads bruise

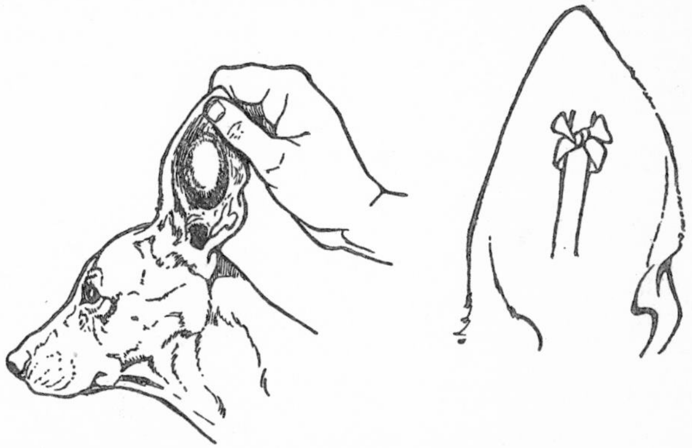

A hematoma in the ear, and surgical treatment to facilitate rapid healing without puckering. The gauze, which is moved back and forth to prevent the middle strip from healing, is removed when the sides have healed down.

the ear flaps on collar hardware. Let the fluid out by a slit through the skin on the inside of the ear. If the blood is not drawn off, it will clot, and the clot will shrink and pull the ear into a gnarled deformity. Let the veterinarian operate. If no veterinarian is available, anesthetize the ear along its base with a few drops of procaine. After shaving the area, make two parallel slits through the skin, three sixteenths inch apart, the length of the hematoma. Clean all clots and fibrin strings out of the pocket. Then tie a small piece of gauze around the narrow slit to keep it from healing. Move the gauze up and down the slit once a day as you flush it out. Let the pockets heal together on both sides of the slit before removing the gauze. The strip of skin will heal in place promptly after the gauze has been removed.

Suturing. SKIN CUTS. The edges are shaved or trimmed with sharp scissors, the tissue cleansed, and the skin brought together. If a cut is long, use Halsted-type suture; if short, an interrupted stitch is adequate. Be sure the lower layers of skin are joined. It is necessary to pull the skin together as quickly as possible becaues it shrinks rapidly. V-shaped areas especially should be treated immediately, since the loosened skin retracts so much that it is difficult to stretch it sufficiently to cover the wound. Where skin grows together from the sides no hair will cover it and a scar is left.

EAR CUTS. Notches in the ear flaps of dogs tend to grow deeper as the dog shakes his head. Healing is often completely prevented, and even after the area has healed, the dog may open the tissue to blood flow by shaking his head incessantly. The bleeding can be greatly reduced by taking a stitch which circles the blood vessel at the base of the notch. A fresh cut can best be repaired by your veterinarian, who will use local anesthetic and carefully suture both layers of skin together separately. One stitch through both skin layers and the cartilage is seldom entirely satisfactory, but if the skin is sutured neatly, the cartilage between the layers will heal together evenly.

Growth Removal. WARTS. Simply cutting a wart off results in hemorrhage. To remove one successfully, the skin below the wart must be dissected out along with the protruding part. A few drops of local anesthetic under the wart is enough to deaden the area. A single suture bringing the skin together usually results in perfect healing.

POLYPS, PAPILLOMAS. Little toadstool growths on the body or in the mouth or on the lips of a dog may often be removed by simply tying them at the base with a surgeon's knot and letting them drop off.

PROLAPSED RECTUM. It is not uncommon to find a pet which from long-continued straining at stool—frequently occasioned by the administration of laxatives, by coccidiosis, or by a disease which produces loose bowel movements—has suffered a prolapse of the rectum.

A red, tumorlike body protrudes from the anus, becomes inflamed and increases in length and diameter, and gradually turns black as the tissues dry and die. If your veterinarian is not available within a few hours, gently push the spongy enlargement back inside. Find a smooth object, such as a one-half-inch rubber tube, insert it into the rectum to be sure no intussusception remains inside and that the prolapse is entirely gone. Withdraw the tube and insert a purse-string suture around the anus, which will have become quite numb from the prolapse. Leave the ends long enough to tie in a bowknot. Release the sutures twice a day to permit defecation.

Eye Surgery. Eye surgery demands a high degree of skill and should usually be left to the veterinarian. At least one common operation, however —the removal of an enlarged, inflamed gland of Harder—can be performed by the owner. The third eyelid (nictitating membrane) sometimes tips forward, exposing this gland which protrudes from the lower lid close to the nose. It appears to be a tumorous growth. If some butyn-sulfate eye ointment is inserted in the eye ten minutes before the operation, it can be done practically without pain.

The spongy growth is grasped with blunt forceps and pulled up, while an assistant holds the dog's head. When the gland is exposed outside the lid, it is snipped off without cutting the nictitating membrane. The eye at once appears perfect except for hemorrhage, which continues mildly for a few minutes. An ophthalmic ointment is used twice daily for two or three days.

Two minor maladies requiring surgery. Left, abscess under the eye, which can be cured by extraction of infected tooth. Right, inflamed gland of Harder, which can be snipped off.

Castration. Millions of farm animals are castrated annually by farmers. Pet animals are also operated on, often very crudely. Without proper knowledge, home veterinarians often kill their pets by clumsy castration. The technique is actually quite simple and applies to every species.

After proper restraint and local or general anesthesia, the incision is made through the skin of the scrotum. This exposes the covering of the testicle (the tunic). It is actually an extension of the peritoneum. Now, too many times the home operator pulls out the testicle and cuts it off. The pet frequently bleeds to death. Instead, the tunic should be incised and the testicle itself exposed. The tunic is folded back over the testicle, remaining attached at only one point from which it must be peeled off. In young animals the testicle and its cord, composed of a muscle, blood vessels, nerves, and seminal vesicle, is then pulled until all these have snapped.

The stretching of the artery prevents bleeding. The tunic withdraws into the abdominal ring and heals quickly.

CAUTION: If any vestige of the tunic is left sticking through the skin incisions, as it sometimes is in castrations, a little lump will grow out and the skin will be prevented from healing. The home operator should always examine the scrotum to be sure the incisions are empty.

A mature pet needs a gut ligature about the blood vessels to prevent hemorrhage. In dogs it is also wise to place sutures through the skin incisions, since they sit with the scrotum on the ground and are likely to pick up infections.

Cryptorchidism. Removing hidden testicles is a task for the veterinarian.

Spaying. Spaying should be done only by a professional. Considering the number of bitches lost by those who have attempted it without knowing some of the finer points, it is far better to leave it to one who knows and can perform the operation neatly, quickly, and humanely.

Teeth Extractions. Loose teeth are so simply extracted—sometimes with one's fingers—that veterinarians often wonder why they find so many in dogs' mouths. Some teeth need special instruments to split them and remove them in pieces, but the incisors and premolars are sometimes so loose that they can be pulled with small tweezers or forceps, or with clean automobile pliers. If you are uncertain about how firmly set the tooth really is, better let the veterinarian attend to it even though you have to wait a week or two. If a tooth can't be moved by the finger tip, it probably is a job for the doctor.

Removing Dewclaws. Dog owners brag about their dogs' extra toes and never have them removed. And, according to show standards, some breeds of dogs—Newfoundlands, St. Bernards, and all retrievers—need dewclaws, the surplus and often useless toe equivalent to a human thumb. Most dog owners, even show enthusiasts, have no objection to front dewclaws but think that on the hind legs they tend to detract from the neatness of the dog. Accordingly, they insist that these useless appurtenances be removed. It would be better to breed dogs without them (they tend to be inherited as Mendelian dominants), but since it is customary to remove them, it should be remembered that the younger the pup is when it is done, the better. More puppies bleed to death from this operation when it is carelessly done than die of tail docking.

When the pup is a few days old these toes may be snipped off with heavy sharp shears. After some healing antiseptic salve has been applied, a little bandage should then be fixed to the leg and left for two days. That usually ends the trouble.

Some dewclaws are large but never come through the skin. Although they bulge out on the leg, they remain only as bones. Since the nail is a skin appendage and not a bone growth, no nail grows on the hidden dewclaws. If these are to be removed, leave the job to the veterinarian. He will use an anesthetic, slit the skin, remove the toe, and suture the skin so you can scarcely tell it has been done—if the pup co-operates by not chewing or licking the site of the operation until it is healed and the bandage removed. I have removed a good many such toes of dogs which have subsequently become American Kennel Club champions and no one would suspect that they had ever been born with dewclaws.

Hernias. A hernia is a protrusion of tissue, organ, or organs through an abnormal opening. They occur commonly in dogs, the tendency to have them frequently being hereditary. Reducing a hernia is a job for a veterinarian, and the treatment is discussed in detail in a later chapter.

Docking Tails. Some breeds of dogs require tail docking for styles set by breed fanciers. Many more are docked by owners than by veterinarians, but it is wiser to have your veterinarian do it if the puppies are much over a week old, because these larger tails are so likely to bleed. The veterinarian can put in a few gut sutures.

In docking thousands of puppies of many breeds, I have found a method of doing the job without danger to the puppies, neatly and cleanly, so that

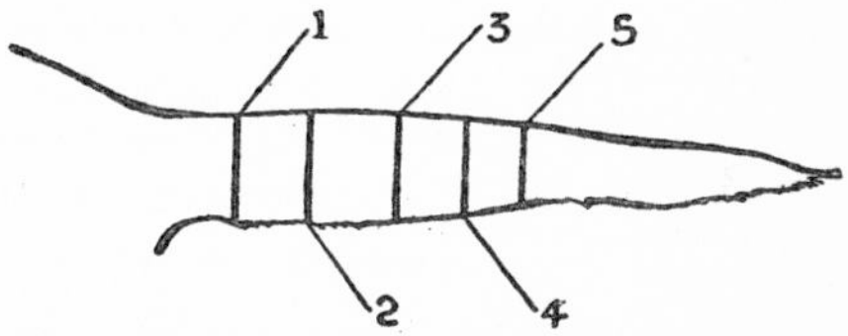

Points at which puppies' tails are usually docked. The lengths shown are those generally preferred, but styles change. If any doubt exists as to the proper length for your breed, consult the breed standard. (1) American fox terriers, boxers, Doberman pinschers. (2) Welsh Corgi. (3) All spaniels. (4) German short-haired pointer, Lakeland terrier. (5) Airedale, wire-haired fox terrier, English smooth fox terrier, poodle.

the tails heal without a hairless stub end. Observing show points, I have also learned the proper lengths to dock; how much to remove; how much to leave of normal length tails. Most important of all, when docking is done by this method there is almost no bleeding and very little pain. The technique I propose is not, of course, the only acceptable one. I have known many a litter of puppies to be docked with a jackknife and docked neatly and successfully.

In docking, remember that every puppy has a limited supply of iron. He can ill afford to lose any blood, because even though he makes up the volume, it will not have quite the iron content of the blood of puppies which will have lost none. The initial loss of blood is not the only thing to consider. Many a litter has been cleanly docked, returned to the mother in excellent condition. She, however, may single out one or two and lick the end of the tail so that the blood cannot clot. If she is not stopped she may lick the pup to death. Every litter returned to the mother should be watched, and if the mother will not let their tails alone, the pups should be removed and brought back to the mother only for nursing while the owner watches to prevent her from unconsciously committing murder.

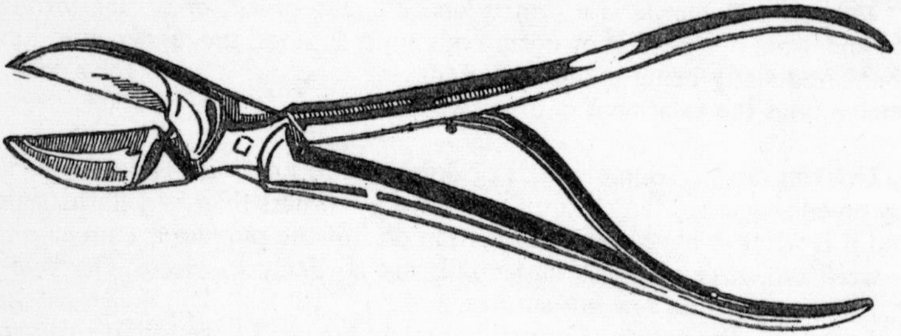

Bone shears. Ideal for docking puppies' tails.

The best instrument for docking is a pair of bone shears like those pictured. The tail is cut with the square side toward the pup. The shears are clamped shut quickly and held a few moments. The end of the tail is jerked back and forth until it comes off. The nerves have been severed instantly, so there is no pain and very little bleeding. If the tail does bleed, a stitch of #0 gut, pulling the skin together, will almost always stop it.

You may have been told that the tail should be "disjointed" at a specific vertebra. People who give you such information have not docked young puppies' tails. You can't feel the vertebrae; you simply cut the tail to the proper length. Only in Doberman pinschers and boxers, where the tails are cut close to the body, does the skin slip to any extent. In their case the skin should be pulled back toward the body before the cut is made. With other breeds the cut is made with only the length the tail will be on the grown dog in mind. The following table shows the proper proportions to leave in all of the breeds where tails are docked. Remember that the tendency of amateurs is to cut too short.

Table V

	PROPORTION TO LEAVE	ULTIMATE LENGTH
American Smooth Fox Terrier	1/8	1″
Boxer	1/8	1½″
Doberman Pinscher	1/8	1½″
Clumber Spaniel	1/4	2″

	PROPORTION TO LEAVE	ULTIMATE LENGTH
Field Spaniel	1/4	2″
Welsh Corgi	1/4	2½″
Cocker Spaniel	3/8	3″
Springer Spaniel	3/8	3½″
Brittany Spaniel	3/8	3½″
Lakeland Terrier	1/2	4″
German Short-haired Pointer	1/2	5″
Wire-haired Fox Terrier	5/8	4½″
English Smooth Fox Terrier	5/8	4½″
Poodle	5/8	5″
Airedale Terrier	5/8	6″
Standard Poodle	5/8	5″

Ear Cropping. I hold no brief for the practice of ear cropping. I know, however, that thousands of dogs are cropped every year, and that most of this cropping is done by men and women who are not professional veterinarians. Only a few states have laws putting the practice in the hands of the veterinary profession, and even in these states violators of the law are seldom punished.

Ear cropping is an art which should be left to those with "know-how." Sometimes, however, a competent person can't be found to do it and the dog owner must perform the operations on his puppies himself. The method I outline here, which happens to be one of my own origination, is the best I know, but it may not be the method that was used on your dog. Ear cropping has been a particularly bloody job; this method makes it almost bloodless.

The equipment needed is: One old-fashioned emasculatome, a pair of straight, sharp surgical scissors, some #0000 catgut, small cutting-edge needles, a pair of curved mosquito forceps, a pair of needle holders, one 5-c.c. hypodermic syringe with a 22-gauge needle, a tube of Duo-adhesive, and pentobarbital-sodium solution for anesthesia. Ether may be used but has definite drawbacks. An assistant is essential for efficiency.

The best age to crop puppies is at seven to ten weeks. They can be done at a year, but chances of success in dogs out of the puppy class diminish with the age of the dog.

The operative procedure is as follows: First, anesthetize the puppy in the manner described earlier in this chapter. To make a beautiful crop on a dog's ear, the line of cropping should be straight. As the ear cups in its natural shape, this produces the effect, when viewed from the front, of a graceful curve. Close to the puppy's head, the flap of the ear starts at a definite bump, and the operator should start his line from as close to this bump as possible. Apply the forceps about one sixteenth of an inch from this spot to act as a guide. Now, depending upon whether you want a tall or short crop, choose the proper point on the front tip of the flap and apply the emasculatome to run from one place to the other. Push the handles together. Leave the emasculatome in place for a minute, then remove it and cut the flap off, trimming along the outside of the line. There will be no bleeding. Now suture it by stitches a quarter of an inch apart to keep the skin from slipping back off the cartilage when healing starts. If you have been rough and caused bleeding, have your assistant gently pinch the artery through the ear with his thumb and first finger, shutting off the blood flow until you have the ear stitched.

Turn the pup over and mark the untrimmed ear with the piece of flap you have removed from the other. Apply your mosquito forceps as a guide, apply the emasculatome, cut off the flap, and suture. If the ears have become bloodied, wash them gently, dry, apply ether, and dry again.

Now cover the outside of each ear tip, two inches down, with Duo-adhesive and press them together, holding a moment until they are firmly stuck. The job is done. Keep each pup in a separate run until the ears have healed.

Aftercare consists of keeping scabs removed and dusting the ears daily with a healing powder. Try to keep the ears stuck together until all healing is completed. If you can do that, there need be no further care. If, for any reason, the ears come apart, they must be taped with the raw edges stretched. When scar tissue heals, it shrinks. And if the ears are allowed to heal hanging over, there is practically no chance they will ever stand up, unless they are recropped and the scar tissue removed.

If ears come apart too early, allow them to heal naturally for a day or two and then stick them together across the top of the head with one on top of the other. Duo-adhesive can be used, but adhesive tape will probably be necessary also, as there will be very little hair to help hold the ears together.

During teething time puppies with naturally erect ears may drop their ears for a month or more. If puppies you have cropped have nicely erect ears and you find them drooping during teething time, remember that they will probably stand erect after the teeth are in. If they refuse and there is no contraction of scar tissue along the ear edges, try rolling them gently around a core of any kind and taping them. A week in this position will usually train them.

Many persons advise massage to make ears stand erect. Massage helps very little and sometimes has the effect of stretching muscles and making them flabby.

FRACTURES AND DISLOCATIONS

The most common disorders of the bones are fractures—all of which can be observed easily by the layman. Dislocations, too, are frequent. The causes of both breaks and dislocations are so varied that it would be of little use to list them; they range from the kick of a horse to catching a toenail in a crack between boards.

Before discussing specific types, let us consider the general categories of fractures.

Three different kinds of break are most often found:

In a *greenstick fracture* the bone breaks but stays in its natural position. Usually one side is broken but the other only bent.

A *simple fracture* is a clean break in which the tissue surrounding the bone is left intact.

A *compound fracture* is one in which there is an opening connecting

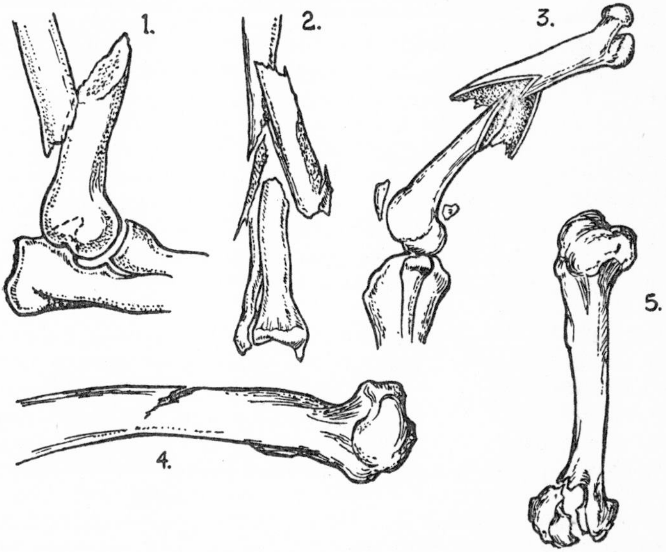

Common fractures. (1) Simple, (2) Compound, when some of the bones penetrate the skin, (3) Comminuted, (4) "Greenstick," (5) Condylar.

the site of fracture to the outside of the body. This opening may be due to a wound inflicted from without or to a hole punched outward by the end of the bone being driven through the surrounding tissue and skin.

In addition there are other descriptive classifications. There are complete fractures where bones are broken clear across; comminuted fractures where bones are splintered; linear fractures in which the break is lengthwise of the bone; neoplastic fractures where the bone breaks from a growth in its substance; sprain fractures in which a tendon tears away a piece of bone to which it is attached, and numerous other variations.

Besides learning a little about the kinds of fractures, it will be helpful at this point if you will review that part of Chapter 2 concerned with how bones heal. You will have a clearer understanding of how fractures should be treated and why.

The owner should know how to treat his dog for shock when it suffers broken bones (see page 135). If a veterinarian is near, the owner is well advised to call him immediately. The animal should be kept warm until the doctor arrives to give the necessary treatment and set the bone.

Dislocations must be "reduced"—slipped back into place—and this, too, usually had best be left to the veterinarian. Breaks of almost any bone can be set. Some, like broken jaws, may need wiring; some may require complicated pegging, or joining by grafting. These matters require specialized study and are definitely outside the realm of this book. The methods require considerable study and a great deal of experience. So does the decision as to whether to use splints, and what kind of splint—yucca, Stader, Thomas—or plaster casts interspersed with cloth, with or without windows, if the fracture is compound. Even the dog's character must be considered. Some dogs will chew almost any appliance off; others will cooperate as good patients should.

Every fracture case should be observed by your veterinarian once a week, so that he can check on the apposition, the healing, the straightness, and so he can remove the splint or cast at the right time. In growing puppies it is often safe to remove a splint three weeks after the break; in mature dogs a month is the usual time.

Pelvic Breaks. Probably the greatest number of breaks are caused by automobile accidents, and, in my experience, of these, pelvic breaks lead all others in frequency.

It is not difficult to tell when the pelvis is fractured. Usually the dog will not be able to stand, or, if he is stood up, his hind legs spread apart and he either collapses in pain or waddles with difficulty. The tail may hang inert.

If the examiner will soap an index finger and, after placing the dog on its side, insert it into the rectum, he will feel the break or breaks clearly. He may even find that a bone edge has cut through the rectum, or he may be able to push a collapsed pelvis back into place by finger pressure and thereby relieve the dog considerably. He may feel a break in the spine where the first tail vertebra joins the last sacral, which would account for the dead tail. If the dog can wag his tail, it is conclusive evidence that the backbone is not broken.

A ruptured pelvis may involve any of the six bones which comprise it (three pairs of bones), and sometimes, as we have said, the spinal column is involved. The bones of the pelvis are the ilium, ischium, and pubis. Look at the diagram of a dog's skeleton (page 27). Now imagine it is covered with flesh and is your dog. Imagine you can see that skeleton through the flesh and skin of your dog. The bones of the pelvic girdle are these six plus the sacrum, that section of the spinal column consisting of five or six vertebrae ending where the tail vertebrae start. When the pelvis is ruptured, any of the six pelvic bones may be broken or torn, or the injury may be to the backbone, the joints where the sacrum and the ilium join, one on each side, to make the sacroiliac joint, or the muscles and ligaments which hold this whole box together.

Fractured Femur. The examiner may find that nothing is wrong in the pelvis, that no bones feel as though they were broken, and yet the dog appears lopsided when viewed from behind. This may be an indication that the head of the femur—the head of the thigh bone—is broken off. It may also mean that the hipbone is dislocated, a condition which we will discuss under dislocations.

In my experience, fracture of the femur is the second most common break. Such a fracture is frequently surrounded by a pocket of blood because, as the dog trots home on three legs, the bone edges rub on the muscles and cut arterioles or venules—sometimes even a large artery or vein. An animal with such a break should be hustled to a veterinarian. He will have to anesthetize the patient to set the break. Anesthetics not only render the dog insensible but also relax the muscles and so make the job easier for the doctor.

Many a well-set bone separates and slips so that it sets in a side-to-side position instead of end to end. If this should happen, the healing process will take longer and the broken leg will be shorter than normal. Even so, the dog will manage to get about with less limp than one would expect.

Fractures of the Toes and Tails. Dislocations which amount to breaks occur in the toes and the tails of dogs of all breeds. Puppies born with tails that bend backward actually have dislocated vertebrae, and bending the tail to straighten it usually results in breaking it or damaging it so severely that the end below the break dies and must be removed.

Toes which are broken at the joints usually are easily repaired by applying casts to the feet after reduction or setting. But when a ligament of the toes is cut or broken, it seldom regenerates and the nail bends upward. This is a familiar sight to veterinarians, who see so many steel-trap wounds. I have repaired feet where these little ligaments were cut on three of the four toes. Thereafter the nails, which no longer touch the ground and wear away naturally, have to be cut at frequent intervals.

Head Fractures. Head fractures result from a variety of accidents—from being struck by a baseball to being hit by a truck. If the skull is cracked above the brain case, the dog may live, but generally so much brain concussion occurs that the prognosis is unfavorable. If the skull over the brain case is not fractured, very often some other part of the skull is. A favorite spot is the bone covering the sinus in the forehead. The sinus itself may be penetrated and infected. Your veterinarian may have to pick pieces of bone out, flush the sinus, and cover the hole with skin.

The arch of bone over the eye, which has a fixed joint through it, often breaks and presses inward, causing the eye to bulge. This necessitates pulling the arch back into shape, where it usually stays because the dog lets it alone after he learns that pressure against it occasions pain. The eye generally becomes inflamed and may even be damaged so that it has to be removed.

Jaw injuries are common. Breaks in the center of the jawbone occur more frequently in my practice than breaks involving either of the bones (mandibles) which together make the jaw. The mandibles are joined by a cartilaginous attachment. When the break occurs here, it is obvious, because the jaw loses its firmness. If it is permitted to heal without attention, it often sets crooked. A veterinarian will wire it together so neatly that it will heal like new and much more quickly than true bone. Nursing is of primary importance. The saliva seems to prevent infection, so that no medication is required unless the wire is placed from below after the skin has been parted. Then the sutures need attention. The diet must be of a nature requiring no chewing—milk and mushy food.

Hip Joint Dislocations. Dogs' hip joints come apart (are dislocated) more often than any other joints. This ball-and-socket joint, like most others, is surrounded by a capsule. Ligaments and muscles, too, hold it in place. In spite of the fact that it is held very strongly in place, falls and blows such as those inflicted by automobiles somehow get the ball on the femur out of the socket (acetabulum).

This dislocation may be such that the ball is above, below, or in front of the rim of the socket. Even the rim itself may be damaged so that it is extremely difficult to get the joint to stay together. Often the capsule, ligaments, and muscles which hold the joint together are so mutilated that the femur can be put back with ease, only to slip out again just as easily.

I have seen some dislocations of this type in large dogs so difficult to reduce that three strong veterinarians struggled until sweat stood out all over them before the muscles relaxed enough to let the joint slip together. I've seen others which were snapped back by merely bending the leg and giving it just the right kind of twist. You may say, if you watch your veterinarian set one, "It's all in knowing how." But no expert, even with the use of a fluoroscope, can get all hip joints together easily.

Shoulder Dislocations. These can be observed by comparing the feel of the two shoulders. Generally a quick forward pull while someone holds the dog firmly will snap a dislocated shoulder into place, with very little resulting pain. But a difficult dislocation should not be pulled more than once. There may be tissue between the two parts. Your veterinarian can locate the trouble quickly, and by anesthetizing the dog and then twisting the leg, he will be able to replace it quite simply.

Wrist and Hock Dislocations. When dislocated, these joints are usually said to be broken. The many little bones of which the joints are composed are held together by ligaments which may be ruptured. The leg may hang sideways with skin and ligaments on one side torn away, and yet when it is straightened in a splint and held immobile, the joint heals and in time the animal will be able to walk as well as before the accident.

Such injuries may require many weeks of careful nursing. Ligaments do regenerate and skin does grow across, but the spot will be bald. That is why the veterinarian tries to draw the skin as closely together as he can—that and because the skin makes the best and the natural covering.

This has been a long chapter, filled with details of surgical methods. No one can tell you just how you will use this information or when you will need it. I can tell you about an incident which demonstrated how useful it may sometimes be.

One cold night a dog hunting with a party of hunters treed what they believed to be a raccoon. They saw eyes shining in the dark, and shot. Out of the tree dropped a wounded lynx. The dog foolishly attacked it. The lynx hooked a powerful claw into the dog's belly and tore it wide open. The dog's intestines fell out and the cat gashed through a section of them so that the lumen was exposed.

All his life the dog's owner had been trying to obtain a dog as fine as this. What should he have done? Should he have shot the dog? He didn't. He saved his life.

Could you have done as well? Here is the way to do it.

Put a muzzle on the dog, improvising if necessary by tearing up your shirt, cold or no cold. You'll get warm carrying your dog.

Pick the dog up and carry him to a nearby brook, wash off the intestines and poke them back inside. With some more strips torn from your shirt wind the abdomen up so the intestines can't come out. Then take turns with your companions carrying the dog to the car or home or to the camp.

No druggist or doctor is available. The only antiseptic you have is a bottle of Lysol. But there are needles and thread. The dog is in a state of shock and feels less pain than when he is normal. Tie him on a table. Soak the needles and silk thread in diluted Lysol. Have everybody working on the dog scrub his hands and then scrub the dog's skin after the binding is removed. As the intestines work out of the wound, hold a flashlight so that you can see whether any intestinal contents have been discharged through the intestinal rent into the abdomen. If so, flush the cavity out carefully. Let somebody continue to rub the dog's ear hard to keep his attention away from the surgical site.

All but the open intestinal loop is replaced, and now the home surgery begins. The outside layers of the gut are brought together and sewed with a row of sutures, Lembert type. The knots are made of three square ties and the ends cut off close. These sutures are inserted at one-eighth-inch intervals. As soon as the job is done, the loop is returned to the abdomen. Now the peritoneum must be sutured. The glistening white lining is brought together with sutures every three sixteenths inch and the ends of the suture knots cut short. Next the muscles are brought together by joining the white covering of them just under the skin. Lastly the skin is joined.

This will be difficult with an ordinary round sewing needle, but it can be done by pushing hard on the needle.

No food is given for a few days, except perhaps some corn syrup and water.

Suppose you do find that an infection develops in your work. By then you will have time to seek veterinary assistance, but you will have saved the dog. You will have saved him because you knew how to perform an emergency operation.

As you read this chapter you may have felt that parts of it were unnecessarily detailed. But these very details may someday save the life of your pet. Isn't he worth it?

8. How to Give Medicines and Apply Accessories

ALL dog owners should know how to administer the common drugs used with animals, how to give their pets medicine in liquid and capsule form, how to apply the standard bandages, how to take the temperatures of animals—in short, how to handle all the little problems of caring for a sick or injured pet.

Your veterinarian will diagnose your dog's condition, prescribe the proper medication, and tell you the kind of care and attention your pet needs. That alone is not enough to restore the animal to health. In most cases you will treat your pet at home, and it is your responsibility to carry out the veterinarian's instructions. The most effective drug ever prescribed will not help your pet if you cannot manage to get more than 5 per cent of the dose down his throat. If you allow the animal to remove the bandage the veterinarian has applied and permit him to expose an open wound to infection simply because you don't know how to apply a bandage that will stay, you can hardly expect a quick and satisfactory recovery.

Your veterinarian will outline a course of treatment for your sick pet, but the way you carry out his instructions and the care you give the animal will usually determine how effective the treatment will be. If you can give the doctor the kind of intelligent co-operation that he has a right to expect, your pet's chances for recovery will be greatly increased.

METHODS FOR GIVING MEDICINE TO ANIMALS

Liquids. You will seldom be called upon to give liquid medicines to any species other than cats and dogs. But whenever a liquid is to be given, you should always remember that if certain of them enter the lungs they can be very dangerous. The first question you should ask yourself is: What would happen if the animal inhaled some?

Pure water solutions of quickly soluble drugs are least dangerous. Hydrogen peroxide turns to water and oxygen when it decomposes in the fizzing effect known to everyone. On the other hand, milk, which is sometimes used as a base or vehicle for drugs, contains solids. Fat is one of them, and fat in the lungs is especially dangerous. If the drug used is harmless if it gets into the lungs—that is, if it is a water solution—it is fairly safe to fill the animal's mouth and throat and force him to swallow it. If some of the medicine trickles down the windpipe, the only unfortunate thing that can happen is a blast of the medicine in your face or on your coat sleeve when the patient coughs. But when a solution dangerous to the lungs is to be administered, a little at a time had best be given.

In either event there are two practical ways of giving a liquid medicine: the lip-pocket method and by stomach tube. Let's see how and when each of these is used.

THE LIP-POCKET METHOD: Although an experienced person can accomplish this alone, you will probably find that two people are necessary for satisfactory results. Place the animal on a table broadside to you. Make him sit. Tilt his head back so that he is looking at the ceiling. With your right hand hold his chin in this position. Slide the fingers of your left hand under his lip, push back and catch hold of the angle where lower and upper lips join. Pull this out and upward. Now you have a cup or pocket which will hold a considerable amount. While you hold the patient thus, your assistant pours the medicine or liquid food in, giving a forty-pound dog perhaps a tablespoonful. As it runs between his teeth and onto the back of the tongue, he will swallow it. When this is gone, more is poured in, and soon he has the whole dose. A word of caution: the assistant should stand out of the line of fire, for if the animal coughs, he or she is liable to be thoroughly sprayed.

If an especially resisting pup is being dosed, the assistant has another duty. With one hand he holds both front paws firmly so that the dog can't pull them loose, and with the other he pours the medicine into the lip pocket.

THE STOMACH-TUBE METHOD: What seems a great task is in reality a simple and safe method if two people co-operate to dose an animal. A piece of rubber tubing, one eighth inch inside diameter and twelve to eighteen inches long, depending upon the size of the animal, is large enough for a dog. You can get both the tube and a syringe—either glass or rubber will do—at your druggist's. The syringe should be filled with the medicine and left within reach. When you are ready to insert the tube, hold the animal as described above with the head straight up. As the tube is pushed over the back of the tongue into the throat, the patient will gulp and swallow it down. If it has been moistened, it will slide down the gullet with reasonable ease.

There is one danger to guard against. You must be extremely careful not to get the tube into the windpipe, for if fluids are squirted down the tube into the lungs by mistake, the results may be tragic. By holding the upper end of the tube close to your ear, you can tell whether the other end is in the windpipe by the purring sound of air rushing in and out of the tube. If the tube has entered the gullet properly, you will not hear any sound at all. Another method of being sure where the tube is is to feel the throat. The windpipe is in front and closest to the skin, and in animals which are not too fat you should have no difficulty in feeling the tube in the gullet behind it.

When you are certain that the tube is where it should be, have your assistant—who needs both hands for the job—connect the syringe to the tube and squirt the medicine or liquid food down the tube. In mature animals the stomach tube may be left in for several minutes without causing strangulation; the patient goes right on breathing normally.

This stomach-tube method is particularly useful in feeding tiny puppies which are too cold or too weak to suck. I have saved dozens this way and have taught many assistants to do it, using a urinary catheter, or small rubber tube. It is a quick way of feeding and one that is most useful in supplementing an inadequate maternal milk supply. To be sure, you must always be certain that the tube is in the gullet, but that is not hard to determine, once you have done it a few times. When you consider that at the clinic we have reared whole litters of puppies experimentally in this fashion, it is easy to see that one man who passes a tube on a litter of eight, five times a day, or a total of 280 times a week, must not experience too much difficulty.

You should never try to squirt a drug into your dog's mouth, snap it shut, and expect the animal to swallow it. Most of the solution runs out. The animal shakes his head and the administration is a failure. You can sometimes overcome the patient's dislike for some drugs by disguising them in sweet syrups thinned down. Glucose (dextrose) is often administered to advantage to sick animals, but if given in the form of corn syrup it is difficult to pour. It must be thinned. If any sweet substance is given carefully and without a struggle, the subsequent dosages will be simpler and dogs in particular can often be trained to open their mouths and take it without a fuss. I have seen many that soon were willing to lick the syrup from a tablespoon.

Pills and Capsules. It doesn't require sleight of hand to get a pill or capsule down the throat of a dog, even when the pet resists. It's all in knowing how. Opening the animal's mouth, dropping in the medicine, closing his mouth, and rubbing his throat may work now and again, but it's not a sure enough method to rely on.

With the left hand (if you're right-handed) grasp the top of the animal's muzzle and pull his head upward. Squeeze the thumb on one side and the fingers on the other, thereby pushing the lips over the teeth and partly opening the mouth. Your patient won't close his mouth because to do so he will have to bite his lips. With your right hand pick up the pill or capsule between the thumb and first or second finger and with the little finger pull down the lower jaw. Hold it open with the side of the little finger and drop the pill as far back on the tongue as possible. With your forefinger, or with the forefinger and second finger, push the pill gently but quickly as far back into the throat as you can. Then withdraw your hand quickly, let the mouth close and hold it together until the dog sticks out his tongue in the act of swallowing. Several pills and capsules may be poked down in this way at one time.

Some capsules contain bitter or choking drugs. If a dog bites them they may cause him fright, suffocation, and a taste so obnoxious that he will try for many minutes to cough or scratch it out. If you are giving your pet medicine of this sort, you will want to be certain that no capsules are dropped between his teeth or insufficiently pushed down his throat.

Short-nosed breeds, such as Boston terriers, boxers, English bulldogs, bull mastiffs, have such fat tongues and restricted throats that laymen frequently have difficulty in properly medicating them. When wet, the pills or capsules become slippery and slide around sideways over the back of the broad tongue. It is wise never to try to give wet pills, especially wet capsules. If you are unsuccessful in the first attempt to give the medicine, take the capsule out and dry it. It will often sick to your finger just enough to enable you to pilot it into the back of the throat properly. Sometimes two fingers can keep it from sliding sideways, and on large dogs even three fingers may work very well.

BANDAGES AND THEIR USES

Of the many kinds of bandage used by physicians and nurses, only a few are very useful in veterinary work. Rolls of muslin and gauze, many-tailed bandages, and adhesive are those needed. Anyone can rip an old sheet into three-inch-wide strips to make a bandage in a pinch. But those strips had best be rolled tightly before applying. Two three- or four-inch bandages, six feet long, will usually be sufficient to bandage any dog.

Many-tails are simply strips of cloth as wide as the area to be bandaged on the patient and torn in the same number of parallel strips from each end toward the central area.

Adhesive tape one inch wide should serve almost any purpose. To cover a wide area it may be lapped, and if a narrower strip is desired, it may easily be ripped.

Most bandages will be applied by the home veterinarian for minor cuts and blemishes, or as stopgap measures before taking the pet to the veterinarian, after which, if bandaging is necessary, the veterinarian will have instructed the client as to how he wants the bandage applied in the future. This may save him giving instructions.

The most common use of bandages in pets is to prevent self-injury. Suppose a dog has been caught in a steel trap. He is found before the part of the leg below the trap bit has died. The skin has been cleaned and the veterinarian has sutured it. If he is not prevented from licking it, he will remove the stitches and open the wound. Moreover, after the bandage is applied, there will be considerable weeping from the wound and, despite antiseptics, an odd odor will develop. This is not a bad sign but rather a good one. The dog smells it and becomes frantic to lick it, since there is something about the odor which animals either enjoy or which excites them to lick. At any rate, they may rip bandages off, necessitating application of new ones fairly often.

In covering such an area, several things must be kept in mind. The bandage cannot be wound too tightly or circulation will be impeded and the area below it will swell from blood and lymph. It must be wound tightly enough not to slip. If swelling occurs, the bandage may be cut but not necessarily removed. New adhesive must then be wound around it.

First some surgical dressing, powder, solution, or salve is applied, and usually a sponge of several thicknesses of gauze put over it. The bandage is unrolled about the wound firmly until several thicknesses have been applied. The end is torn lengthwise to make two tails, which are tied in a knot at the bottom of the tear and then wound around the leg in opposite directions and tied in a knot again. When the bandage fails to go on smoothly, or when it is necessary to go from a thin place on the leg to a thicker section, if the roll is twisted occasionally, as shown in the illustration, it will go on with professional smoothness. If one layer of adhesive tape is then applied, making sure that at least one half inch sticks to the hair above the bandage, it will hold the bandage material in place and be sufficient protection against the patient's efforts to remove it.

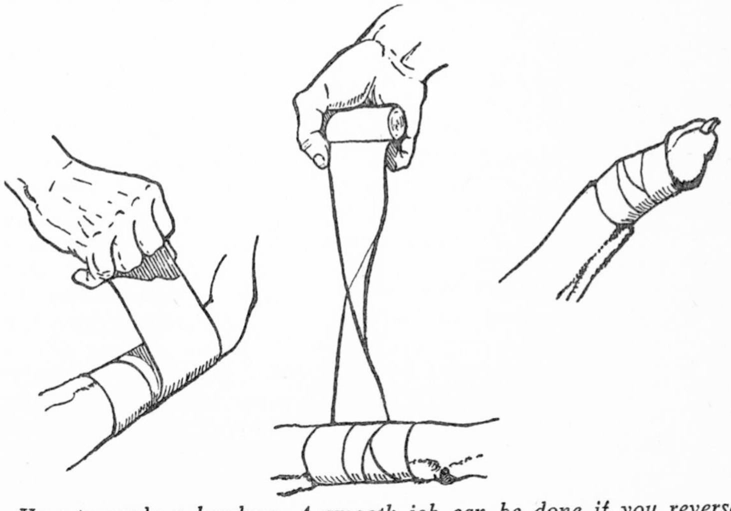

How to apply a bandage. A smooth job can be done if you reverse the roll occasionally. Right, pressure bandage to stop blood flow. Usually these bandages are applied too loosely.

One of the most frequent uses made of bandages is to check blood flow. In this case we call them pressure bandages. Dogs often cut their feet on glass, tin cans, or other sharp objects. Since the feet are extremely vascular (full of blood vessels), even a small cut may bleed enough to leave a large blood spot everywhere the dog steps. Cuts higher on the foot can cause sufficient hemorrhage to make a dog anemic, but I have never seen one bleed to death from such a gash.

To stop the flow of blood, apply a small cloth sponge directly to the cut and quickly wind a bandage tightly about the foot many times. It may become red from blood soaking through it, but it will slowly stop bleeding.

Tourniquets are so often recommended to stop bleeding in human beings that pet owners sometimes resort to them injudiciously. With a pet, a strong elastic band can suffice or even thumb pressure over the cut artery. If a tourniquet of any sort is applied to a whole limb, it is important that it be released occasionally to let blood in and out of the part tied off.

Many-tailed bandages are usually used about the body. When dogs scratch and chew holes in themselves because of skin infections, there is often no better accessory treatment. Skin remedies are applied and the bandage put on. Depending upon how much of the body it is to cover, the bandage generally has two or four holes cut to allow the legs to go through. Then a row of knots is tied along the back and left in bows, so that it can be untied to remove the bandage, which may be used again. Long surgical incisions on the sides, back, or belly can sometimes be kept covered by many-tails. Head operations, ear troubles, such as splits or sutured ear flaps, can best be protected with many-tails.

USING THERMOMETERS

Ordinary rectal thermometers, which one can purchase in any drugstore, are adequate for taking the temperatures of our dogs. It is a simple matter to shake one down, then dip it in vaseline or mineral oil and insert it three quarters of its length into the rectum. It should be left in for more than sixty seconds, removed, wiped clean with a piece of cotton, and read. Don't wash it in hot water. Anyone can read such a thermometer by twisting it slowly until the wide silver stripe appears and reading the figures opposite the top of the column. Most thermometers are graduated in fifths, and since each fifth equals two tenths, the reading is usually expressed in tenths, i.e., 102⅕°F. is 102.2°F. A dog's normal temperature is 101°.

9. Problems of Reproduction

THOUSANDS of people breed and raise animals. Some enjoy breeding to improve a species, to originate a new strain, or even to originate an entirely new type of animal. But for thousands more, pleasure in their dogs is contingent on security from their pets' reproducing. In crowded city areas, in small homes, among busy people, litters of animals are out of the question. Whether you want to breed your pet or prevent your pet from breeding, you will want and need to know how your pet's reproductive organs function.

Biologically speaking, the basic reason for the existence of any animal or plant is to pass along the germ plasm of which it is the custodian for the next generation. Everything about it which helps it to live in harmonious relationship with its environment is working toward that end. The creature is a bundle of tricks of nature to insure its perpetuation. One of the most interesting tricks or arrangements is the female mating cycle.

At maturity the female usually is said to come in heat or come in season. Most animals come in season in what are called mating cycles. The primary influence which causes different species to start their mating cycles is the length of the day. We do not understand how light accomplishes these changes which vary from one species to another. Dogs have a mating cycle summer and winter, and that is usually all. There are dogs which regularly come in heat only once a year. This is the case with wild, doglike animals—the wolf and fox, for example—which have litters only in the early spring. How long ago it was that the dog developed the propensity to come in heat twice a year, we do not know; nor do we know whether the dogs that come in heat once a year inherit this idiosyncrasy.

As we have seen when we discussed body regulators, the pituitary gland initiates the mating cycle, the follicular hormone carries it through, and when the follicles rupture and discharge their eggs, the luteal hormone ends it. At the same time a rather complex series of changes is going on in the animal's body. The mating cycle of the dog is fairly typical. An understanding of this process will help you to handle your pet intelligently —and may save you embarrassment if you own an unspayed bitch.

Outwardly, the first signs of the season are the slight swelling of the vulva and increased appetite. For perhaps five days this swelling continues until a few drops of blood drip from the vulva. Some bitches bleed scantily and clean themselves so that no blood is ever seen. Others bleed fairly copiously. The first, or bleeding, period lasts from four to fifteen days. By the end of this period the discharge is a pale red, nearly cream-colored.

Inside: The ovaries, which appeared smooth at the start, are showing the protrusion of the follicles as they enlarge. The uterus is growing longer and larger in diameter.

The second stage is initiated by a willingness on the part of the bitch to copulate. There may be a long teasing and playing period with the

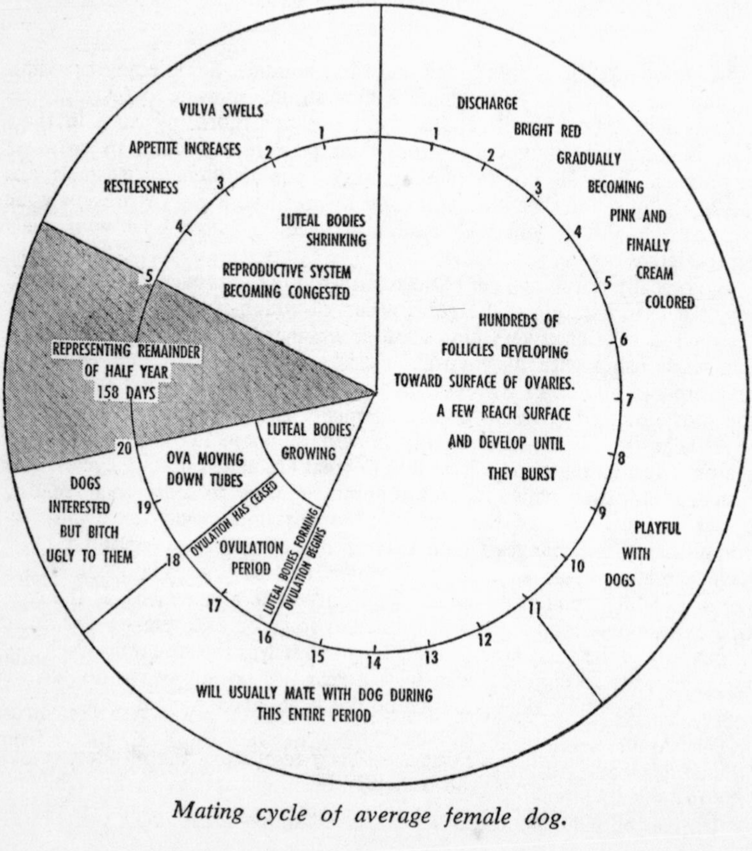

Mating cycle of average female dog.

male dog, but eventually she will accept him. This is considered the first day of the second, or acceptance, period.

Inside: The follicles are enlarging on the ovaries, and the uterus and blood vessels are greatly increased in size. By about the sixth day of the acceptance period the follicles of the average bitch have ruptured and liberated their eggs. It is possible to find bitches which ovulate the first day of the acceptance period, and others will be found which ovulate toward the end. If copulation has occurred, the sperm from the male (thousands of them) will be waiting around the ovaries for the discharge of the eggs so one may fertilize each egg. Then the fertilized eggs move down the Fallopian tubes and eventually come to rest at fairly even spaces from each other.

As soon as ovulation has occurred, a blood plug forms in each follicle. This changes into the luteal body which secretes the hormone whose presence in the blood effectively stops the mating cycle and mating behavior. Luteal bodies remain throughout pregnancy. If they are dislodged, the bitch aborts. After birth, the luteal bodies last for several months and their presence prevents another mating cycle.

Outside: During the copulatory, or acceptance, period the bitch mates repeatedly, if allowed, but toward the end she "goes out" rather suddenly. As the luteal hormone takes effect, her behavior changes. She may fight off willing males, and then just when the owner is sure the period is over she may play and be teased by a male until she accepts him. These late matings often result in large litters, certainly larger than those of very early matings.

When dogs are mated the first day of the acceptance period, the sperm must live several days, waiting for the eggs. But when mating occurs late, the eggs are ready and the sperm find them waiting.

Gestation is the time from fertilization of the eggs until birth, not the time from mating until birth. If an animal is mated late in the period, the gestation period will be shorter, since the eggs are waiting for the sperm and fertilization takes place immediately.

COPULATION

How is copulation accomplished?

The doglike animals accomplish mating by a unique physical device. In the dog's penis there is a bone. It is thick at the base and tapers toward the point. Through it runs the urethra. The penis is of a spongy tissue which, when an exit valve in a large vein is closed, fills with blood under pressure from a large artery. Right behind the bone there is a plexus of nerves which is very sensitive. Pressure on this point causes a violent thrust reflex. At the same time the valve regulating the exit of the blood from the penis closes and the dog develops an erection, which is a distention of the penis with blood.

Unlike the penis of any other group of animals, the dog's penis has a large bulbous enlargement at the base. When the dog's penis enters the vagina of the bitch, it must go through a muscular ring or constriction of the external opening of the vagina. The bitch must elevate the vulva to make a straight tube of the vagina. As soon as the penis is pressed through this restricted opening, it passes into the vagina, which is much larger and very elastic. The moment the penis is through, the pressure of the tube on the reflex nerve center causes a violent thrust and the dog clings to the bitch with all his strength. And in that moment the penis swells to large proportions, three times its normal diameter in the smaller part and five or six times at the bulb.

The swelling of the bulb prevents the dog from withdrawing his penis. At this time he ejaculates semen and the sperm it contains. A pressure is built up and the semen is forced through the cervix and up the horns of the uterus, through the Fallopian tubes, and into the capsule which surrounds the ovaries. In twenty minutes after copulation starts, the semen will have ascended this far.

Dogs remain "hung" in this manner for from one minute to two hours. The average time is slightly less than twenty minutes. The male turns around and faces the opposite direction from the bitch. While the two are hung in this manner, they may get their nails into the dirt and pull with far more than their own weights. No one should be alarmed when they pull this way; neither dog is being hurt. As the valve relaxes, the blood leaves the penis, usually from the bulb part first, and allows the enlarged penis to slip out.

Very little has been written about copulation in dogs. The author has made notes on hundreds of matings, including such data as the length of time the dogs were hung, the number of times various dogs copulated in a day, and certain idiosyncrasies about individual dogs and breeds of dogs.

There have been many instances where a pair of dogs have been raised together, in the same home, and the owner has wanted puppies from the pair. While the bitch seemed to be willing to mate, the male showed no inclination. Then, toward the very end of the acceptance period, the owner has found them copulating, and good-sized litters of puppies have resulted. One pair of Boston Terriers which were kept together never mated until the seventeenth day. A pair of Great Danes were mated toward the end of the period only. Another pair of dogs, when kept away from all other dogs, behaved in this manner; but once when they were placed in a kennel where there were other dogs close by, their sexual behavior pattern changed and they copulated every day during the whole acceptance period.

Some dogs are never willing to mate more than every other day if left alone with bitches in the acceptance period. One Foxhound, owned by the author, mated five times one day and three times the next and was hung at least twenty minutes each time.

STERILITY

Sometimes successful matings do not result in offspring. An animal's breasts may develop, her belly may increase in size. She has a much larger appetite, makes a nest, but produces no litter. This condition is called a pseudo-pregnancy—a perfectly natural phenomenon in all fertile animals which normally occurs when they are bred but fail to conceive. It also occurs even when they are not bred, provided they ovulate.

Everyone who has bred an animal unsuccessfully wants to know why the female failed to conceive. There are several possible explanations.

The male may have been infertile at the time of the mating even though he was known to be fertile at other times. Overbreeding, infection in the genital tract, improper diet, sickness of a general nature—one or more of these and other less obvious conditions may cause his temporary sterility.

If males are too young they will produce sperm which are not virile enough to fertilize the ova.

To amplify some of the above points, overbreeding can easily render a male infertile. It has been found that a good "sperm swarm" is necessary to insure proper fertilization. At one service several million sperm are discharged to fertilize only half a dozen eggs. If only half a dozen sperm were present, there would be no offspring. Thousands surround an egg, yet only one enters to combine its germ plasm with that of the egg and start the new individual.

How often may a vigorous stud animal be bred? One thirteen-year-old dog bred a bitch a day for a week and all conceived. There seems to be no harm in mating studs every other day, and such activity will not diminish their fertility. To insure a fertile mating, bitches should be mated to stud dogs every other day as long as they are willing. It used to be thought that this would constitute a strain on the male dog, but, as we have seen above, such is not the case except in debilitated males.

Among common misconceptions concerning breeding is the belief that if a female is bred to several males she will conceive from only one mating. This is not true. An animal can produce young in one litter which have been fathered by different males. Since the female produces a varying number of eggs or ova, it is possible for a sperm of the male with whom she has mated to fertilize one egg and for a sperm of another male to fertilize another. If a purebred female is bred to two males which vary greatly in type, it is easy to distinguish the young sired by each father. When mongrel dogs mate with other mongrels, or when animals of like appearance mate, it is impossible to tell which male sired which offspring.

Infection of the genital tract is explained in Chapter 16.

Improper diet can cause sterility. Lack of vitamins, such as vitamin A and the B complex, lack of proper amino acids, minerals, and possibly certain fatty acids may produce sterility. Animals which have been fed dog biscuits or kibbled food exclusively are often sterile.

Undescended testicles are another cause of sterility. It is not advisable to breed to a male unless both testicles are in the scrotum, because this defect often runs in families.

Sickness of a general nature will debilitate a pet so that he will lose his vigor. Even though he can copulate, he will often be unable to produce virile sperm. Convalescing males are generally sterile. Severe worm infestations also decrease virility.

Cysts on ovaries are a common cause of female sterility. They may be removed surgically. Improperly developed reproductive tract, infection in the tract, tumors, or general debility due to disease all cause female sterility.

Improper development in the female's tract is not common. In bitches, however, there is an obstruction due to a web of tissue which runs vertically across the vagina. This is not unlike the hymen in humans. This narrow web sometimes has to be cut before a dog's penis can enter the vagina.

In rare instances females fail to come in heat because of juvenile reproductive organs. Nothing practical can be done with such animals. Hormone injections usually fail. Medication can bring the animal in heat, but she will not conceive.

Great quantities of vitamin E have been fed in the form of wheat-germ oil to produce fertility. Its value is questionable. Many wild animals eat nothing for three months before they copulate and still produce young successfully, even though their fat may be almost exhausted. Grain-eating animals, such as rats and squirrels, probably do not need supplementary vitamin E because their diet is abundant in it and they have not built up a means of doing without it as other species have.

Copulation stimulates ovulation in all small pets except the dog. Dogs will mate only at the right time. While most bitches ovulate in the middle of the acceptance period, some ovulate at the beginning of the period and some at the end. A bitch which ovulates the first day may copulate for seven days more, but obviously, if she is bred, her eggs will be fertilized shortly after ovulation, not seven days later. By the same token, a bitch which ovulates late in her acceptance period cannot conceive from a mating early in the period, perhaps six days before ovulation. Therefore, if you do not know a bitch's peculiarities in this respect, it is best to mate her several times.

It is common for very old animals, which will still come in heat, to breed normally, conceive, and then to resorb their fetuses. One may feel the little lumps along the reproductive tract as they grow large, day by day, and then feel them grow smaller and softer until they disappear. One remedy for this is the female sex hormone in small doses. Your veterinarian can supply it in proper dosage for your female provided you are interested in breeding valuable old animals whose strain you want to perpetuate.

There are cases where animals are accidentally mated when pregnancy is most undesirable. Today your veterinarian can use either of two, or possibly three, hormones to terminate the pregnancy, usually without serious aftereffects. A series of injections is required, but the effect is generally achieved in from two to five days. There is no need for permitting fetuses to develop to full size and for pregnancy to continue to full term. If the young will be destroyed at birth, it is better to arrange for the mother to give premature birth while the fetuses are small, so that her task will be made easier.

BIRTH

After the female's ova have been fertilized—that is, after each has become united with a sperm—they nest against the uterine wall. As they grow, each fetus is surrounded by amniotic fluid which is enclosed in an amniotic sac. Each has a placenta attached to the lining of the uterus from which nourishment is carried to the fetus, through the navel.

It is difficult to predict the size of a litter from the appearance of a pregnant animal. If she is very large, it may mean that she is carrying a small litter of large young or that she is carrying a large litter of small young. X ray is the only dependable means of determining the number, and it is easily employed if advisable.

As the whelping time approaches, an animal will make a nest. If she is a house pet, she may fix a nest in a closet, on a bed, or out in the garden. As time of birth draws near, she will settle in her nest and appear to strain. The frequency and intensity of her uterine contractions increase.

As the puppies start to pass through the birth canal, there is an even greater effort of expulsion which is probably due to a reflex occasioned by pressure on the upper part of the vulva. This is a useful fact to know in helping a bitch to whelp. If you want to make her strain, insert a finger in the vulva and pull upward and backward. She will nearly always strain and assist you. The average whelping time for dogs is five hours. Small dogs, such as cocker spaniels, usually finish whelping in three hours, but large dogs, such as Danes and St. Bernards, often take seven or eight hours. Twelve hours is the limit of normal time for a large dog, although bitches have been known to take thirty-six hours with no particularly abnormal aspects to the whelping.

The contractions of the uterus push the young animal out through the vagina. The puppy appears in one of several ways. It may still be in the amniotic sac. If so, the sac must be broken or the young will suffocate. If the mother doesn't do this, her attendant should do it for her. The puppy may still be in its sac, but the sac may have ruptured. Or the young may be born with the sac remaining inside the mother. In this case the navel cord is still connecting it to the sac. The mother may chew this cord to break it, and the sac and placenta will be discharged later. But an attendant can wrap a cloth about the navel cord and pull gently until the sac comes out with the placenta.

If a placenta is not discharged from a pet she may develop peritonitis, a serious infection. It is essential for her health that every placenta be discharged shortly after the birth of a litter.

Normally a female will chew off the navel cord at varying distances from its socket, then eat the placenta and lick her young dry. This is unpleasant for most people to accept, but it is part of a natural function and there is no indication that interference is called for. However, it may be necessary to crush the navel cords with blunt scissors an inch from the body if the mother is unable to do it efficiently.

If you attend a mother animal during birth you will find that your assistance and affection is reassuring and that she will trust you with her young. If she has a large litter, it is a good idea, when she is not looking to hand the first ones to a helper, who can put them in a warm, dry place to stay until the mother is relaxed and ready to take care of them. In this way she can attend each one as it is born, without injuring others from whom her attention has been diverted.

Two post-parturition infections are common—uterine infections and infection of the breasts. Infection of the uterus is unlikely if no placentae remain in the uterus. Normally a female discharges from her uterus the lining to which the placentae were attached during pregnancy and through which the young were nourished. This takes the form of a dark red discharge and may last for ten or twelve days, or even longer in a dog, and for several days in small animals. Infected breasts are extremely serious to both a mother and her young. They require immediate attention (see Chapter 16).

The preparation of a nest has a great effect upon the success of a litter. Avoid using loose material that is likely to get into the mouths of the young and interfere with their nursing. Dehydrated sugar cane is excellent bedding material. It should have cloth under it, so that it will not irritate navels should bedding be pushed aside. Thousands of puppies die each year from infected navels, the result of irritation and wearing, and these infected areas are difficult to cure because the bacteria work in under the edge of the protecting skin.

A litter of animals should be watched carefully to see that they are all getting enough milk. When they are a few days old they can starve in a very short time. Frequently old animals have some teats so large that the young will suck from the side or be unable to suck at all. They sometimes have to be helped so that they can find the teats which are small enough for them.

Before and after birth a mother needs an inclusive diet. The health of both the mother and young depends upon it. When the mother is carrying her young her food must not only keep her nourished, but must also build bones, blood, and bodies. She needs more fats, proteins, and minerals than usual. And a mother requires more water than usual while she is suckling her young, especially immediately following their birth.

Before the young are born, the animal should be prepared for suckling by being carefully cleaned and having long hair cut away. It often prevents the young from reaching the teats.

Breasts often cake because a mother produces more milk than her young need. This is inevitable when her litter is small. Caked breasts are normal and disappear without medication.

Sometimes a mother dies during parturition or when her litter is very young. Although it is not easy to save the orphans, you can probably raise them successfully if you understand their needs. This means that you have to understand what their mother would supply if she were living.

A wise dog owner will look carefully at the puppies' navels every day to see that they have healed over. The dried-up umbilical cord drops off sometime during the second day, although occasionally puppies will wear it much longer. After this, healing should progress rapidly.

People who are desperate to save an orphan often rush to buy goat's milk. Most people think there is something magical in it which will save the young of any species. Actually, goat's milk is very similar to cow's milk and much more expensive. It is richer in fat than most Holstein milk but not so rich as Jersey. About the only important difference is that in goat's milk the fat is broken up into much finer particles than in any cow's milk.

Table VI—Composition of Milk in Different Species of Animals

	FAT	PROTEIN	CARBOHYDRATE	ASH	WATER	TOTAL SOLID
Cow	4.0	3.8	4.9	0.7	86.2	13.8
Goat	4.1	3.7	4.2	0.8	87.1	12.9
Dog	11.2	5.7	3.1	1.3	78.7	21.3
Cat	5.0	7.0	5.0	0.6	82.0	18.0
Rabbit	16.0	14.0	2.0	2.2	65.0	35.0
Guinea pig	7.0	5.0	2.0	1.9	85.0	15.0
Rat	15.0	12.0	3.0	2.0	70.0	30.0

Every year we see newspaper pictures of queer foster parents—adopted pet combinations—a cat nursing a young rat or tending a chicken, a mare pony caring for a puppy or a goat, a bitch nursing a kitten. Behavior of this sort is because of an excessive "mother complex." In the case of a bitch that has not had pups and has no milk a hormone (prolactin) can be injected which will make her into such a good mother that she will steal other bitches' pups in order to have something to love and protect. She'll curl up with them and accept them as her own.

Almost any female with enough prolactin in her blood will try to mother some animate thing. Perhaps it is a bitch mothering a duckling, or a rat mothering a young mouse. The trouble with getting a foster mother to adopt young not her own is generally that she already has got used to her own and then it is difficult to make the substitution. Most people have heard what pains a shepherd must take to get a ewe which has lost her lamb to accept an orphan.

The best way to encourage an adoption is to smear the orphan all over with vaginal fluids and milk from the foster mother. This makes the orphan smell like one of her own. She licks the fluids off and this licking tends to make her want it. There is no quicker way. Persistence will win over a foster mother even if she at first refuses an orphan. It may be necessary to hold it to her breast, remove it so she can't bury it or kill it, and bring it back at the next nursing. If you are there, she won't harm it, but if you are not, she may kill it. However, once a foster mother starts licking an orphan it is usually safe to leave them alone.

If no foster mother is available, the hardest thing in raising orphans is to arrange for a nipple of the right size, and then to induce puppies to nurse from it. Some people use medicine-dropper rubbers through which they punch holes. Others find children's doll nipples. Puppies will usually thrive on small baby nipples.

Many small orphans are killed through the careless use of medicine droppers. Unless you are very careful to put a drop at a time on the baby's tongue and see that he is swallowing it, his mouth may fill with the milk. Then he may cry or wheeze and inhale some of the milk. This often causes pneumonia, and from this the little thing dies. Few of those using medicine droppers know how much milk to give. A day-old puppy of a small breed needs five dropperfuls six times a day; one from a large breed needs twenty. The following table gives an approximation of the requirements for puppies by weights. As in humans, it varies with the individual.

Table VII

WEIGHT OF ORPHAN	AMOUNT OF MILK REQUIRED	FREQUENCY OF FEEDING*
3 oz.	3 c.c.†	Every 3 hours
5 oz.	5 c.c.	Every 3 hours
8 oz.	½ oz.	Every 4 hours
12 oz.	1 oz.	Every 5 hours
1 lb.	1¼ oz.	Every 5 hours
2 lbs.	2 oz.	Every 6 hours
3 lbs.	2¾ oz.	Every 6 hours

*All orphans under one week old do best on 4-hour feedings or oftener.
†A c.c. (cubic centimeter) is ¼ teaspoonful.

SPAYING

For many years opinions about the results of spaying (not spading) a bitch were bandied about by "experts" on a purely conjectural basis. Mr. James found his bitch became obese; Mrs. Jones found her dog did not change; Mrs. Wilson thought his Dane became timid after the operation; Mrs. Doe thought her Doberman became bold and ugly. Even veterinarians couldn't agree.

Considerable research now shows that spaying has little effect on the general characteristics of the animal. Spayed greyhounds race as well as unspayed and have very little tendency to be fatter than unspayed sisters. Other species are not spoiled, except for reproduction purposes, by the operation—if properly done.

This is true with one qualification: that the operation be done when the animal is nearly full grown or later. This is very important. Studies show that when animals are spayed very young there is a disharmony in their glandular development. If it is desirable to produce a chicken which will be large, awkward, lazy, and fat—a capon—the operation is not put off until the bird is full grown. If it were, the result would be merely a sterile rooster. No, the operation is done in the early life of the bird because at that time it accomplishes precisely the changes which we want to avoid in spayed pets. Exactly the same thing is true of bitches. A spayed puppy becomes neither male nor female in appearance and grows very fat. The waddling, turtlelike, lazy, spayed bitches are usually those which were spayed as puppies.

The fact that some spayed bitches get fat is not in itself a valid argument against spaying. Unspayed bitches, too, get fat. Some of the most grossly overweight dogs I know are whole animals. They are overfed. If they had been spayed and placed in the hands of the same owner, his or her explanation for the overweight condition would have been that the bitch had been spayed.

It is now believed that spaying has little effect upon a mature animal. The animal does not have mating cycles and the urges which they bring. This may have a very slight effect on weight and personality. Spaying in babyhood causes abnormal development. The only reason for spaying bitches young is to prevent the bitches of vicious breeds from becoming dangerous as they get older. If they are spayed as puppies, they tend to remain gentle.

In some remote localities, female puppies have almost no sale because of the expense of the spaying operation. Dog dealers refuse to buy puppies for resale unless they have already been spayed. In such areas, there is some justification for the operation; it is better to operate on young puppies than simply to destroy them.

Spaying a bitch has a number of definite advantages:

1. The animal is spared the risk attending birth.
2. The owner is spared raising or having to destroy unwanted animals.
3. The owner avoids the annoyance of males surrounding his home, killing shrubbery, breaking windows, and following members of his family.
4. The spayed female does not wander at certain seasons as the unspayed does.
5. Spaying almost certainly prevents the formation of cancer in the breast, which sometimes occurs in bitches three or four years of age and commonly in older dogs. It also prevents metritis, an affliction of unspayed bitches.

6. The owner is saved perhaps forty dollars a year for boarding his pet twice a year.

7. Food is saved, since a pregnant, or lactating, mother consumes more food than a spayed one.

8. In many places the license fee for a spayed bitch is less than for an unspayed bitch. Where this is so, the owner will save the cost of spaying many times.

There are also disadvantages in spaying:

1. An owner may someday regret that his female can't reproduce.

2. As spayed animals grow older they sometimes lose control of the bladder sphincter. But this can be corrected (Chapter 16) by giving a drug—stilbestrol—occasionally.

Does spaying harm a hunting dog? Some of the greatest hunters ever known have been spayed bitches. In fact, it helps hunting dogs, because unspayed bitches so often come in heat in the all-too-short hunting season. Because of this they often miss the training and experience that makes better hunters of the spayed bitches which are never incapacitated.

Months after bitches have been spayed and returned home, dogs sometimes collect about the house as if she were in heat. The owner should first look to see if the bitch is bleeding and swollen. If she is not, she is not attracting the males. Occasionally a chip of ovary, or even a whole ovary, may have been left. Gynecologists often spay their own animals, using the technique of removing the uterus but not the ovaries. These bitches have not been spayed in the veterinary sense. If ovaries are not entirely removed, a bitch will come in heat, copulate, but fail, of course, to conceive.

Very often spayed animals which are thought to be attracting males actually are not. Another bitch which is in heat is probably the basic attraction. She may have urinated in many places about the neighborhood. Dogs smelling the urine detect nothing of the keep-away odor of normal urine and therefore conclude that the bitch in front of whose house they find it is in season. When she appears, the dogs attempt to copulate. She thinks they are playing, and if she has a mild disposition, she will not fight them as a bolder animal would. Not being repulsed, they hang about until the dogcatcher comes in answer to a complaint and removes those he can catch to the pound. A bold spayed bitch will fight off any intruders and the dogs will stay away.

CASTRATION

Much the same arguments hold for castration as for spaying. Generally it is done to make males stay home. Those which congregate around the abode of a bitch come home torn or punctured with tooth marks from the frequent fracases attending such meetings. Such dogs frequently wander away and are brought home by the dog warden, who collects his fee. They are expensive animals. Castration usually alters their wandering habits because the sex urge is often the cause of it.

There are many other reasons for castrating animals. Dogs of breeds whose members tend to become vicious with age are often rendered gentle and lovable when castrated young. Castration also tends to prevent indiscriminate wetting and thus saves shrubbery.

Whether or not castration will cause dogs who are chronic wanderers to settle down and stay home is a moot question. It definitely has had that effect in numerous instances but has produced no diminution of the wandering tendency in others. It is worth a try, however, if your choice is either to alter the dog or dispose of him.

It seems to be the opinion of many that animals should not be spayed or castrated because copulation is essential to health. This is not the case. Any animal, whether whole, spayed, or castrated, is just as healthy if it is never bred as those which are used for breeding. Considering the risks of pregnancy and birth, a female's chances for longer life are actually greater. And as for males, only a small percentage ever copulate in their whole lives. This is true of many species, not of our pet animals alone.

10. Sanitation and Hygiene

YOUR first concern as a dog owner must always be the maintenance of your pet's health and well-being. To be able to care for a pet in sickness is a necessary skill, but for many obvious economic and humanitarian reasons the prevention of disease is even more important.

The proper care of a pet requires that you have a fundamental knowledge of animal hygiene and sanitation, that you recognize the necessity of keeping the animal clean, that you provide quarters which are free not only of visible dirt and debris but also of disease-carrying agents. In short, it is essential that you have a thorough and realistic understanding of how to establish and maintain environmental and personal conditions which actively promote and preserve your pet's health.

Let us start first with the care of the animal itself and then consider its surroundings and how to manage them.

COAT CARE

When you think of an animal's coat condition, you must think both of his hair and of the skin under his hair.

You undoubtedly have noticed that when dogs are brought into the warmth of a house in cold weather they have a doggier odor than they do in warm weather. This is due largely to the greater secretion of sebum, a protective substance emitted by glands embedded in the skin and deposited mostly against the shafts of the hair. To some extent it coats the skin, acting as a waterproofing agent and helping it to shed rain and dampness, and it also serves as a protection against some types of bacteria. The sebum serves several useful purposes, but when it is allowed to accumulate on the dog's coat it produces a strong odor which must be removed by bathing.

The animal's skin, as we have seen, functions as an organ of the body, just as do the kidneys or liver. Its exposure subjects it to all kinds of abuse which better-protected organs never experience. In a healthy animal, glandular secretions of the skin keep the coat shiny. But a coat must be combed often. Dead hair must be removed and snarls untangled in all long-haired breeds. Only a comb and elbow grease will accomplish this. Burrs must be removed by hand. Hard mats have to be cut with scissors. To do this, push the scissors under the wad, pointing them away from the body, and cut the wad in half. Large wads may be cut into many sections which then comb out with the least pain to the pet. It is almost never necessary to do the easy thing—snip across the hair. With patience, all the dead hair can be separated from the wad, leaving a lovely coat.

Combing of long-haired dogs should be done as frequently as necessary to keep the coat in good condition. Animals should be taught from puppyhood to stand or lie on a table, or, in the case of a large dog, on the floor, and expect and enjoy combing.

Short-haired animals need less attention, but a fine comb, even for them, is more efficient than a brush. Some people take a hacksaw blade and drag it, like a comb, over the coat. The teeth catch loose hairs and pull them out. The bare hand, moistened and rubbed over a short-haired dog's coat, will pull out many loose hairs and leave the coat looking glossier.

Brushes should not be the mainstay of grooming. Running brushes over the outside of a long-haired animal's coat accomplishes little in the way of loose hair removal. It does sweep out some of the finest skin scales, accumulated dust, and a few loose hairs. There are many kinds of specialized brushes. Thousands of elaborate grooming brushes, with wire bristles on one side and fiber bristles on the other, are sold, but professionals do not use them. You can get along very well with: (1) a comb with very strong teeth, ten to fourteen to the inch, which can pull out snarls and do rough work; (2) a fine comb with twenty teeth to the inch; (3) a strong scrub brush for a dog; and (4) a pair of scissors.

If the animal to be groomed is a small, smooth-coated pet, a fine, strong comb plus a small scrub brush will suffice.

PLUCKING AND CLIPPING

Should wire-haired breeds of dogs be plucked or clipped? Wire-haired-terrier breeders who show their dogs express dismay at the mention of clipping. A clipped terrier does not have a typical show appearance. But those who are not interested in showing their dogs will find that the dogs like clipping better than plucking. The clipped coat is smoother, the dog is not subjected to the annoyance of plucking, and the job costs only about half as much. A dog may be clipped every three or four months and be in trim condition all the time at a cost no greater than that of two pluckings.

Summer clipping is advisable for long-haired dogs for hygienic reasons as well as for the dog's comfort. At one time it was generally thought that since dogs have few sweat glands in the skin it was unnecessary to clip them in hot weather. Some people even insisted that the long hair served as a protective insulation against heat. My own experience with hundreds of long-haired dogs has convinced me that this reasoning is fallacious. Clipped dogs are definitely and obviously much more comfortable in extreme heat. In addition, a clipped dog is more easily cared for. It requires less combing, keeps cleaner, and does not shed long hair throughout the house. He is also much less likely to catch fleas or develop skin disease, since parasites prefer skin which is under heavy coats of long hair. If, in spite of clipping, he should get a skin disease, it is more readily curable and requires less remedy.

If you want to do your own grooming or plucking, a stripping comb or a plucking comb is indispensable. Most dogs are groomed by professionals who know how to do it correctly. It requires great skill in grooming to turn out a poodle, for instance, in style. It generally pays to have the work done by those who know how. An amateur cuts off the hair all right, but sometimes the result resembles a moth-eaten garment. Professionals with efficient clippers do a much smoother job.

But then, so do many non-professionals when properly equipped. If you have never clipped or plucked a dog, the following brief instructions should enable you to make a workmanlike job of it. In addition to the equipment mentioned above, you will need, depending on the breed you beautify, a stripping comb, a dog razor, and an electric clipper. The Oster clipper, made especially for trimming dogs, comes with several kinds of replaceable blades. Blades number 10 and 5 will be adequate for

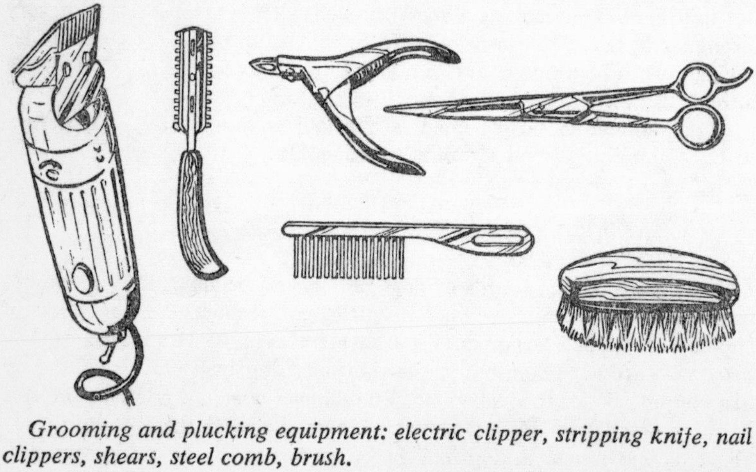

Grooming and plucking equipment: electric clipper, stripping knife, nail clippers, shears, steel comb, brush.

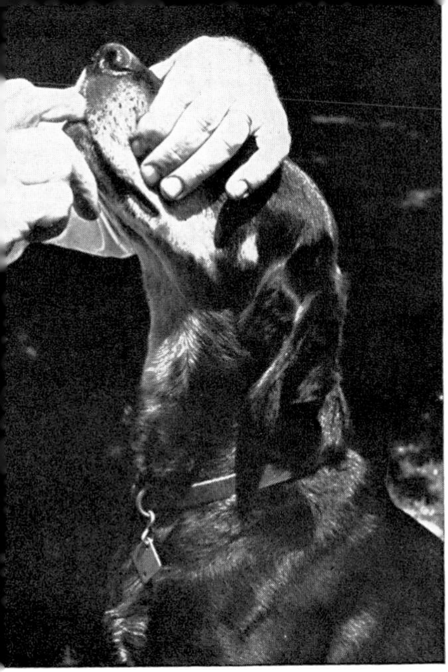

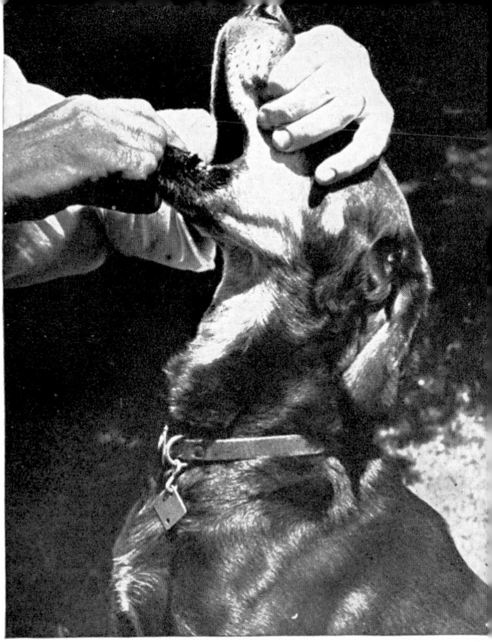

TO ADMINISTER CAPSULES OR TABLETS

LEFT: Hold dog's head upward with left hand over top of face, fingers pressing lips between teeth. RIGHT: Pull lower jaw down with right hand. Left continues to hold head upright.

LEFT: Drop capsule into mouth as far back as you can while you hold lower jaw open with fingers. RIGHT: Push capsule down throat with first two fingers, keeping thumb and last two fingers outside mouth.

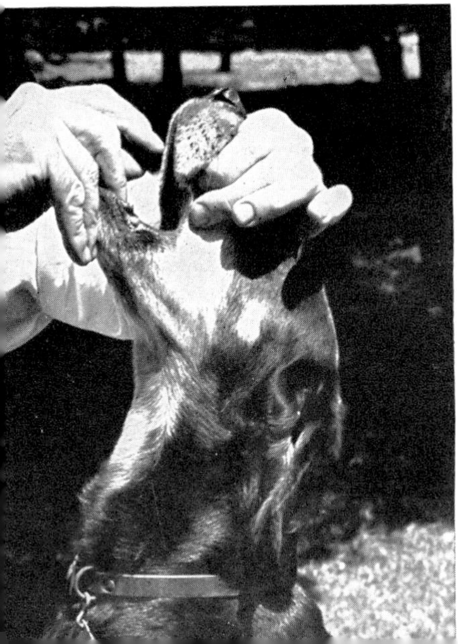

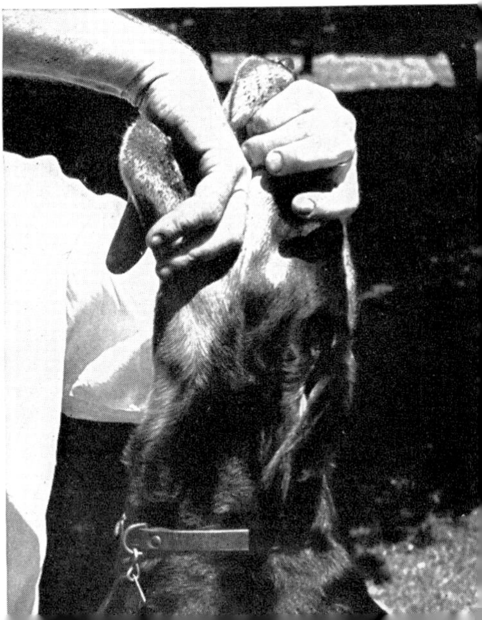

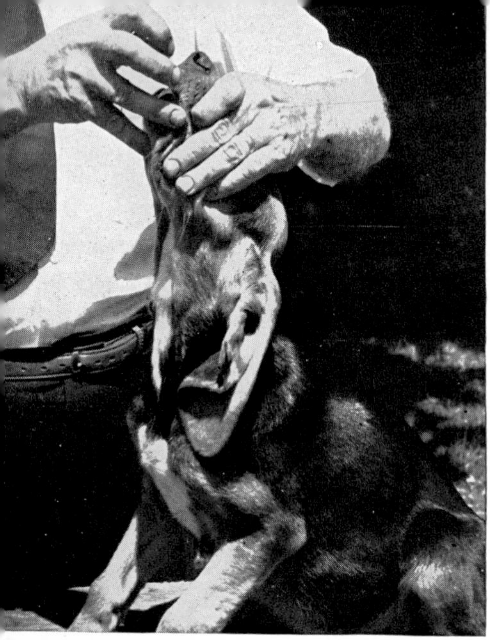

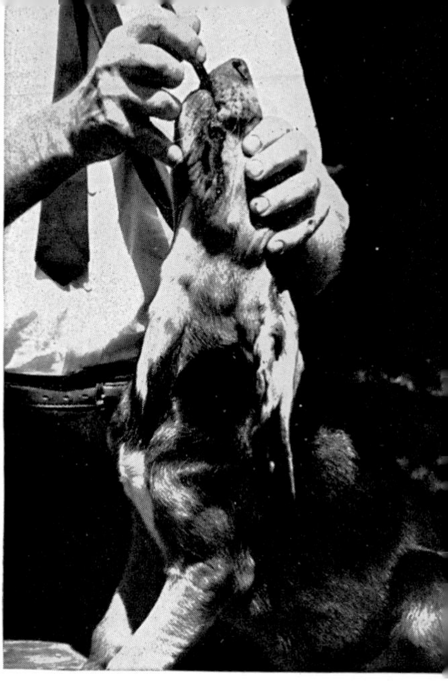

PASSING A STOMACH TUBE

LEFT: Hold head upright. Push tube over back of tongue and down throat. RIGHT: Before pouring fluid through it, listen at end of tube to be sure it is not in windpipe.

The lip-pocket method of giving medicine or liquid food: Hold head up and pull lip out to make a pocket.

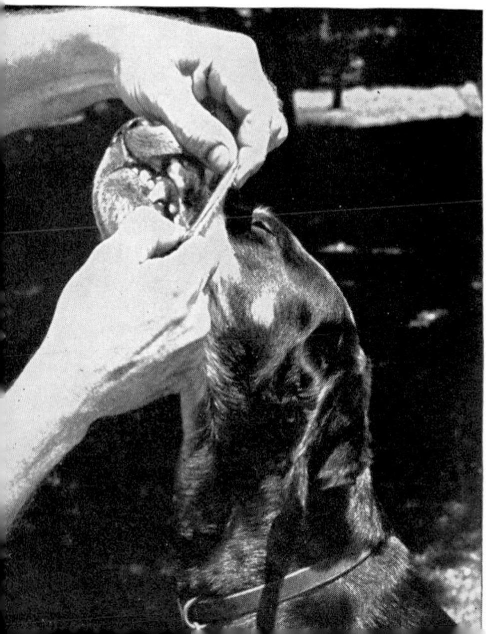

Continue to hold head up by pulling on lips while assistant pours fluid into pocket. It will trickle between teeth.

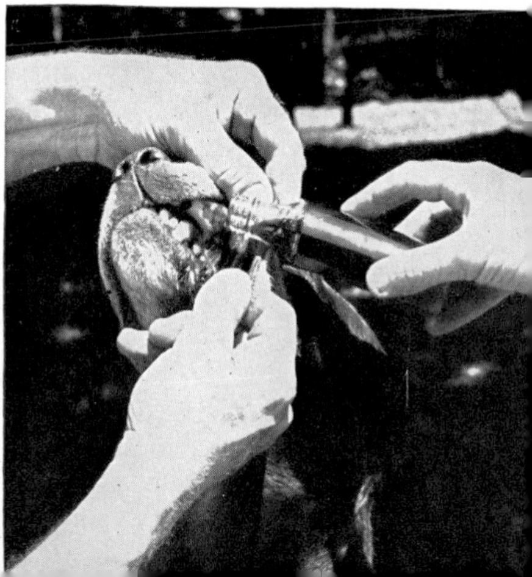

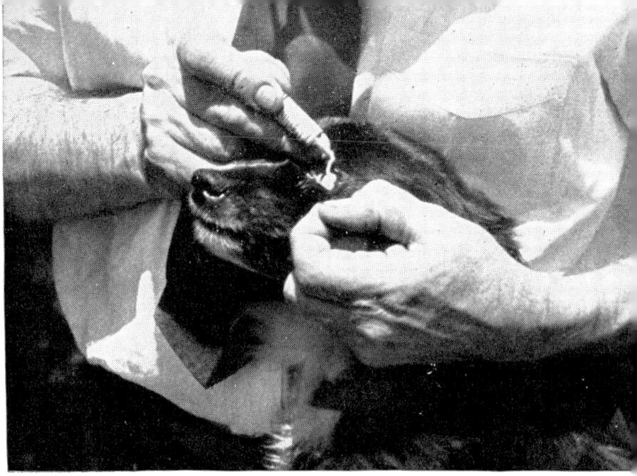

PLYING OPHTHALMIC OINTMENT

ll lower lid out and squeeze a small amount of medicine into pocket so produced. Allow it to close and wipe surplus off lids.

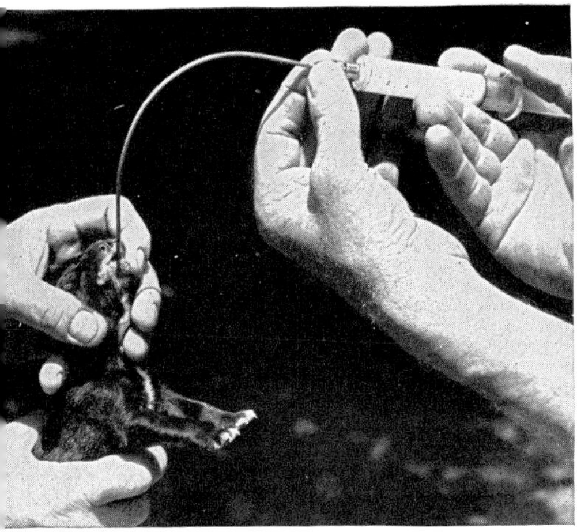

FEEDING DAY-OLD PUPPY WITH STOMACH TUBE AND SYRINGE

Be sure tube is in stomach, not windpipe, and have the milk at body temperature.

TAKING A DOG'S TEMPERATURE

LEFT: Insert a greased thermometer into the anus, two thirds of its length. RIGHT: An assistant can help by holding one hand under dog, and dog's collar with other hand.

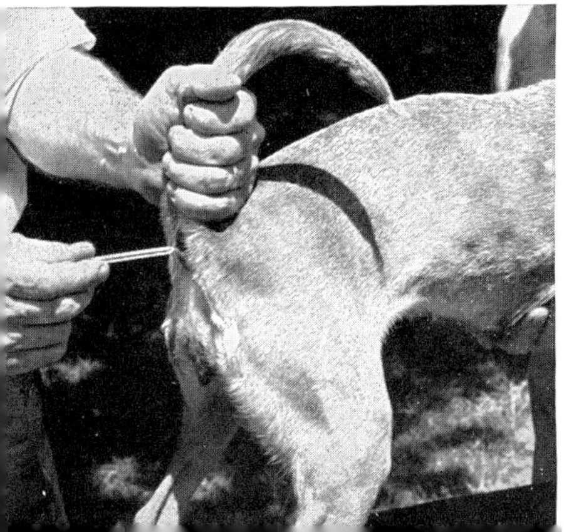

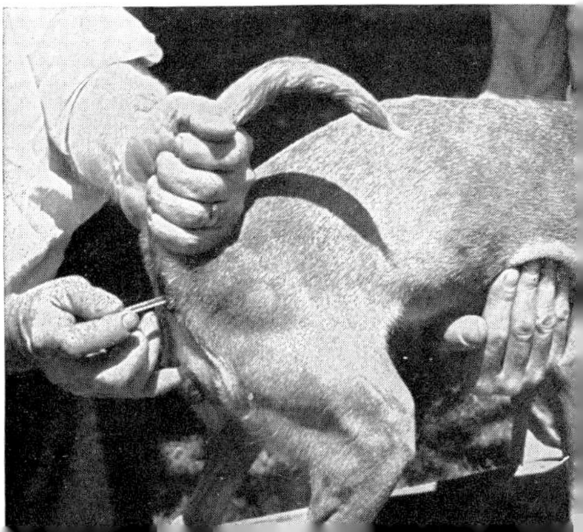

REMOVING THE ACCUMULATION FROM ANAL GLANDS

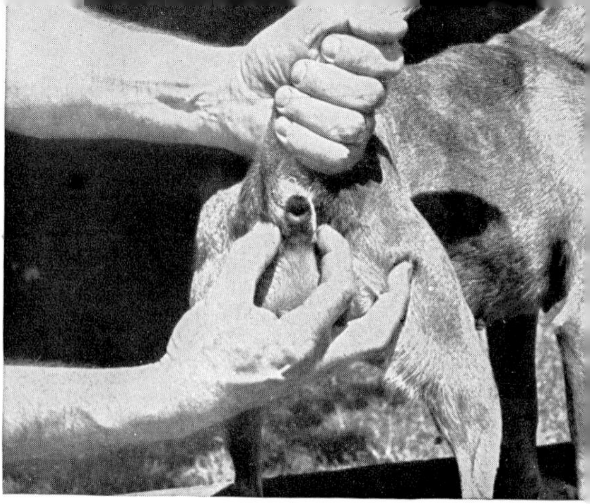

Thumb and index finger are placed just under each gland. They are shown here in proper position to squeeze glands.

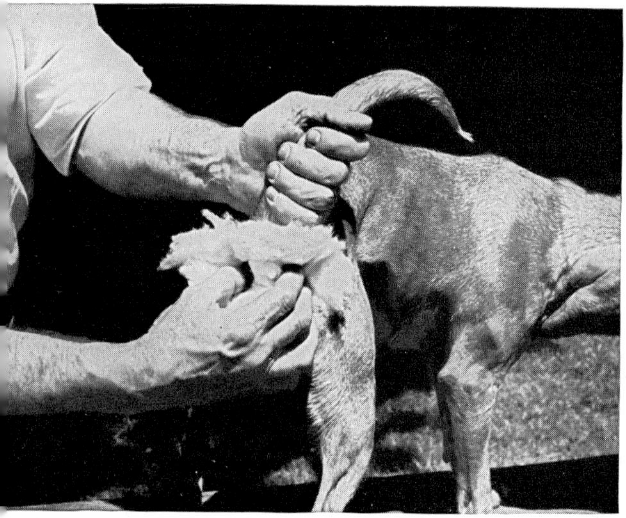

Cotton should be used to cove fingers as material expresse is obnoxious. Firm, stead pressure is required to empt the glands completely.

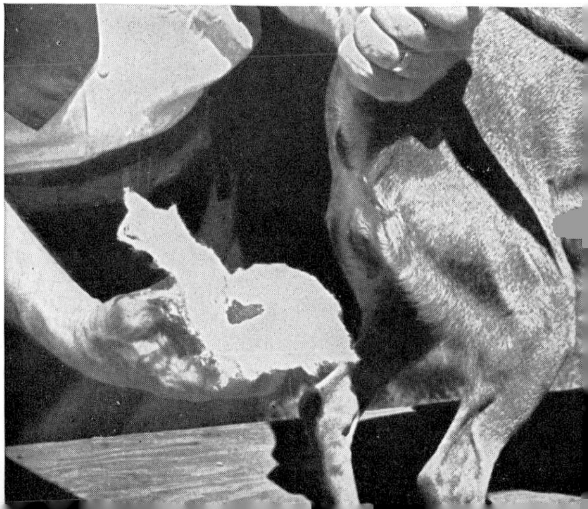

After glands are emptied dog will be relieved and in a few days will stop "playing sleigh ride."

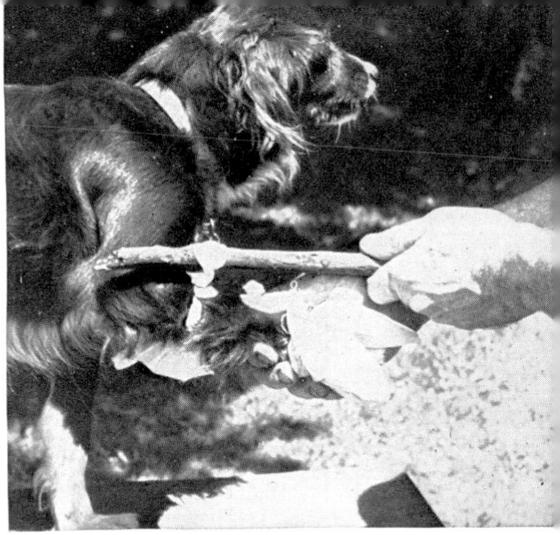

APPLYING A PRESSURE BANDAGE TO A CUT FOOT

LEFT: Wind firmly, occasionally twisting bandage to insure even covering. RIGHT: A tourniquet is sometimes necessary to stop blood flow. Loosen every ten minutes to allow blood circulation.

In bandaging the head it is necessary to cross over and turn the bandage roll frequently. Placing the bandage on both sides of the ears will keep it from slipping off.

'ight abdominal bandaging is helpful after accidents when the dog is bleeding internally.

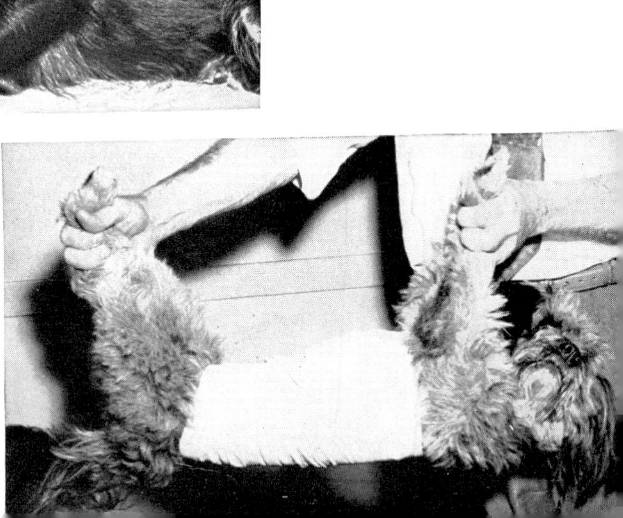

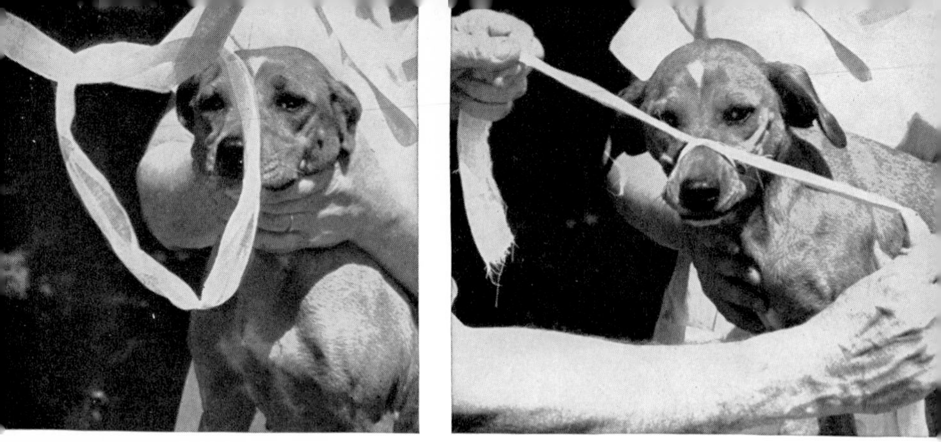

APPLYING CLOTH MUZZLE

LEFT: Holding ends of noose, approach dog slowly. RIGHT: Slip noose over and behind soft end of nose. Pull tight.

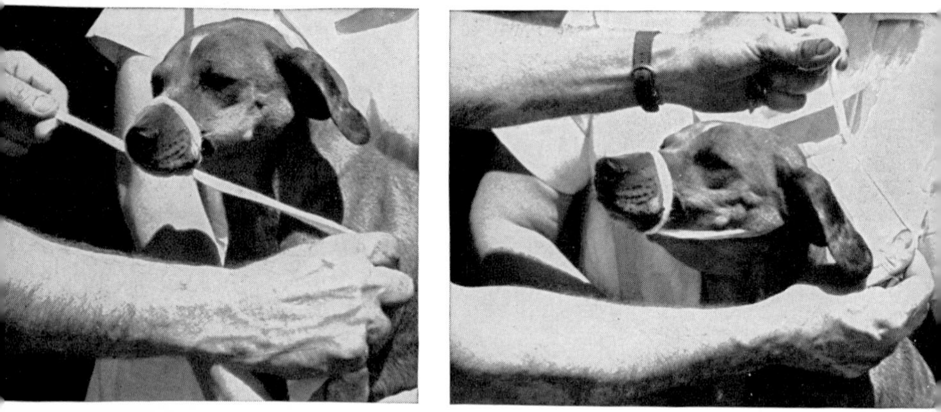

LEFT: Make another knot below jaw and pull tight again. RIGHT: Bring ends under ears behind head and tie with single knot.

Finish with a tight bowknot for quick release.

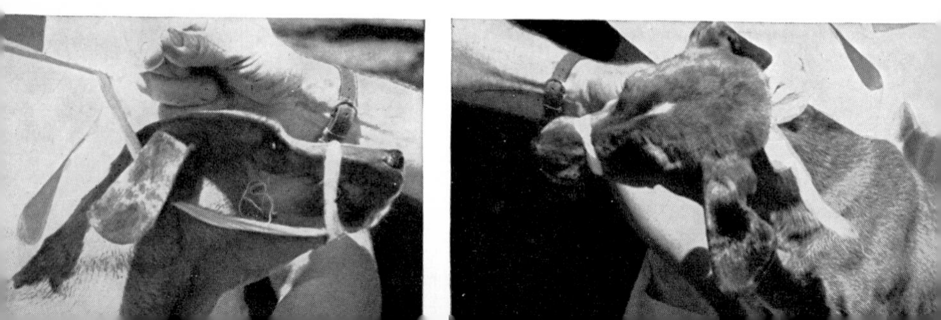

RESTRAINING A DOG

The warden's pole is a hardwood stick with a row of metal eyes threaded with a stout cord. Loop at end is slipped over dog's neck and pulled tight.

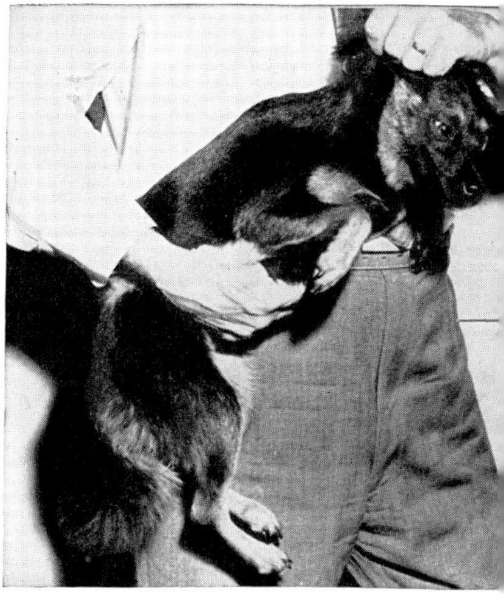

Holding an injured dog by nape of neck and under his chest restrains him so that he is comfortable and yet can't bite.

Double-lasso method is only safe way to handle particularly dangerous dogs. The dog is easily controlled in this fashion.

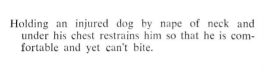

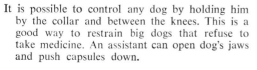

It is possible to control any dog by holding him by the collar and between the knees. This is a good way to restrain big dogs that refuse to take medicine. An assistant can open dog's jaws and push capsules down.

CLIPPING NAILS

A dog's nails should be cut back with clippers until tip and toe pad are even. Try not to make the nails bleed, but if you do, they will not become infected.

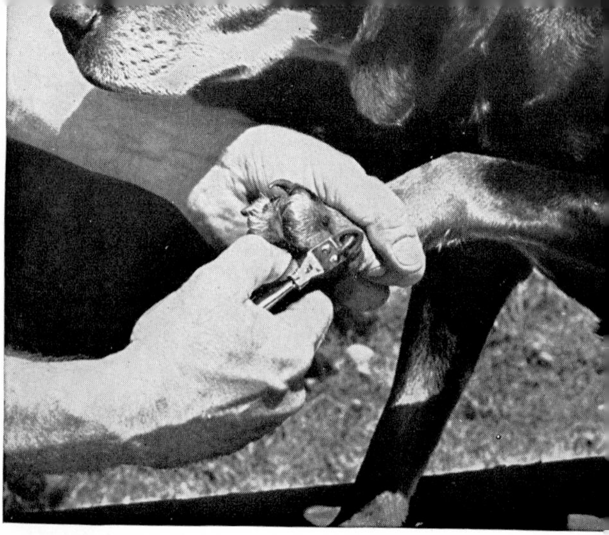

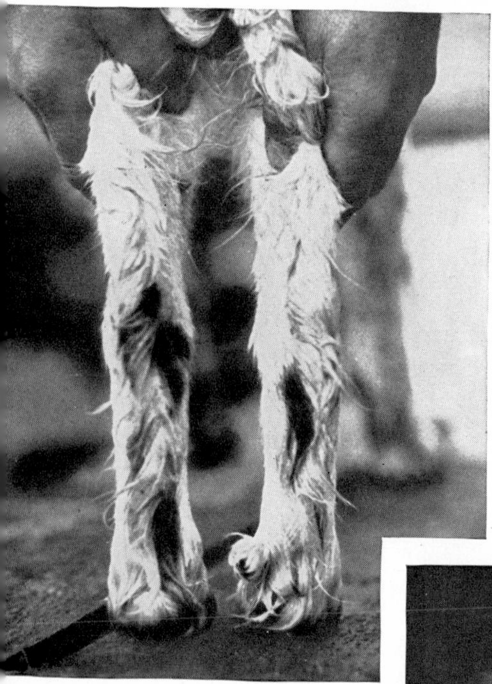

The dewclaws—useless appendages—can be removed with benefit to most dogs. This dog had only one. They are inherited characteristics.

EXAMINING TEETH

Some dogs' mouths are partly black and some all black. This puppy's teeth are all grown in, but the gums are still swollen.

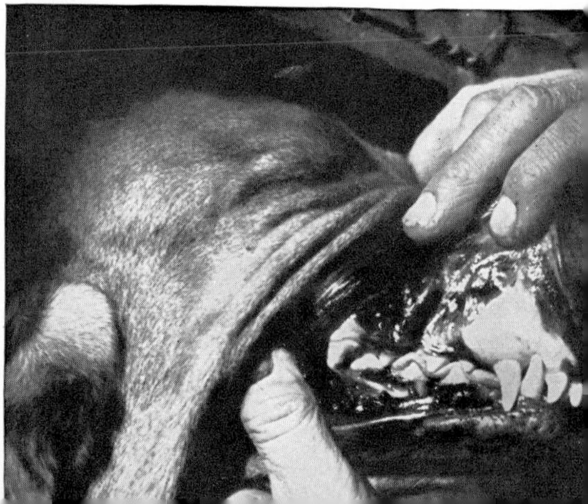

almost any work. The number 5 blade is perhaps the most useful attachment. It cuts hair approximately plucking length but does not pull out the loose hair. The short stubs, when they do fall out by themselves, are not noticeable about the house.

Some experts deplore the use of electric clippers. Most people who have had experience with both methods, however, feel that a clipped dog looks as well—to the owner at least—as a stripped one. Certainly clipping is a much quicker way of removing surplus hair and obviously it is much easier on the dog. Some plucking adherents insist that clipping causes a dog's hair to become finer each time it is done. Recent research has shown, however, that it has no such effect. Whether an owner prefers clipping or plucking seems to be largely a matter of what he has done in the past. Among the thousands of dogs clipped at the Whitney Veterinary Clinic there have been hundreds which had previously been plucked. In almost every instance the owner has been so well pleased with the appearance of the clipped dog that he changed to that method exclusively. In any event, the choice between clipping and plucking seems relatively unimportant since a clipped dog soon has hair long enough to look plucked.

There are times, of course, when plucking is preferable. If your dog is one of a breed which is ordinarily plucked and you intend to show him, by all means have him plucked. For example, if you own one of the wire-haired breeds and have lots of time, you will probably want to groom him with a plucking comb which can be obtained at any pet shop or drugstore. However, most people have found that plucking household pets is only a waste of time, since they look just as well after they have been clipped.

HOW TO CLIP AND PLUCK

The Wire-Haired Breeds. Our illustration of the wire-haired terrier will serve as a clipping guide for that breed as well as for the Airedale, Irish and Welsh terriers, and the schnauzers.

The dog to be clipped should be stood on a table. Above him there should be a hook of some kind to which a leash from his collar may be attached. By placing your hand under the crotch you can make him understand that he must stand, and he will eventually learn to pose like a statue.

When you are plucking, hold the handle of the plucking blade in your right hand with your thumb at a short distance from the serrated blade's edge. Press the edge against the hair, apply thumb pressure, and pull. Out comes the hair, which you release by removing your thumb. Repeat these steps for another combful. The motion becomes quite rapid as you learn the method. Pull, pull, pull, pull as quickly as you can make your hand go. The long, old hair gives way quite easily and, in a short time, you can pluck out a good-sized patch, leaving only the curly undercoat.

All of the neck and body is stripped. The legs are left as they are, and only the very longest hair is pulled out to make the legs look large, straight, and cylindrical. The hair on them is left considerably longer than the body coat. All this is plainly shown in the illustration.

The head receives different treatment. Showmen often clip the head with electric clippers, trimming the cheeks, the top of the head and the ears. If you have no clipper, however, you can safely use a razor. The guard will prevent shaving the hair too closely. Cut the hair on the top of the nose to the same length as that on the top of the head, but, starting at the brim, allow the hair down along the lips to be increasingly longer, to form the beard. From the rear angle of the mouth backward and underneath the eye, the hair is short. The only long hair is on the eyebrows and beard. When you have finished with the head, the long hair of the beard should produce a line under the face, parallel to the line from the eye to the top of the nose. The hair on the feet should be cut with scissors to give them the appearance of round cat feet.

There is no reason to make grooming a chore. You need not try to complete the job at one session. If your dog is uneasy or gets tired, stop for a while and let him rest. After you have finished, look at another dog of the same breed which has been plucked by a professional—at a dog show if possible. You will soon see where you have gone wrong and learn how to improve your technique.

Sealyham terrier and wire-haired terrier.

Scottish Terriers and Sealyhams. Dogs of these two breeds are especially easy to clip or pluck, and their appearance is greatly improved by proper grooming. They can be plucked, but many professionals recommend clipping instead. After you have finished clipping the dog and look at him from behind, he should have the shape of a half circle whose edges drop straight to the ground. More beard is left on the foreface of these breeds than on the wire-haired terrier, but otherwise the clipping is similar. The eyebrows are also usually left a little longer. No hair should be removed from the underbelly. The trimming line ends halfway down the dog's side and the hair below allowed to grow progressively longer so that it appears to be continuous with that on the legs.

West Highland Whites, Cairns, and Others. Although owners often mistakenly think that these breeds should be trimmed or plucked, "tidying up" is a better description of the kind of grooming they need. Certainly no clipping is necessary, only the pulling out of stray or long, unruly hair is needed.

Cocker Spaniels. These include the old and new types of American cockers and English cockers. The old type of American cocker is the one which has made the breed so popular. The illustration shows how he and the English cocker should be clipped. All the long hair is removed from the top of the head and from the top third of the ears (the insides

Old type of American cocker spaniel.

New type of American cocker spaniel.

are trimmed out too). The back, the top, and the sides of the tail and both sides and the front of the legs are also trimmed, as are the feet all around and for an inch up the back of the leg. The hair which forms the "feathers" on the backs of the legs and the belly hair are left long. When the clipping has been finished, the whole coat should be combed to remove snarls. When that has been done, the scissors may be used to trim away any scraggly hair to enhance the clean-cut, gay appearance of the dog.

The new type of American cocker is clipped the same way as the old type on the head and back, but the long hair on the legs is left uncut. The feet are clipped all around and the hair combed down straight. This bushy-legged clip, though preferred by some, has undoubtedly done much to harm the popularity of the cocker spaniel. Those who advocate it also breed for a heavy coat. This huge coat gives the owner more to work with in grooming the animal, but the average pet owner will also discover that such long, abundant hair has an unfortunate tendency to become a snarled mass of burrs and twigs—in short, an ideal breeding place for parasites. Not only does the long hair on the legs become matted and unsightly, it also collects dirt which the dog distributes about the house.

The Bedlington Terrier. When properly groomed, the Bedlington has a unique appearance which can be developed only because the animal has a peculiarly thick, linty coat without wiry texture. The coat of the show dog stands straight out and should be about one inch in length. It can be encouraged to grow in that manner by frequent combing and brushing toward the head.

The head of the Bedlington is clipped in a most distinctive way. The hair on the ears is clipped short except for a flat tassel an inch long at the tip of each ear. The topknot on the head should be the highest at the occiput and from there permitted to taper to its shortest length just behind

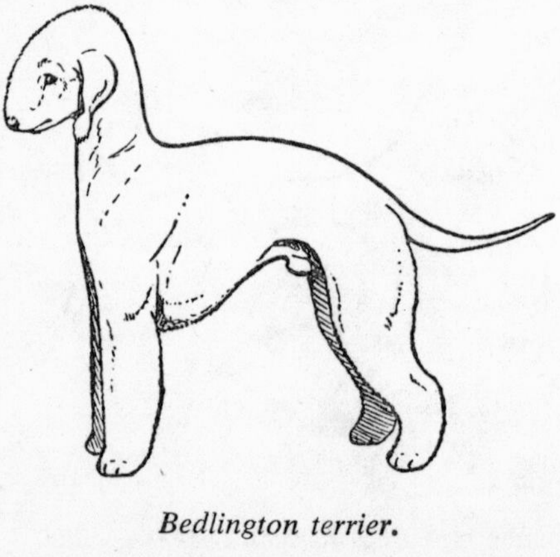

Bedlington terrier.

the nose. It should be rounded over the head, starting from the eyes and the point where the ears are attached.

The leg hair is somewhat longer and straighter than the body hair and should be trimmed to give the typical terrier appearance—cylindrical. Some experts use only scissors and combs for the entire job, some use the razor, and many laymen simply clip the body close and let the hair grow again but leave the leg hair, which they trim with scissors and comb thoroughly.

Poodles. Trimming poodles is not nearly so difficult as the fancy styling might lead one to believe. Still, clippers, combs, scissors, and

Continental clip and English saddle clip.

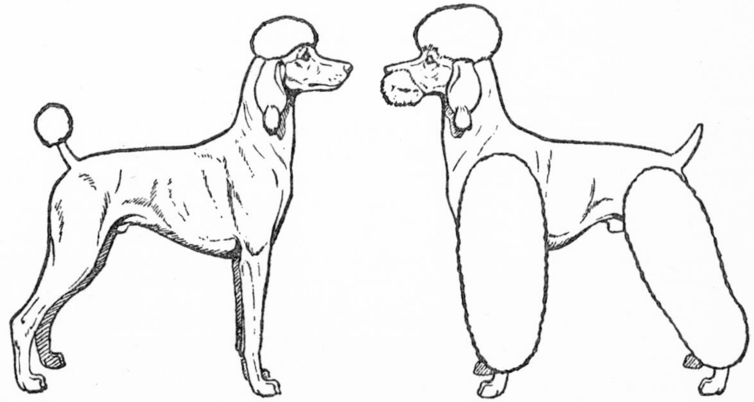

Field clip and Dutch clip.

razors will all prove useful. The hard part is knowing the basic designs and then being able to start with a great ball of hair and give the dog that oo-la-la! appearance. Many poodle owners prefer to have the dog clipped in a more masculine fashion, without decoration, holding that poodles are really hunters and general-purpose dogs. This is true—but for every man who owns a poodle there are dozens of women who prefer the fancy styles.

The illustrations show the four most popular clips, and for each there are variations.

THE FIELD CLIP: Usually all the coat is clipped with the number 10 blade, leaving long hair only in a pompon on the top of the head and another on the tail. Tassels on the ear tips are sometimes left also. Clipped in this manner, the poodle is comfortable, easy to care for, and ready for action in any going.

THE PUPPY CLIP: As the coat lengthens on a growing puppy it is necessary only to keep it combed and clean. The only parts that really require trimming are the face, the tail close to the body, and the feet and legs up a few inches from the ground. When the first fancy clip is executed the coat is all there to trim in whatever style the owner prefers.

THE DUTCH CLIP: In the Dutch clip, the distinctive features are the pantaloon effect, the whiskers, and the head pompon. The whiskers are left to form a long fringe about the face. The head, feet, part of the tail and body are clipped short, and the pantaloons are trimmed with scissors only. There is considerable variation in the clips. Some owners prefer the top of the long hair to start high up on the body with only four inches of the back separating the two sides. Some clip the chest clean while others leave it covered, the long hair running from one "pants leg" to the other. Considerable combing and scissor trimming are required to produce the proper cylindrical legs.

ENGLISH AND CONTINENTAL CLIPS: In these clips there are three distinct hair lengths. However, a good deal of variation is permitted. A number of experts clip the ears and leave the eyebrows with a bare area between them and the pompon on the head. Others leave the hair on the ears long and the hair from the eyes continuous with the pompon. Show dogs need the full topknot and feathers on the ears to give the essential poodle expression.

The feet are always kept clipped. In the Continental a pompon is left on each hip only, but in the English clip there is a blanket of medium-short hair. A modification of the English clip omits the upper bracelet on the front legs, and instead the long hair over the shoulders and chest is left unclipped down to the position of the bracelet. Follow the design, study poodles groomed by experts, and each time you clip you will come closer to perfection.

The Kerry Blue Terrier. The Kerry's soft wavy coat should be trimmed in such a way as to leave the body well covered but neat. In the proper trim, the head is clipped on the cheeks, ears, and forehead, but a long bang is left over the eyes and down the nose. The whiskers are full and flare out. For pets, it is most practical to reduce the whiskers by shearing them short. If they are left long, they will require too frequent washing and combing. The legs are trimmed cylindrically.

Kerry blue terrier and Cairn terrier.

Setters and Springer Spaniels. For showing, English, Irish, and Gordon setters and springers are clipped on the head and part way down the ears. The hair on the neck and shoulders is smoothed and all scraggly hair removed from the back. The sides and top of tail and the feet should also be carefully trimmed. The finished dog must look sleek. Such meticulous and careful trimming is unnecessary with pets or hunting dogs. Some hunters do, however, remove a goodly part of the feathers and long hair when they hunt their dogs in rough territory, especially where burrs are present.

CARE OF THE SKIN

The skin of many species of animals, including the human, has large numbers of sweat glands. Dogs, however, have them in restricted areas—under the tail, for instance, and fewer about the rest of the body. But if dogs do not sweat, how is the skin cleaned? Cleaning is accomplished by the renewal of the outside layer, which is constantly being sloughed off by growth in the layers beneath, and by the shedding of the hair itself. There is always a fine scaling of skin going on, more at some times than at others. Healing skin often sheds large, flaky, dandrufflike scales which must be combed or brushed out of the hair. Sometimes the shed-off scales will stick to hairs and one may find little disks of skin clinging to them, an eighth of an inch out from the body.

Many pets are equipped with another pair of skin glands, the anal glands, which are situated at either side just under the anus. They discharge their contents through the anus via two ducts. Pressure on them will cause the expulsion of the contents. These glands are found in a great many related species and their purpose has not been fully explained. We do know, however, that the anal glands discharge automatically when the animal becomes terrified. Dogs, cats, skunks, and weasels have them, and each species is characterized by a distinctive odor. Everybody recognizes the penetrating odor of a skunk. Farmers are often able to detect the presence of a weasel by his odd musk. Many dog owners do not realize that their pets have these anal glands and that part of their body odor comes from them. When you see Fifi sit down and drag her hind quarters along by her front legs—"play sleigh ride," as one youngster put it—you may usually assume that her anal glands need emptying. Ordinarily it is not worms which cause this, although many dog books claim it is.

Because nerves are everywhere in the skin, it takes very little—only a fleabite, for example—for a pet to show his annoyance by scratching. With the other basic information necessary to care for an animal's coat properly, you should learn something about the nerve patterns in the skin. If you scratch your dog in certain places on the back, he will scratch, but he may not come within ten inches of scratching the spot where you are scratching him. When veterinarians use an electric clipper on the backs of some dogs, particularly the members of wire-haired breeds, they find areas along the sides which cause a dog to scratch so violently that they often have trouble clipping. Clipping in other parts causes no such reaction. The dog's hind leg may not even reach the sensitive area and he doesn't try to chew at it—he merely scratches in a random sort of way. I mention this reaction only because dog owners frequently do not realize that when their pet scratches his shoulder it is no indication that he is itchy there. He may have a sore spot at the base of his tail. A better indication in locating an itchy spot is to watch where he chews most.

NAILS

The nails are appendages of the skin. Each nail has a hard outer crust protecting it, while inside there is a blood and nerve supply. Nails, being organs of defense as well as being useful in holding food while the teeth tear it apart, are strongly attached to the toes—much more so than our nails.

Dogs' nails are constantly growing to make up for the loss of nail which, in a normal wild dog, would be worn off by contact with rough surfaces. House pets seldom have the opportunity of wearing the nails sufficiently. Dogs running the streets keep their nails filed off on the pavements, but dogs walking on carpets or sleeping most of the time have no such opportunity and often their nails curve back under the foot until they press into the toes. Dogs differ markedly in the rate of nail growth. In some the rate of growth is so rapid that even running on city streets fails to wear them off.

When nails get too long they cause foot misery and sometimes real lameness. If the tips are below the pads of the feet, the pads have no traction on smooth surfaces like linoleum or hardwood floors and the dog slides on the kitchen floor, has trouble climbing stairs, and often appears to get lazy. Nails of house dogs need trimming or filing regularly. Some dogs object so strenuously that they must be muzzled. If you cut too short and the nails bleed, the capillaries will soon close if the dog is kept off rough surfaces for a while; there is no danger of infection.

If you use an electric cautery to stop bleeding from your dog's nails, don't apply it long; barely touch the raw surface. Heat applied to the nails will destroy the live tissue a long way up the nail.

SHEDDING

"Doctor," thousands of people ask of their veterinarians every year, "what makes my pet shed the year round?" The answer is—light. All my own kennel dogs live outside, subjected to the light of the sun only. That's the way nature intended them to live—without the benefit of electric lights. It has been found that as the days get noticeably longer the influence of these lengthening days on the dog's body (probably via the eyes) causes the hair to stop growing and fall out. New hair replaces the old. If, now, the day is suddenly made much shorter, the new coat will grow faster and reach the acme of its beauty far sooner than if the days gradually shorten. Pets which are not subjected to the normal light cycle shed a little all the time and heavily in the late spring. Combing helps in remov-

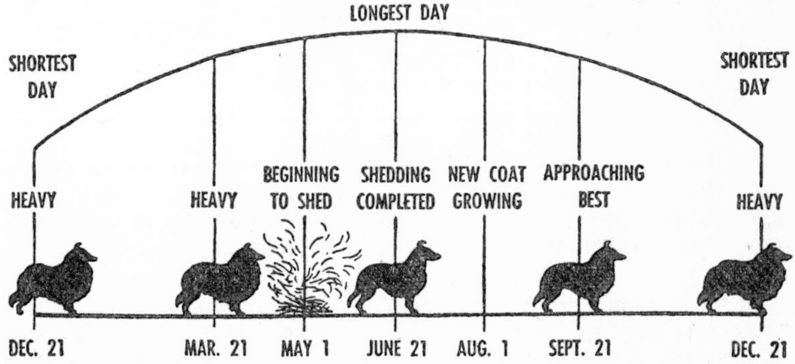

How the length of the day influences the shedding of the dog's coat when he is kept out of doors.

ing the loose hair before it falls or is rubbed off on one's clothing, rugs, or furniture.

BATHING

Dogs and cats are the only pets ordinarily bathed, and they are bathed simply to remove dirt and odors. The odors disappear with the dirt. There is no best way to bathe a pet, and no way has yet been found to eliminate the need for "elbow grease." The human fingers surpass any mechanical device for efficiency in bathing.

Because the coats of dogs are water-resistant, one needs the help of a chemical to wash a dog with ease. Soft or liquid soap is excellent and can be procured with either a 20 per cent or a 40 per cent coconut-oil base. You will save money by buying 40 per cent soap and adding an equal amount of water. A 20 per cent product is ideal. You can either add it to a bucket of warm water which will then wet the pet's coat easily or you can put some on the pet's back, pour on the warm water by the cupful, and mix the soap and water on the animal. Professionals use a tub and allow water to run onto the patient from a hose. Cake soap can be used instead of liquid, but it requires considerably more work.

By whatever method the soap and water are applied, the solution must be well worked into the coat and rubbed until the dirt has been loosened or dissolved. After the lathering, the soap must be thoroughly rinsed from the coat. This is best accomplished by working the fingers through the hair, just as one does in applying the soap solution. Usually one soaping and rinsing is enough, but if necessary, the process may be repeated.

There are soaps which contain vermin poisons. If one is used, no further medication is required. However, there are vermicidal dips and rinses available which are well worth using for topping off a bath on any pet. The solution is prepared just before the bathing starts. After the pet has been rinsed, the dip or special rinse is poured all over the coat, but this is not rinsed off. It is allowed to saturate the coat for a few minutes, the surplus is squeezed out with the hands, and the patient is dried.

A loosening of hair is generally a result of any bath. After the pet is dry, considerable combing is generally necessary to free the coat of the loosened hair and give it a sheen and tone.

Bathing small dogs or puppies may be easily accomplished by using a basin and towels. The whole animal may be dipped in the basin, leaving only the head out. The soiled water is allowed to run out and fresh water quickly drawn while the pet sits on a towel, waiting for the next immersion.

One of the questions about bathing most frequently asked is whether it is safe in winter. It is safe in winter provided the pet is well dried before being allowed outside in the cold air. For that reason many pet owners bathe their pets at night, knowing they are sure to be dry by morning.

Another common question is at what age it is safe to bathe a young animal. There is no rule about age. Small puppies which have become soiled and evil-smelling must be bathed if we are to keep them in a home. I have never seen a bath harm a pet provided it was properly dried. The fact is that puppies of all breeds are frequent sufferers from parasites and diseases. When one gets sick shortly after being bathed, the bath is all too often assumed to be the cause. Most of the harm that has come from bathing has been of this nature: the pet was going to be sick anyway; the bath didn't cause it.

There are several dry shampoos available which are quite effective cleaning agents. These should be used according to directions, which vary with the type. Then there are also harmless detergents on the market which remove dirt without lathering.

REMOVAL OF ROAD TAR. Dogs often run in newly tarred roads and return with a ball of tar and sand around each foot. Kerosene will dissolve the tar but it also irritates the skin. In most cases it will be necessary to rinse each foot in several washings of kerosene and quickly wash off the kerosene with strong soap and water each time. The discoloration of the tar is hard to eliminate completely but does no physical harm. Remember that it is as necessary to wash out the kerosene as it is to remove the tar.

REMOVAL OF PAINT. Paint removal is a frequent problem. Paint is not so poisonous as many people think—that is, white paint. Some of the paint pigments are poisonous, however, such as Paris green. If the dog comes home with fresh paint, still wet, on its coat, turpentine will remove it, if plenty is used without allowing too much to come in contact with the animal's skin. The turpentine must be removed by thorough washing with soap and water.

If the paint is dry, it will probably be necessary to clip the hair, even though it causes a temporary disfigurement. It will grow in again. If your dog's skin is especially tender, use linseed oil to dissolve the paint. When you have diluted the paint greatly, wash it and the oil out with soap and water. Don't cut the paint out with scissors except as a last resort.

ANIMAL ODORS. The sources of animal odors, aside from those of excrements, are ear canker, anal-gland secretions, and the sebum from thousands of body glands and dog collars which absorb sebum. All of these can be eliminated—as already mentioned—by cleaning the ears, by expressing the anal-gland secretion, and by thorough bathing.

PARASITE CONTROL. Bathing in itself will not eliminate parasites, as many people seem to think, but preparations of excellent efficiency for use with the bath may be had for the purpose. Some are used as a rinse or dip following the bath, as described above; others are liquid soaps or soap cakes with insect killers added. Some manufacturers claim that their products will prevent fleas and lice from reinfesting dogs for several days after their use. Some claim their products will kill the eggs of lice (nits).

In eliminating lice, it is necessary to apply the killing agent every eleven days, as this breaks the generation and so eliminates the lice.

The more effective way to control pests is to use a liquid dip, soap, or rinse to kill all the insect pests during the bath and then keep the dog well powdered with a nonpoisonous flea powder.

THE MOUTH AND TEETH

An animal's unpleasant breath is often caused by dirty, broken, or infected teeth. Tartar is sometimes an eighth of an inch deep. Your veterinarian can snap it off and clean the teeth, which will do much to sweeten the breath. Cleaning an animal's teeth is not difficult. You can do it yourself with a tartar scraper which you can get from your dentist.

Examine your pet's teeth at least once a month. Look for tartar and loose or broken teeth. Animals fed soft foods have more tartar than those fed on hard foods. All animals enjoy chewing soft rib bones, which help to keep teeth clean and prevent tartar from building up. Animal teeth do not need brushing to keep them clean.

THE EYES

Our dogs' eyes require very little attention. The only hygiene necessary is the removal of surplus hair that may curl inward and irritate the eyes, and the removal of exudate on the nasal side where the eye overflows in many breeds. Spaniels and toy poodles are two breeds which often exhibit soiled spots which may discolor the hair. Pekinese dogs with large wrinkles of skin close to the eyes need to have the hair on these ridges kept short to prevent it from touching the eyeballs.

Most people believe that dogs such as poodles, old English sheep dogs, Kerry blue terriers, and many mongrels will become blind if the hair is clipped from in front of their eyes. This is not true. The hair is harmful. These dogs sometimes have mats and caked areas where the eyes' secretions have built up a mass of material under which the skin is generally sore. Only very fastidious owners who groom their dogs frequently should let hair grow long over the eyes. Even then the eyeballs may easily be injured.

Every hunter knows how his dogs' eyes look the day after a hunt. Hounds hunt with heads to the ground and plow through reeds, brush, and tall grass. Seeds, dust, and vegetable fibers which fill their eyes are sometimes too coarse to wash down the tear ducts into the nose and run over the rims of the lids, caking around the eyes. In such cases the eyes should be washed with warm water and a soft cloth. Tears are a better antiseptic than boric acid. For comfort use a mild anesthetic like butyn sulfate combined with a mild antiseptic in an innocuous ophthalmic ointment, which your veterinarian will prescribe. It is wise to keep a supply of these drugs on hand for all dogs have a tendency to sore eyes.

THE EARS

Ears are often troublesome in dogs. Examine them occasionally under a good light. Dirty ears have a nasty odor which pervades the animal and may cause him to shake his head and dig constantly at the ear with his hind paw. If you see a pet moving his front paw over an ear as if it itched badly, he probably has canker or ear mites.

Drop a mixture of ether and alcohol in the ear to dissolve wax and dirt. Propylene glycol will serve as well. After the application swab out the ear carefully with cotton on the end of a toothpick. If a little alcohol and ether are left, they will evaporate.

COLLARS AND HARNESSES

An animal's health should be considered when collars and harnesses are bought. Salesmen do not always have this in mind in making recommendations. Round collars for long-haired dogs, strap collars for short-haired dogs, are usually most satisfactory. Harnesses are used for all small dogs, but it is sometimes difficult to hold a large dog with a harness. Big dogs tend to do less pulling than small ones because they are more often properly trained. Yet it is easier to train a small dog than a large one, because it requires less strength. A properly fitted collar isn't cruel on any dog, and harnesses could be dispensed with if all dogs were trained not to tug on their leashes.

Every collar or harness should be examined to see that no sharp points or rivets protrude to scratch the animal's skin or wear off the hair. It is most important not to get a lot of hardware on these accessories which can injure a dog's ears. When a hound shakes his head and his ears flap against a heavy buckle and license tags, the ears are often damaged. A dog that has worn a heavy combination of hardware sometimes has the hair entirely worn off his neck.

Small chains used for collars can be cruel if a dog is kept chained. It is not uncommon to find such chains cutting deeply into the neck of their unfortunate wearers.

BEDS AND BEDDING

Bedding for pets is a problem. For indoor dogs you may buy several different kinds of mattresses, canvas stretched across metal or wooden frames, and all sort of beds. You can make beds out of pieces of thick carpet or castoff mattresses cut down, or you can allow pets to sleep in old chairs.

Some people like the smell of cedar in bedding, but stale cedar mixed with dog odors has an unpleasant aroma. After a while the smell pervades a whole house—even the clothing hanging in closets. If wood shavings or other wood products are desired for bedding, ordinary pine can be bought for a fraction of the cost of cedar. By sprinkling some flea powder in it a very much better flea and louse destroyer and repellent is made without the cedar smell.

Many dogs refuse to sleep on soft beds. Great Danes often develop large joint swellings from irritation caused by sleeping on hard surfaces, and almost everyone has known at least one dog which insisted on lying right by the crack under the door. Heavy dogs which refuse to sleep on the softer bedding provided for them sometimes develop sores or stiffness. Light dogs usually show the marks only at their elbows.

In outside kennels, oat or wheat straw is as satisfactory as any bedding. Marsh grass is excellent. Wood shavings are likely to be tracked out and create a disorderly appearance, and they are difficult to rake. If straw is placed in a kennel, there should be at least four inches of the packed material under a dog for a mattress in cold weather. In summer less is needed. It is seldom necessary to dust outdoor dogs for fleas if a liberal amount is shaken in the bedding each time it is changed. In muddy weather the bedding may have to be changed every two days, while in dry weather it may serve a month. If it stays over a week, flea powder should be dusted over it every six or seven days.

RUN SANITATION

In a dog run, sanitation can keep a pet in sound health. The lack of it may be responsible for his death.

Runs for pets of every kind are made of wire, concrete, sand, soil, gravel, grass, or of various combinations of these materials. Wire runs which are elevated from the ground permit all excrement to drop out of the cage, and they can be cleaned and hosed readily. Kennel dogs which are kept in these are freest from parasites. Dogs kept on concrete suffer most from parasites, since concrete is splendid as an incubator.

Grass is also objectionable. It is impossible to do even a halfway job of removing stools where grass grows. Worm eggs stick to the leaves as they grow, and dogs may eat the leaves and become infested or reinfested. Even when grass is started in a run, it soon dies out, leaving bare top soil which becomes muddy.

Washed builder's sand makes an excellent run floor. It costs little, it is easily removed and discarded and easily replaced. It shakes off a dog's feet even when wet. In addition it doesn't track into his kennel, as does soil with clay in it.

Sanitation, of course, consists of removing stools and replacing the material in the run. Proper stool removal requires that not only the stool itself but also the layer of sand under it be lifted out with a shovel. If rain has washed some of the outside surface of stool off, any worm eggs in it may be carried down a fraction of an inch into the floor, since these eggs are much smaller than the pores between even the finest kinds of soil granules. A little soil or sand should always be hoed up with the stool to be certain that all contamination is removed.

In cleaning a dog run, do not rake all the stools into a pile and then shovel them up together. When a stool is even partially pulverized by raking or sweeping, its parts, including worm eggs, are scattered and washed into the soil, which soon becomes thoroughly contaminated. Worm eggs that have become embryonated may resist the elements for years, waiting to be consumed by dogs. When hookworm eggs hatch and the larvae have reached the infective stage, they move upward from fairly deep in the soil with capillarity. They will be found close to the surface of the soil, even somewhat above the surface if they can find a little stem or stalk to climb.

Too much care cannot be exerted in gathering stools. Stools cannot be gathered efficiently from cinders, gravel, or grass. They cannot be removed from concrete without leaving eggs in the pores. Only by burning or daily scrubbing can concrete be freed of parasite eggs or larvae. Some kennel owners use flame-throwing oil burners which heat the soil surface sufficiently to kill worm eggs and hookworm larvae, but such methods are, of course, impractical for the owner of one dog.

It is difficult to clean any kind of dog run in winter. The problem is not so serious as it might be, however, since worm eggs do not incubate in cold weather, nor do fleas develop. How is this problem managed in kennels where runs are full winter and summer? All spring and summer the sand runs are cleaned with hoe and shovel. A summer's cleaning removes at least two inches and sometimes four from the run's surface. In the fall this is replaced so that the surface is above surrounding ground. Since the sand will pack down an inch, six inches of sand should be added if four are gone. If a dog has infested a run with eggs of parasites, deworm the dog, shovel off the top two inches of sand, and fill the run with fresh sand.

All winter little run covering can be removed, except on balmy days when the surface may melt enough to enable shoveling. When snow covers the run the owner does the best he can, which usually isn't satisfactory even from the standpoint of appearance. As soon as the surface has thawed in the spring, the top two inches should be removed and replaced with fresh sand.

In a dog run the stools are generally deposited within a few square yards. It is easy to dig away this soil and replace it with sand. But don't merely turn it over for a depth of a few inches and think that the whole problem has been solved. Dogs dig holes, and when they do they will scratch old buried worm eggs to the surface. Even the necessary removal of bits of earth with the stools will in time dig away enough soil to reach the eggs again.

There are few disinfectants which will kill worm eggs. Roundworm eggs can stand even carbolic acid. But hookworms can be destroyed by a very strong salt solution poured over the surface of the runs until it stands in pools. It has also been found that a 2 per cent solution of household lye applied in the same manner will destroy hookworm larvae. Neither method works very well on a slope. In addition, dogs must be kept off the lye until after a hard rain.

A more efficient method than either is the use of borax-sodium borate —made into a strong solution (2 pounds per gallon) and poured over the run's surface at the rate of 2 gallons per 100 square feet. Borax may be procured from kennel-supply companies and wholesale drug distributors.

OUTDOOR ACCOMMODATIONS

If a dog is left outside from spring on, he will be healthier than if kept indoors. He will have a better coat, he will shed less, and he will be in less danger of being overfed. Thousands of hunters believe that making house pets of their dogs ruins them for hunting.

Scientific studies on acclimatizing animals show that they should not be exposed to sudden changes in temperature. An animal which might die of exposure when taken suddenly from warm to cold can stand much lower temperatures if it is introduced to them gradually. One reason for this is that cold stimulates the growth of the coat, which in time becomes much thicker and so provides better protection. When southern dogs are brought North, their coats are so much heavier in their second winter in the North that they look like different animals. An animal that has become accustomed to cold can stand a great deal.

Northern outdoor dogs often prefer to be out in the snow when they might sleep inside of a comfortable doghouse.

Every fall outdoor kennels need to be prepared for the winter. There should be no cracks for the wind to blow through, and the doors should have burlap bags hung over them. The dog's own heat will keep his house at 60° on a night when the outside temperature is 15°. These burlap front doors do not always stay in place, however, since dogs seem to enjoy pulling them off. Because of this habit I have known my own dogs to have spent nights with temperature 10° below zero curled up on straw beds open to the wind. So far as I could see, they showed no ill effects from the cold. In fact, many dogs enjoy sleeping curled up in snow on bitterly cold nights even when they can sleep inside in what would seem to be far greater comfort.

DISINFECTANTS

Disinfectants must be chosen with care. Dogs are quite resistant to most of the ordinary forms, but cats and foxes cannot stand phenol derivatives. Their nest boxes, beds, and their coats should not be disinfected with these products. Some time ago, when an owner used a phenol disinfectant in fox nest boxes, many of the fox kittens were killed from the fumes long after the product had dried out or soaked into the wood of the boxes.

Odorless deodorizers are excellent and can be purchased reasonably. "Phenol coefficient" on a label may not mean a phenol product. It simply compares a product with phenol in germ-killing ability. Some of the odorless deodorizers do have high phenol ratings.

Some pet owners like the odor of pine oil; others prefer phenols, which often simply outsmell the odor to be removed. Good soap-and-water cleansing is usually adequate around pets, and if there is an odor left after scrubbing, it is a safe assumption that the spot or place is not clean. Disinfectants which give off chlorine are good but are also bleaches and must be used judiciously on that account.

ENCLOSURES

Dogs allowed to run loose are least infested with intestinal parasites, except for the rabbit form of tapeworm. Country and suburban dogs kill and eat rabbits and are thus infested. Dogs in small runs or on short chains have the most intestinal parasites.

The dog on a chain defecates, then runs around dragging the chain through the stool, spreading it over so wide an area that it is usually impossible to take it up. Dogs hitched to overhead wires have a better chance to remain parasite-free because they generally drop their stools at one end of the wire and spend most of their time away from the dirty sections of their runs.

Long, narrow runs are preferable to square runs with the same number of square feet. The dog usually defecates in one end of a long run, generally at the end farthest from the house. But if that is the end where the dog first sees you, he will spend most of his time in daylight hours watching for you, and thus remain in the filth. If possible, the arrangement of the run should be such that this is avoided.

If enclosures are built, the wire needs to be of such strength that dogs cannot chew through it, and it should be of a mesh which is difficult to climb. It should be buried at least eight inches in the ground. A foot is better.

RAT CONTROL

Rats should not be allowed to remain as kennel parasites any more than insects should be permitted to infest the kennel inhabitants. It is generally easy to eradicate them. Red squill, a drug nonpoisonous to pets other than rodents, will keep rats at a minimum. When rats are known to exist on the premises, put out a small bowl of dog food and let them eat it. Do this every night until the rats are bold enough to eat it all and then you know how much they will take. When you have encouraged them to feel at home, mix one part of red squill with eight parts of food and leave it for them as usual. As a rule this one poisoning will eradicate the rats and no more will be seen for a month or more.

Some of the new rat poisons are extremely effective but dangerous to pets. If they are used, they must be covered so there can be no possible chance that the pets can dig them out or uncover boards or boxes to get them.

PERIODIC HEALTH EXAMINATION

One of the best bits of advice a veterinarian can give to his clients is that they keep most careful track of the health of their pets, especially those that have passed middle age, by periodic physical checkups. If you have a competent veterinarian to whom you entrust your animals' health, he can make some tests which may be instrumental in prolonging their lives by many years.

He can determine the presence of some diseases by temperature readings and other signs. He can detect external parasites, intestinal parasites, heartworms, skin disease, ear canker, kidney disease, bad teeth, overweight and underweight conditions, eye defects, and deafness. These defects need correcting, if possible.

Any of these conditions can shorten an animal's life. When you take your pet to the veterinarian's for a periodic health examination, take along a small sample of stool and a urine specimen. To catch the urine from a dog, take him for a walk on a short lead and, if a male, hold a cup under his penis when he lifts his leg; if a female, push a small shallow dish under her when she squats. A person with a good sense of touch can press against both sides of a dog's abdomen simultaneously, get the bladder between the fingers, and exert sufficient pressure to cause a relaxation of the bladder sphincter muscle. A pan placed under the dog will catch the urine squeezed out.

Let us consider how a periodic health examination can prolong the life of an animal. Suppose you know of nothing wrong. All you notice is that Rover hasn't the pep he used to have. You take his urine and feces and ask your veterinarian to examine him. But don't expect him to make an examination worth the name unless you have the urine and stool, because so many facts may be learned from them.

The veterinarian asks you whether the dog drinks more water than he used to. You have noticed that he has. So when he tests the albumin and learns that it shows XX, indicating kidney disease, he gives you medicine to administer at home and tells you not to feed any more meat, fish, liver, and just about everything Rover loves. He explains that Rover will learn to love his new diet as well when he gets accustomed to it.

He may see that Rover, who weights forty-three pounds, is thirteen pounds overweight, and show you how to reduce him. The number of diseases which can be uncovered in dogs is legion. Fortunately the majority of them can either be eliminated or relieved by proper care and medication. A proper examination, which reveals many diseases in their early stages, when their treatment is most effective, is one of the surest ways to insure the health and longevity of your pet.

11. Health Hazards in Hospitalization, Boarding, and Shows

DOG OWNERS sooner or later face the question: What shall I do with my pet when I have to leave him? There are a number of other questions closely related to this first one. If the dog becomes sick, shall I keep him at home or leave him in a veterinary hospital? Shall I exhibit my dog in a show? Shall I take my dog to a training class? Is it safe to allow my pets free access to neighborhood animals?

Actually all of these general questions are part of a still larger one: To what extent shall I isolate my dogs?

In order to answer these questions intelligently, there are certain basic facts you should know. Every proprietor of a veterinary hospital or a boarding kennel, every dog warden and humane-society officer, knows these facts. If every pet owner knew them as well, sickness among pets might be greatly reduced. Omitting for the moment any consideration of the emotional side of the question, let us discuss only the purely physical factors, the health hazards which "mingling" entails.

Let's assume that every dog owner and every dog handler is honest, and that every person owning an animal he or she knows is sick will isolate it. Let's assume, too, that no dog warden knowingly puts a sick animal in the pound. And last, but not least, let's assume that no veterinary hospital exists without isolation wards where dogs with each kind of disease are separately segregated. It is obvious that none of these assumptions can be completely true. Pet owners are no more and no less ethical than other groups of people. Certainly not all of them are sufficiently concerned about the health of other people's pets to isolate their own when they know them to be sick.

But suppose that all these things were true. Could you even then be certain that your dog could be safely placed with a lot of other healthy animals and never contract a disease? You could not.

The average dog show probably furnishes the best example of the risk involved whenever animals are brought together, in spite of the fact that every dog exhibited is supposed to be a healthy animal. Although veterinarians examine all dogs at the entrance gate and reject those which are sick, dog shows are still one of the prime means by which disease is spread. Here is a case in point from my own experience. A few years ago, just after one of my bloodhounds, Barbara of White Isle, had weaned a beautiful litter of puppies, she was "shown" at the Westminster Kennel Club Show in Madison Square Garden. Twice a day she was walked to the exercise space. In that space one day there was a Dalmatian bitch from Texas. She looked sick to me, but her owner refused to keep her leashed and when she walked up to Barbara I was unable to shoo her away. On the following Saturday, six days later, I was showing Barbara at the New Haven, Connecticut, show when I noted she was squinting. A little later she vomited. Her temperature was only 102°. Car sickness can produce vomiting. Dust in the eyes can cause squinting. But Carré distemper can cause and was causing both symptoms. It so happens that on the sixth day after infection a dog's temperature drops when it has that disease—which accounted for Barbara's 102°—and rises again the seventh day. Barbara's puppies and seventy-five other dogs of mine contracted distemper.

The Texas Dalmatian—via a dog show—had spread distemper to Connecticut and probably to many other localities, and who knows but that the Connecticut bloodhound spread it to California, since there were dogs from California on the circuit of eastern shows. Yet who was to blame? We had no means of conferring immunity at that time.

Today we have the means, and distemper is rapidly disappearing, but distemper is only one disease. The dog show remains a good example of the hazards of "mingling," because, if we face the facts honestly, we must admit that it is impossible to recognize disease in animals when in the incubation stage.

Here is another example of the way disease is spread. The kennel owner accepts Mrs. Williams' dog in all good faith. The dog is placed in a building with many others. All of them appear to be in good health. After three days the kennel owner notices that Mrs. Williams' dog is gagging. She isolates him in another room. But suppose your dog had been in the first room. Many of the dog diseases are spread by droplet infection. A day after you take your dog home she starts to sneeze. You telephone the kennel owner immediately and take your dog to her to cure. She tells you your dog was contented and well on its first visit. But the chances are she remembers Mrs. Williams' dog, and when two days later she finds that most of the dogs in that room are sneezing, what is she to do? Whose fault is it? Is the kennel owner under obligation to take your dog back and keep it until it is cured or dies? Legally such an occurrence is considered along with lightning, wind, and fire as "an act of God." Pure slander! But lawyers have to have a pigeonhole for everything, and so dog diseases are blamed on God.

Perhaps your dog contracts distemper while being boarded, and when you return she is dead. The owner of the kennel has spent hours, half sick herself because of worry over what has happened, trying to nurse the dogs under her care to health. You are hurt, indignant, and angry that your dog has been lost. Perhaps you refuse to pay even the board. Actually, considering the work and worry she has had, you owe the kennel owner far more than if nothing had happened.

This is a frequent occurrence in dog-boarding kennels. Everyone with very much experience could tell of many similar instances. Clients will bring their dogs in, stating they don't want them kept close to other dogs because of the possibility of disease spread. They choose an outdoor run. The dog goes home infected with coccidiosis. Who's to blame? A fly, more than likely. Did the fly first feed on an infested stool of a dog in the same kennel or did he fly from a kennel five miles away? Flies may easily travel eight or ten miles in a single night. An act of God? Slander! Nor can you call it an act of carelessness.

Needless to say, no boarding-kennel owners ever *want* such things to happen. It hurts them every time it does. It causes worry, anguish, extra work, and loss of money. So what, then, should be one's attitude? Shall every pet owner say, "I left a well animal; now he's sick. You're to blame"? Or shall he look at it from a reasonable point of view, difficult as that may be when one's individual pet's health is involved?

It is impossible to assemble a large group of animals of any species and be 100 per cent certain that no one is infested with parasites or is incubating some disease. So long as this is true you can't board a pet and be 100 per cent sure the pet will be well, uninfested with parasites, and neither incubating a disease nor showing symptoms of it when you call for it.

The best and safest thing you can do is to leave your pet in a kennel where veterinary attention is given or where the owner knows diseases well enough to be able to recognize the first symptoms and is willing and able to treat them properly. It is, of course, essential that there be an isolation ward in conjunction with the boarding facilities.

If, when you call for your pet, he is sick or even dead, don't at once conclude that there has been some dirty business or blame the kennel owner. Be sorry for him or her, knowing your animal has occasioned great inconvenience and, in the case of conscientious individuals, considerable mental pain. Loving animals as I myself do, I know that it is difficult to be wholly reasonable at such times, but this is the only fair attitude to take.

Dogs corralled by the city dog wardens may be placed in a truck with half a dozen others, taken to the pound, and there put in a cage or a pen with many other dogs. Some of these will be dogs from homes where they received the best of care, but in general those who think so little of their pets as to allow them to run are not the citizens who have fine dogs and take good care of them. In fact, many cruel owners purposely abandon sick or mangy dogs, and when your pet is picked up by the warden he is subjected to all the infectious diseases known among the dogs of your city—all concentrated in one room.

When your male dog knows where a bitch in heat lives, if he is healthy you may be sure he will be camped near her home, and so will all the other dogs that know—another potent source for the spread of infection.

Unquestionably dogs can contract diseases in veterinary hospitals. The most careful veterinarian, in the best of faith, accepts animals, apparently free from disease, for operations. Two days later those same animals may be sneezing and filling surgical wards with invisible virus-filled droplets. Even though utraviolet lights and germ-killing vaporizers may have been installed, they are not 100 per cent guarantee that a few healthy dogs will not be infected. I have never known a veterinarian to tell me that no disease was ever contracted in his hospital. But neither can the superintendent of a hospital for humans make that boast. Who doesn't know of at least one case of a patient in a hospital contracting virus pneumonia or some other of the contagious diseases? What of the diseases which sweep through the infant wards, or the women who even today are infected with "childbed fever"? I doubt that the risk of leaving a pet in a scrupulously clean veterinary hospital, complete with isolation wards, is any greater than the risk of contracting a disease yourself while in a hospital.

Remember that not everything that happens to your pet in a hospital or kennel happens *because* he is there. Many of these things are the result of normal health hazards; many are the direct result of the age, habits, idiosyncrasies, food, and appetite of your pet.

If you leave an old animal, remember that the older he is, the nearer he is to the end. If he should die of a heart attack or a kidney ailment, even though lawyers blame the death on God, be just enough to call it old age, remembering that he had to die sometime. And be grateful it wasn't in your arms. You were spared a heart-stopping anguish.

Most animals are boarded in the summertime. If your pet has died and been cremated or buried, don't feel animosity toward the responsible kennel owner or the pet-shop proprietor in whose care he was left. The bodies of animals can't be preserved in summer. Those who have to see death and shield the rest from such unpleasantness know that. Those who never have seen death often find it difficult to understand.

You may have left a very fat pet and return to find him thin. You should be pleased that he has lost dangerous excess weight. Or a comfortably fat pet may have grown too fat by the time you call for him. A few days' attention to his diet will correct that.

Remember the characteristics of the breed and of the individual animal. If you own a great Dane, you can expect he will brood, be homesick, refuse food, and probably lose at least twenty pounds in a week. If he does, it will be your fault for ever having allowed him to become so dependent upon you. The cure is to leave him more often and to use at home the same food the kennel uses, if it is a wholesome brand, so that he won't have to be starved to eat it every time you have to board him.

If you own a lively pet, the first day after you take him home his stools will probably be quite loose. This does not necessarily mean he is sick. Any hunter will tell you that though his dogs' stools may be perfect when in the kennel, he won't have run a quarter of a mile before he may be passing liquid stools. Excitement after confinement—not sickness—always causes loose stools. Your pet was probably in a small run or even a cage; at home he has the whole outdoors to run in and he jumps and frisks. Expect loose stools until he gets back into his old regime.

Most pets seem thirsty after leaving boarding establishments. They have had pans of water in their runs, but take them home and they seem thirsty. Expect this too.

Your pet may seem starved. This is not strange. He's been learning to know a new food and you take him back to the old one. Of course he enjoys it. It's like a newlywed husband going back home for Sunday dinner and Mother's cooking!

Try to be reasonable about the food and care you expect for your dog while he is being boarded. Too many owners seem to think to themselves, "A dollar a day! A lot of money!" Then they proceed to tell the kennel owner what to feed: one pound of top round hamburg for the evening meal; this, that, and the other thing at stated intervals throughout the day. On such a menu the cost of the food alone may run to three dollars. No wonder the kennel owner smiles. His food cost can't be more than 25 per cent of the dollar or he'd have to go out of business. As we shall see in Chapter 13, this is enough to buy adequate, wholesome food. If you want your dog fed fancy things, it is best that you supply them and pay seventy-five cents a day for the other expenses incidental to the care and maintenance of your pet. For the average pet, where the cost of everything is considered, the boarding-kennel owner is lucky to make twenty-five cents a day on the average dog when he charges one dollar a day, or on the average cat when the charge is seventy-five cents a day. If you have boarded a setter for two weeks, the kennel owner actually got $3.50 for the care of the animal—not too large a fee for his services. Would you assume the responsibility of keeping a neighbor's setter for two weeks, feeding it, keeping it free of external or internal parasites to the best of your ability, changing its bedding every three days, cleaning its droppings twice a day, renewing its water twice or three times a day—all for $3.50? I doubt it.

The reason the kennel or pet-shop owner is willing to do this is because he is equipped to keep large numbers of dogs. And this very fact throws a sick animal now and again next door to a well one. This is a normal and unavoidable condition which the pet owner must learn to accept.

Which brings us to this observation: If you find a boarding accommodation for your pet which suits you, keep using that establishment and don't shift around. In time your pet will become immune to any disease which may infest that place, and your troubles are over. Just as children in a certain school and community become immune and thereafter are glad they did have measles, mumps, and chicken pox so they don't have to have them later, so pet owners can be glad their pets were first protected against all the diseases they can be protected against by inoculation and then by having built up natural immunity to the others. This much is certain: Animals can't assemble in large numbers and remain free from disease any more than children can be expected not to contract the infectious diseases from their classmates in school.

One other factor or risk in boarding pets is escape. Don't expect the kennel owner to be responsible if your dog chews a hole in a sound fence and escapes. You owe the kennel owner for the damage. Or if your dog jumps a six-foot fence and you haven't said he would jump, or perhaps didn't know it, that is your misfortune.

The tendency of most human beings to blame the other fellow for their own shortcomings is evidenced to the fullest in their reactions to the loss of a pet in a boarding institution. If you will consider the facts as I have presented them, you will see the problem in a fairer light.

One precaution you can and should take: Consider the age of your pet. Young puppies are far more likely to die than are grown dogs, because they have less resistance. Intestinal parasites are more harmful to young animals than to older ones. Virus diseases go very much harder. Distemper may be 100 per cent fatal to whole litters of puppies, but less so to older dogs. House-dog disease destroys a high proportion of puppies but very few older dogs. More older dogs than puppies will live through distemper. Knowing these facts, you will be wise to keep your puppies—and all your young dogs—isolated, so far as it is in your power to do so, until they are over a year old. Thereafter the ravages of diseases will be less severe.

After you have read this book you will be in a better position to judge where your pet contracted any disease, because knowledge of the incubation period will help you. If you know that Carré distemper incubation period is five days and you have had your pet home from his vacation place for ten days, you may be sure he "caught it" while he was in your hands. By the same token, if you are informed by the boarding-kennel owner that he started to be sick a few days after he was accepted to board, you may know he was infected before you left him.

Nor can we neglect the viewpoint of the owner of the establishment where our pets are left, be it a boarding kennel or veterinary hospital. I think you would be amazed if you knew the number of times people who were aware that their dogs were sick tried to leave them "to board" at our clinic. Every hospital owner has had the same experience. Kennel owners, too. Veterinarians with "weather eyes" out for such animals are not often fooled, but boarding-kennel owners often have diseases introduced by such unscrupulous dog owners because they fail to recognize the disease and are grateful to have another boarder.

One final thought: The risk to health where pets congregate or are congregated is unavoidable. It can be greatly reduced. Nothing does more to minimize the hazards than proper vaccination. If you neglect to take this simple precaution, you not only are not doing the sporting thing to the pets of others, but you are failing to take the most obvious step to protect the health of your own.

12. When the End Comes

THE death of a dog is a very serious problem to a great many people. Too many otherwise intelligent pet owners simply can't bring themselves to realize that every life has a limit. When their conscientious veterinarian assures them it is time to say good-by to their pet, instead of taking his advice they say good-by to the veterinarian and take their pet to another.

It is interesting and helpful to consider the life expectancy of the breeds of dogs. If you know what to expect in advance, you will not be surprised at death, nor will you ask the impossible of your veterinarian.

In the table below, the average age at death means *from natural causes* in animals which have survived infanthood.

Table VIII

BREED	AVERAGE AGE AT DEATH	OLDEST KNOWN TO THE AUTHOR
Cocker spaniel	12 yrs.	17 yrs.
Chihuahua	13	15
French poodle	12	19
Great Dane	9	14
Foxhound	12	20
Airedale	12	20
St. Bernard	10	15

There comes a time when we must ask ourselves, what's best? Shall we let our dog die of old age, general breakdown, a growth, kidney disease, or other causes? Or shall we bravely say, "He has led a good life, he's no longer enjoying what little is left of it, he's blind and deaf, he's in some pain; we'll have him put painlessly to sleep"?

It takes courage to make such a decision. When the time comes for the owner to decide what to do with his aging pet, there are some general facts which he should know. They may make the decision easier for him.

There is no pain to euthanasia if properly administered. A humane veterinarian can inject a few c.c.s of an anesthetic into a pet's vein and he droops his eyes, nods his head, sighs as he feels release from pain, goes to sleep. He just never wakens.

An animal does not miss tomorrow. Suppose that you couldn't think ahead. If you had no imagination, you couldn't project yourself into the future. Mentally and physically you would live only in this moment—not even two seconds in the future. We can anticipate a fine dinner party and see images of it in our mind's eye. We can look forward in winter to next spring's flowers and thus make our winter more bearable. But an animal lives in the present alone, without any thought of the future. If he dies, his existence merely terminates. He is being deprived of nothing, for he has no conception of the future.

The death of a pet is not his loss so much as ours. The home will be empty without his presence. True, for the past year he probably hasn't been the friend we knew and loved; he's been ailing and not himself. But propinquity has endeared him to us and *we* see him as he used to be; we remember all the fine qualities he once had. When we hesitate to bring his life to an end, we are unconsciously thinking of ourselves. We may even allow him to suffer pain and discomfort because *we* don't want to lose him; we don't want our serene existence upset by no longer having our pet.

He's going to die someday. We must face this fact, even though we shrink from it. Isn't it better to stop his suffering by terminating his existence by our own volition than to allow him to linger in pain or extreme old age?

What might he say if he could think? He would probably say something like this: "I don't want to leave you any more than you want to be without me, but please give me comfort and freedom from misery. I can't see, so I bump into furniture. I can't hear you. I no longer enjoy the meals you prepare for me. I'm a burden to you, and certainly no good to myself. If I go outside, I might be crushed by an automobile. What good am I, anyway? Couldn't you be unselfish and grant me a blessed release?" And he might well add: "And if I gave you so much fun and companionship, get yourself another pet to fill my place, just as quickly as you can. Start giving him the attention you gave me when I was young. It will give you lots to think about and help to keep you young."

METHODS OF EUTHANASIA

The methods employed in euthanasia in the past—and, unfortunately, even today in some places—are largely responsible for the fact that so many people simply refused to consider ending a pet's life. They were shocking, inhumane, and often clumsy. Usually the animal was shot, gassed, or electrocuted. The drugs that were occasionally used were unsatisfactory: the injection of strychnine was certainly inferior even to shooting; ether and chloroform brought a kinder death, but even with these there was some struggle.

Today there are a number of drugs available which are both quick and painless. When you decide that it is best to terminate your dog's existence you have every right to insist that drugs of this type be administered. The best of these, in my opinion, are the barbiturates; and of them I prefer sodium pentobarbital. When injected into a vein or directly into the heart, its effects are almost instantaneous. A sudden sleep overpowers the animal and in a matter of seconds it is completely unconscious. The heartbeat and breathing cease; the end comes quietly and quickly. I have administered this drug to many pets in the presence of their owners, and without exception they have been tremendously impressed by the humane and painless death it has brought.

The lethal dose of sodium pentobarbital is usually considered to be one and a half times the amount required for anesthesia. In nearly every case such an injection is adequate, but I have known cases in which it produced only a prolonged deep sleep and a second injection was necessary. To eliminate even the possibility of such occurrences, I administer three grains for each five pounds of the animal's weight. A dose of this size is completely and immediately effective.

In spite of the fact that sodium pentobarbital is inexpensive and easily available to qualified persons, it has not been adopted so widely as it deserves to be for euthanasia. If your local humane society or dog warden is still using the methods of a decade or so ago, you will be doing a service to both the pets and pet owners in your community by discussing with the proper authorities the possibilities of using pentobarbital.

A saturate solution of magnesium sulfate (Epsom salts) is also satisfactory as an injection to produce euthanasia. It is now used by agents of many humane societies as well as by some veterinarians. The anesthesia which is its first effect is followed closely by death. Fairly large amounts must be administered, however. A 50-c.c. syringe will be necessary for large dogs.

CARE OF THE REMAINS

Should you have your dog buried? If so, where? The back yard? This is illegal in many cities. In a cemetery for pets? A grave and perpetual care cost about sixty dollars in some communities. Should the animal be embalmed? Why? What happens after death, anyway? Slow oxidation is the answer. Oxidation is a chemical name for burning. Wood in a fire oxidizes with a visible flame. A decaying stump oxidizes slowly, with no such fanfare. An animal's body oxidizes slowly too. So it is actually a matter of deciding between quick or slow oxidation. Burial or cremation is the choice. I unhesitatingly recommend the latter. What matters if the oxidation be quick? Isn't it better to know it is over in a few minutes rather than slowly taking place in the cold ground over a period of years? Chemically, there's little difference; esthetically, choose cremation.

POST-MORTEMS

Sometimes the question arises: "Shall I permit a post-mortem examination?" A study made in a large hospital for humans to determine the percentage of persons who refused to allow free post-mortems on their loved ones showed that 26 per cent disdained the thought, refused permission. Even though the interviewing doctor could say, "The examination may be of help to you personally; such things run in families, you know," 26 per cent still refused. A similar study at the Whitney Veterinary Clinic revealed the astounding fact that 24.3 per cent refused to allow free examinations on their pet dogs after death. Many of the findings could have been of great help to other dogs, if not always to their owners.

Occasionally pets die of diseases which are transmissible to their owners. If the veterinarian is willing to risk his health performing an autopsy, one would think the owner should acquiesce. The same applies when such an examination could help the veterinarian to help other dogs, or when it would add to our knowledge of cancer, or parasites, or growth, or blood, or heredity.

When your doctor finds your pet's malady of sufficient interest to give his time to studying its body, you need an excellent reason to justify your refusing him permission. If you love pets, you love to see them well. You can hardly do less than to help the doctor to help other pets—and perhaps, incidentally, yourself.

Part Three

13. How to Feed Your Dog

A DOG OWNER frequently has his own unique conception of what his pet should eat—and from a scientific standpoint his ideas are often startling. Sometimes his notions about the proper diet for Fido are derived from scraps of theories that have long since been completely exploded; sometimes they are reflections of the owner's own food fads and foibles. But whatever the source of his ideas, he usually clings to them with remarkable tenacity. If he really has a full set of preconceptions about what a dog *must* be fed and little specific knowledge of modern research in the field of nutrition, it takes a considerable amount of proof and persuasion to get him to the point where he is willing to forget his old theories and look at the facts with a receptive and inquisitive mind.

FOOD FALLACIES TO FORGET

Any scientific discussion of proper feeding must begin with a listing of food fallacies. There is a surprising number of them, and in the aggregate they do a vast amount of harm. Anyone who is really interested in feeding his dog properly should discard them completely. He should forget any ideas he may have had that dogs can't digest starches or sugars; that they can't digest fats; that they must have lean, raw meat; that if a dog doesn't like something it is bad for him, and, conversely, that whatever he likes is good for him. Along with these should go other common misconceptions, such as "milk makes worms," "potatoes cause skin rashes," "garlic eliminates intestinal parasites," "raw egg white makes a dog's coat shine," certain foods are "heatening to the blood," and "sulfur in drinking water keeps dogs healthy."

None of these things is true. They are all fallacies which for years have prevented people from feeding their pets intelligently.

VARIETY IN DIETS

In Chapter 3 we discussed canine evolution and mentioned some of the natural foods dogs are known to enjoy. The average one-dog owner whose pet is fed canned or dried foods, or table scraps with some meat added, will scarcely credit some of the "diets" on which dogs have been maintained in good health. Here are a few, listed simply to show the diversity of foods that dogs *can* digest.

In Scandinavia a dog breeder feeds his dogs mostly cooked whole fish with a little cooked grain—and they thrive.

In Kentucky a fox hunter leads an old mule or worn-out cow over the hill, shoots it, and lets his hounds live on the carcass until only the larger bones remain. Usually the organs and intestinal contents are first to disappear.

At a large university the physiology department feeds cane sugar, lard, bone ash, casein, vitamin concentrates, and a mineral mixture.

I feed my dogs a diet of dehydrated dog food in meal form and nothing else but water.

A certain chick-hatchery owner feeds his dogs on infertile cooked eggs and stale doughnuts from a nearby bakery, with alfalfa-leaf meal mixed in.

A Maine potato farmer gives his dogs boiled small potatoes in their jackets, mashed and mixed with hamburger and alfalfa meal.

Stray city dogs live after a fashion by rummaging through garbage pails.

During World War II many United States Army dogs were fed on horse meat and corn meal boiled together.

And yet I know a poor misguided housewife who prepared the following menu for her pet. *Breakfast:* 2 crumbled zwieback slices, yolks of 2 raw eggs, 1 glass of milk, 1 vitamin capsule, 1 calcium-gluconate tablet, 2 yeast tablets; *Lunch:* ½ cup kibbled dog biscuit soaked in a cup of warm soup made with parsley, fresh, canned, or frozen spinach, together with 1 jar of baby's liver soup; 1 fried lamb chop trimmed of all fat, diced in cubes with 1 teaspoonful of cod-liver oil added; *Supper:* 6 tablespoonfuls diced top round, 2 ounces tomato juice, 1 tablespoonful limewater, ½ cup cooked vegetables, ½ cup kibbled biscuits soaked in warm water; *Late evening:* 2 puppy biscuits, 2 lumps dog candy, and a bowl of milk.

A neighbor of this woman's buys kibbled dog biscuits, soaks them, mixes cooked vegetables and meat with them, and feeds the mixture to her dog with good results.

Another dog owner on the same street opens cans of dog food, spoons out the contents, and her pet thrives on it.

DIETARY ESSENTIALS

The important thing to keep in mind is that in order to be balanced a dog's diet requires protein, carbohydrate, and fat, just as do the diets of human beings and all other animals. A safe general rule is to have 14 per cent protein as a minimum (dry basis); 20 per cent fat, and the balance carbohydrate and minerals with some indigestible residue. These essentials, in their proper proportions, can be supplied easily and inexpensively without figuring percentages with paper and pencil, as we will see when we consider the specific foods available for our dogs.

Fat in the Dog's Diet. Let me stress again the fact that dogs can handle to advantage much more fat than most people give them. Idle dogs can utilize as much as 25 per cent of fat in their diets, whereas hard-working dogs, such as those drawing heavy loads in the Arctic, are often fed diets with 70 per cent fat.

"Fat burns in the flame of carbohydrates." Fat and protein alone are not so well tolerated by a dog as fat and protein with carbohydrate. Everyone knows that a fat steak eaten without bread soon becomes sickening, but that when bread is taken along with it much more fat can be enjoyed. If all starchy foods are omitted, the proportion of fat should be lower.

Breaking Down Starch for Digestibility. Carbohydrates are so often locked up by nature that foods containing them need preparation if they are to be of most value to any dog. As we have said, starch granules are broken by heat; heat also reduces starch into dextrose—one step in the digestive process. It is amusing to hear dog owners say that they never feed their dogs starch and in the same breath announce that they feed lots of dog biscuits—which are mostly baked starch.

Carbohydrate is found in liver in the form of glycogen (animal starch), and this, too, is digestible. Many starches are locked up in cellulose (the chief component of the cell walls of plants). Heat helps to break down cellulose so that dogs can digest the starch. Carrots, potatoes, turnips, and other vegetables; apples, pears, and other fruits are often relished in their raw state by dogs, but much of what is eaten is found in an undigested state in the stool. Boiled or baked, and then mashed, these foods are assimilated almost entirely.

GENERAL TYPES OF FOOD

The following are general types of food available nearly everywhere in the United States, any of which can be fed to your dogs. Prepared foods will be considered later.

Meat and By-Products of the Slaughterhouse. There are few parts of any meat animal a dog cannot eat and digest. Hair, skin, bones, and blood have little value to him, but all the rest has, even the intestinal contents.

The by-products of slaughterhouses, not ordinarily fed to dogs, are excellent sources of nutrition. Ox stomach is a good example. It is rich in fat, cheap, and digestible. It is relished by dogs, and the protein is excellent. Unfortunately its odor is offensive even after thorough washing. Lungs and udders of slaughtered cattle make good dog food. I have heard it argued that dogs get a lot of milk when they eat udders, but this is not so. The udders are often from dry cows and, even if they are not, contain only a small amount of milk. If either lungs or udders are fed they should be well cooked.

Canned poultry refuse is one of the most inexpensive canned foods and one highly relished. It contains unlaid eggs, pinfeathers, and a great deal of other material that seems most unappetizing to humans, but dogs love it either despite or because of such things.

Most dog owners think that meat is a must, but this is not so. Other proteins are equally good. But meat and its by-products in general constitute readily procurable foods. Muscle meat is in itself no better than organs such as liver, lungs, tripe, udder, brain, and in some cases is not so valuable.

Needless to say, meat is less expensive when cut from poor-grade animals, such as old cows, bulls, or horses, and has almost as much nutritional value as meat from prime steers, except that there is usually less fat. There is little choice between beef and horse meat from the standpoint of value, though some sentimental persons can't bear to think of feeding a noble horse even to a noble dog.

Now, as to how to feed meat—cooked or raw, ground or in hunks. The answer is that it makes little difference in its digestibility if it is cooked or raw, but boiling meat brings flavor out into the water which can then be mixed, fat and all, with other foods, such as bread and cereals. Meat in chunks small enough for a dog to swallow is digested better than meat ground into hamburger.

Bones occasionally cause trouble by splintering. Raw chicken bones splinter badly, while well-cooked bones snap at right angles. Once a healthy dog gets a bone in his stomach it is quickly dulled and digested. Occasionally one sticks in the intestine. If a dog crunches through a soft rib bone he usually pushes a good deal of tartar off his teeth, thus cleaning them. Such bones are the best kind to give your dog, if any are fed. They contain worth-while nourishment in protein, fat, and minerals, including iron.

However, dogs will often drag large bones about in places where they or other dogs have defecated. Worm eggs in the stool stick to such bones, are lapped off by the dog, and thus infect him. This should be kept in mind by the pet owner.

Milk. Research shows that milk is as good for dogs as meat. Both contain a high percentage of water—meat about 65 per cent and milk about 87 per cent. Meat has approximately eight hundred calories per pound and milk about two hundred and fifty per pint. A dog, therefore, needs three times as much milk by weight as meat to produce the same nutritional effect. Milk has much more calcium than meat, and more vitamins. It is one of the very best dog foods. It does *not* produce worms, as so many believe.

Fish. Raw fish fed over a long period produces a form of paralysis. Cooked fish is fully as valuable a source of protein as is meat and will keep dogs in sound health. Almost all kinds of fish eaten by humans make excellent dog food. Fed alone, the whole fish, including the bones and intestinal contents, is better than fillets. What is left of the fish after the fillets have been removed is too high in bone content for efficient dog food, although it contains much good protein.

FISHBONES. More fish could well be fed to dogs than is now being fed. Nearly everybody wonders whether the bones won't stick in their dogs' throats and, without knowing the answer, decide "when in doubt, don't." There have been instances of fishbones which have actually done serious damage by sticking in the throat or between teeth, but such instances are rare. It might be dangerous to feed a dog a pan of fishbones left over from the family meal. If he chewed and swallowed them, the stomach fluids would soften the bones quickly; the danger would be to the mouth and throat.

Bones subjected to the 250°F. temperature of the canning process become harmless, as anyone will remember from having chewed bones in canned salmon. Whole fish with the bones embedded in the meat seldom do harm. In fact, whole cooked fish constitute a substantial part of dog diet in many parts of the world.

Cereals. Many cereals, such as corn, wheat, oats, soybeans, barley, rice, and their by-products, when cooked, make worth-while dog food. The protein of corn is zein, which is incomplete. Wheat comes nearer to being complete. Oats are especially valuable. Brown rice is useful—much better, in fact, than white polished rice. All furnish calories or heat units and many nutritional essentials. Bread is one of the most worth-while dog foods; not by itself, to be sure, but it may compose a large proportion of the diet to good advantage. It contains, besides well-cooked wheat or rye flour, skim milk, salt, and yeast. The devitalized white bread has almost as much value as whole wheat, since much so-called whole wheat has a large proportion of white flour.

Vegetables. Since vegetables contain such great quantities of water, most of them are low in calorie value, but dogs can be taught to eat large amounts. Potatoes in their jackets and other below-ground vegetables can be utilized admirably if they are cooked and fed with meat, fish, or milk. Green vegetables are especially valuable as sources of vitamins and minerals and furnish some calories if they are well cooked but not overcooked.

Probably the best vegetable available for dog food is alfalfa-leaf meal. This is generally ground so fine that much of it is digestible without cooking. However, in the raw state it is very laxative, almost like raw bran in this respect, so it must be fed sparingly. Only the highest grades (20 per cent protein) should be used in dog feeding, the lower grades being too laxative because of the large amounts of woody stems they contain.

Fruits. These are a canine luxury and more in the nature of trick foods. Dog owners delight in showing how their dogs eat even apples, pears, peaches, or bananas. Too little of these fruits is digested to make them efficient dog foods, but they do no harm.

PREPARED DOG FOODS

There are hundreds of conscientious manufacturers of dog foods earnestly working to turn out products which, when fed exclusively, will nourish dogs from weaning until they die of old age. There are also charlatans turning out foods that have no other qualification than that dogs like them. I have tested scores of these foods. Some were deficient in half a dozen essentials. Dogs fed such foods developed rickets, showed vitamin B deficiencies, failed to reproduce, developed sore eyes characteristic of vitamin A deficiency, and became anemic because of iron deficiency. And every one of these foods was eaten eagerly by dogs. Appetite is definitely no guide to the goodness or completeness of a food. Good or bad, prepared dog foods fall into three general classes:

Canned Foods. There are many brands of canned foods on the market. The chances are good that, if you patronize a large market where many brands are sold, there will be at least two made by one packer from the same formula. That packer and the proprietor of the store know that most dog owners buy on the basis of what a dog likes. If you are such a person, he knows that you may buy one of each of his brands. At noon you may offer your pet food from one of the cans. He does not happen to be hungry then, so he turns up his nose and leaves it. At suppertime you try another can of the same formula, but packaged under a different label. Naturally he's hungry by that time and eats it, and you think, "This is wonderful food." Don't judge on these grounds. The taste test is no test at all of a good dog food.

The best canned foods on the market today are known to the trade as *pudding foods*. They are poured into the cans as a thick soup which contains enough gelatinizing substance to make a solid cake after processing. Most of them contain 70 per cent or more water and about four hundred and fifty calories, which is just about enough food for a dog weighing fifteen pounds. An active, medium-sized cocker spaniel requires two cans a day if fed canned food exclusively. An English setter weighing sixty pounds needs four cans—and that is correct no matter what the directions on the can say.

Dog Biscuits, Cakes or Kibbled. Nearly all dog biscuits are palatable to every dog, being composed mostly of flour. They are among the most advertised of all dog foods, and they do serve a purpose. However, the baking process by which they are manufactured—heating to sometimes 450°F. for an hour or more—destroys the heat-labile vitamins and some amino acids of which proteins are composed. Some biscuits are not baked so long as others, and the insides do not become so hot as the crust, so that some of these destructible essentials are preserved.

In all of the tests I have conducted, dog biscuits stood at the bottom when compared with other foods and judged on the basis of growth promotion. Earnest efforts are being made to improve them. Kibbled biscuits—those broken into small pieces—are often referred to as fillers. Dog owners expect to add meat and vegetables when feeding them. Manufacturers know this, and some of them have been less eager than others to make their products complete foods, realizing that the dog owner will provide the essentials.

Until recently fits and paralysis in dogs were often attributable to too many biscuits made with bleached flour. But now that the cause has become known, manufacturers are using flour that will not produce such troubles. It is still true, however, that dog biscuits, if fed in too large amounts, are constipating—especially when they are supplemented only with meat and bones.

The claim is often made that dog biscuits are essential for good teeth. This is not true. Teeth are made from the inside, not by rubbing the outside, although chewing hard foods may remove a certain amount of tartar. I have a number of very old dogs with beautiful teeth though they have never eaten anything but mushy food.

Frequently dogs are made overfat by the constant feeding of dog biscuits between meals. These pathetic creatures—canine "five-by-fives"—are the victims of their owners' ignorance or lack of will power. They can't say "no" when a dog teases, and the easiest thing is to hand their pet a dog biscuit.

Biscuits have their place but should be used sparingly, as a filler in kibbled form. They also are useful as a reward, or to piece out a diet when taking the dog on a vacation. Because Fifi begs for it is no more indication that she *needs* a biscuit than a child's teasing for a lollipop is an indication he should have one. Both biscuits and lollipops, when given more than occasionally, spoil the appetite for more complete foods essential for health.

Dry Foods. During World War II some manufacturers dehydrated mixtures of wet dog foods because tin cans were not available and sold the new product in cardboard containers. When water was mixed with this food the resulting mixture was much like the canned dog foods, except that it contained less meat and more cereals. Many dogs thrived on these foods, which were truly *dehydrated* foods.

But before, during, and since the war, other dog foods, made by mixing separately dehydrated ingredients, have been available. These have come to be known as *dry foods*. They usually consist of approximately half cereal ingredients and half foods of animal origin. The cereals may be corn flakes, wheat flakes, bread meal, soybean meal, or peanut meal. Such mixtures often include raw cereal products, such as middlings and cheap flour, and some manufacturers who make dog biscuits include the crumbs of broken biscuits in the mix. The products of animal origin may be meat scrap, fish meal, liver meal, or mixtures of organs dehydrated, skim-milk powder, and other such items. Vitamins and minerals are added to make doubly sure that every known dietary essential is included in the food mixture.

Dry dog foods are usually called "complete foods." All they require is the addition of water. Actually, despite the fact that dogs will thrive on them, they are all low in fat content, seldom having over 4 per cent. As we have seen, a balanced diet requires approximately 20 per cent fat. The wise dog owner buys dry food, melts any wholesome edible fat—used lard, oleo, chicken fat, roasting fat, bacon drippings, or fat skimmed from the soup kettle—and mixes it with the dry food. House dogs should not be fed a richer mixture than one part fat to four parts of dry food. In the average home there is usually enough fat left over from cooking to furnish all the dog needs and relishes. It is not essential to the digestion of dry dog foods to add this fat, but it makes for economy and palatability. If I were feeding a dry dog food which I had not tested, I would add fat to it and mix it with milk and water. Then I could be sure that my dog had every essential.

Do bugs in dog food cause worms? Are they poisonous to dogs? These are frequently asked questions. The answer to both is "No." Inquiry into the natural food of foxes, coyotes, and other doglike animals indicates that bugs are often eaten from preference. All the meal bugs and larvae are harmless.

ECONOMICS OF FEEDING

Now for the economics of dog feeding. Disregarding for the moment the time and trouble that may be spent in the preparation of some foods, suppose we consider only the cost of feeding a pet—let us say a forty-pound dog, which is about the average size.

If you buy a little more food for the family than is needed—and what housekeeper doesn't—it will cost you about forty cents a day minimum to feed your dog.

If you use canned dog food, your forty-pound dog will need three cans at a cost of approximately thirty-eight cents.

If you feed him dog biscuits at fifteen cents a pound and add the necessary supplements, the cost will be at least fifty cents, even when you use the cheapest meat.

Dry dog-food meal, mixed with water, will cost about ten cents a day. If you add 25 per cent fat and reduce the amount of meal, it will cost you even less—one cent for the fat (two ounces) and six cents for eight ounces of meal, a total cost of seven cents per day. This is probably the most economical method of feeding dogs, and I doubt if a better one is known.

People who have fed their dogs on meat, with its eight hundred calories per pound, are hard to convince that a dog can thrive when a mixture of one third the amount of dry dog food and fat is used. Actually, a simple problem in arithmetic should hardly need explanation. Because dry meal fortified with fat contains three times as many calories per pound as meat, only a third as much need be fed, but of course the water added for moisture increases the bulk.

All these methods require only common sense, and most dogs can be made to thrive without digestive disorders on any of the foods we have discussed or on combinations of the different types of food.

In spite of the higher cost, you may decide to feed your dog on foods you eat yourself. If you do, remember that feeding a forty-pound dog in this manner is practically equivalent to feeding half of another adult member of the family. The following table gives you, in round numbers, the approximate calorie value of many foods fed to dogs. From it you can decide on the proper amount to feed.

Table IX—Approximate Water Content and Calorie Value of Some Human Foods Fed to Pets

	PERCENTAGE OF WATER	CALORIES PER POUND
Beef		
Round	68	800
Hamburger, lean	74	520
Heart	63	1100
Liver	65	550
Lungs	80	410
Marrow	3.5	3800
Suet	14	3400
Pork		
Ham	55	1350
Leg	60	1210
Veal	65	720

	PERCENTAGE OF WATER	CALORIES PER POUND
Lamb		
Leg	51	1350
Flank	46	1900
Chops	50	1570
Poultry		
Chicken	65	1000
Turkey	55	1300
Soups		
Beef	93	116
Chicken	85	265
Meat stew	84	355
Bouillon	98	5
Milk Products		
Whole milk	87	310
Evaporated	73	635
Skimmed	90	167
Cream, 20%	70	990
Cream, 40%	55	1600
Whey	93	120
Cheese		
Cheddar	34	1850
Cottage	72	490
Cream	38	1700
Ice cream	63	930
Butter	12	3450
Oleo	5.5	3750
Cereal Products		
Bread	36	1150
Bread, dried	7	1760
Frosted cake	18	1700
Doughnuts	18	1900
Rolled oats	11	1700
Corn flakes	12	1550
Macaroni	10	1600
Vegetables		
Dried beans	12	1500
Beets	87	190
Cabbage	91	121
Carrots	88	180
Onions	87	200
Lettuce	97	75
Potatoes, boiled	75	400

ACCUSTOMING YOUR PET TO A SPECIFIC DIET

A dog accustomed to any specific diet that satisfies him and keeps him healthy will generally have a difficult time becoming accustomed to any other diet. In making a change, the point to remember is that once you have decided on a sound diet, every member of the household must cooperate to see that nothing is fed to upset the schedule you have adopted. If Toby is put on a diet of canned dog food when he has previously been eating chicken with buttered broccoli, he must be starved, if necessary, until he eats the canned dog food. Any member of the family who feels sorry for him and gives him even a scrap of chicken or broccoli will defeat the whole plan and will be punished by having a spoiled pet continually begging for more tidbits.

As I have said, I feed only a good type of dry-meal dog food. There are a number of excellent ones on the market. Sometimes when I have bought new dogs which have been brought up on fancy diets, it has been most difficult to change their feeding habits to the food of my choice. I remember one large dog that lost eighteen pounds before she accepted the change. It was seven days before she would touch a morsel of the meal-type food. Now she gulps it with evident enjoyment and is fat and sleek.

HOW OFTEN AND HOW MUCH TO FEED

Once a day is often enough to feed a grown dog, no matter how much he teases between meals. It is all right to let a growing puppy eat all he wants. But a house dog on such a schedule soon becomes overweight. It is much simpler to keep a dog's weight down than it is to reduce him. If he seems famished when he has finished his meal, give him a little more. If he doesn't eat it all, he has been given too much. If he is gaining weight, or losing, the owner should provide more or less food as is indicated to keep the dog in proper condition.

HOW TO REDUCE A DOG

Reducing a dog is in most cases part and parcel the question of how much to feed. If you don't give your dog more to eat than he needs, he won't be overweight. If he is already too fat, you can get him back into shape by regulating his diet. If you have a reasonable amount of will power, reducing your dog will be a fairly simple matter. I have worked out a chart (page 64) which should provide all the information you need. The left side of the graph is divided to show weight in pounds. On the base line you will find a series of figures representing the number of calories necessary to maintain a given weight in a dog. This is the way to use the graph:

Weigh your dog. Let us say he weighs sixty pounds. Find the sixty-pound mark on the left side of the graph. Follow this line until it strikes the curve. From that point on the curve, drop straight down to the base line. There you will see how many calories he needs—nineteen hundred for a sixty-pound dog.

Or you can work the graph backward from the calorie line to see how the diet your dog is getting compares with his actual needs. He is getting two cans of a good grade of dog food, plus three large dog biscuits, three candies and assorted tidbits from the table, and a bowl of milk every night. Let us figure just the first two items. Two cans of food have nine hundred calories, three large dog biscuits (one half pound each) have twenty-two hundred. That makes a total of thirty-one hundred calories, when he needs nineteen hundred. Add the table scraps, candy, and milk and he is getting nearly twice what he requires. This will explain why your dog weighs ninety-three pounds when the correct weight for his breed is sixty pounds.

How are you going to reduce him? There are two or three ways. First, you can feed him nineteen hundred calories and—knowing that a working dog needs many more calories than an idle one—exercise him enough to take off the excess weight. By exercise I don't mean walking him around the block. You can easily find ways of really making him exercise. Hitch him to a wagon and give the neighborhood youngsters rides; take him for ten-mile hikes, if you yourself are energetic; or get him retrieving. If you throw a stick or rubber ball only fifty yards and he runs after it and brings it back, remember that seventeen such retrieves will mean he has run a mile. If he is very fat, you will have to accustom him gradually to this work, a little more each day. But if you make him work, the fat will melt off him—provided you and the rest of the family all see to it that he gets his nineteen hundred calories a day and no more. He won't be starving until he has used up the energy stored in his excess weight. When he is down to sixty pounds he still will have plenty of fat.

The second method is underfeeding. Switch him to a totally different diet, say dry-meal dog food. You know it is good for him, but it is so different that he won't eat it. Fine! The less he eats, the more of his own fat he consumes. By the time he is eating the new food well, he will have reduced considerably. Then feed him half his daily caloric requirements and his fat will melt away by this method too. It is well to give a complete vitamin capsule with his food once a day while he is losing weight, because he may not have sufficient vitamin content in his restricted diet.

A combination of exercise with a restricted diet is good. But one must be cautious. Some very fat dogs become so inactive that their hearts cannot stand exercise. Their spirits are willing, but their hearts may be weak, their muscles flabby, and their lung capacity greatly reduced. A gradual daily increase in your pet's activity is indicated.

Thyroid extract, which causes a dog to burn up his food and fat more rapidly, should be used with great care, if at all. Owners have been known to kill their pets through giving human doses of thyroid extract. Drugs are not necessary if common sense and will power are used.

Some people find it easier to pamper a dog by overfeeding than to take care of his health by regulating his diet. It may be easier for a time, but *only* for a time. The wise owner knows that obesity is dangerous to his dog and that in the long run firmness in matters of diet is perhaps the greatest kindness he can show his pet.

EATING FILTH

One of the most disturbing features of running a kennel or even of owning certain dogs is the habit which some animals have of eating dung (coprophagy) or eating dirt (geophagy). It is quite understandable how puppies during their teething age want to chew on objects and will sometimes chew them up and swallow them. This also is one of the manifestations of rabies and occasionally of encephalitis. In those cases the behavior is due to disease, and some of the puppies' actions are due only to a desire to exercise the teeth and gums, but sometimes other seemingly healthy dogs will eat mouthfuls of dung or dirt. The owner immediately wonders what is wrong, as well he should.

In the old days, when there were horses in the city streets, it was not at all an uncommon sight to see house dogs eating horses' droppings. Farm dogs, too, will eat horse and cow manure, and many dogs will eat their own or other dogs' stools. Some dogs display a passion for eating cats' stools. What is behind all this? Probably many causes, some of which we may not as yet know.

Undoubtedly nutritional deficiency is the principal cause of both coprophagy and geophagy, but it is not the only cause. When it is the cause, the dog is trying to conserve nutritional essentials. If you visit rat laboratories where nutritional tests are in progress, you will find all the rats kept in cages with wire bottoms elevated so high that the animals can't reach down and obtain stools to eat. If they could, the tests would be invalid. Another cause is some peculiar odor in the stools that attracts dogs. An important cause, especially in kennel dogs of a retrieving nature, like Cocker Spaniels, is their desire to retrieve. They will pick up stools, carry them around in their mouths, and eventually eat them, thus more or less training themselves to this obnoxious habit. Another cause is underfeeding. Some dogs get so hungry that they become stool-eaters. Parasites, especially hookworms, which cause anemia are also a cause of the habit.

Cures are effected by first considering the causes of the condition and eliminating them. Nutritional deficiencies can be overcome by feeding complete diets. It must be remembered that a great many vitamins are manufactured by bacteria working in the intestines, and it can easily be that dogs need vitamins when you find them eating stools. They may also need essential amino acids or minerals. Consider everything carefully and supply what you think your dog or dogs may need. You may quickly cure your pet.

The use of chlorophyll, which will eliminate some peculiar stool odors, sometimes produces dramatic results. This can be supplied by a lot of dark green vegetables boiled lightly and added to the food. Alfalfa-leaf meal may also be added to the food, but not in large enough quantities to physic the dog. Chlorophyll pills, obtainable in any drugstore, may also be given.

In the case of retrieving breeds, if the dog is given something to carry, coprophagy usually immediately ceases. I have seen a whole kennel of Cocker Spaniels miraculously cured by putting a rubber ball in each pen. The ball gave them something to carry and play with, and that was all it took. Sometimes house dogs can be cured by having a bone to chew on.

If the trouble is parasites, especially hookworm infestation, see that the dog is dewormed (pages 83–91). After deworming, the pet can get enough iron to help replenish his blood supply and does not feel the urge to conserve the mineral by eating dung or dirt.

14. Raising Puppies

HAVING attended many of the eight thousand puppies that have been born in our kennels and hospital, I find that I have a natural tendency to assume that dog owners are more familiar than they really are with the details of puppy raising. To avoid making such a mistake in this chapter, I am going to assume that you are expecting your pet to whelp a litter of puppies and that you know nothing whatever about how to raise them—what to do, how to plan, how a bitch gives birth, what to arrange for, or how to feed the little fellows when they are ready to wean. This is probably unfair to you; but it is one way of making certain that this section will include all the facts you need to know in order to raise a sturdy litter of pups.

THE MOTHER

Few things that can be done to attain success in raising a healthy litter of puppies are as important as insuring the mother's (or dam's) health before the puppies are born. This insurance must go back to the period before she is bred. She probably would not have come in season unless she had been in good health. Your primary consideration, therefore, is being certain that she has no opportunity to become infested with parasites. They are enemy number one of the puppies to be born. If the dam is infested, her puppies are almost certain to be infested either during the embryonic period or after birth. Infestation after birth can result from contact with the mother's breasts or feet or with the infested run.

As shown in Table XV puppies under three weeks of age can have worms in them old enough to be laying eggs; that can only mean that the puppies were infested while still embryos. Because this condition is not readily apparent, the pups may become so unthrifty that death occurs very soon after birth. It is most important, therefore, to make sure that the dam is free of parasites of all kinds, both external and internal, and that the run is free of worm and flea eggs. Fleas and lice make the mother scratch and increase the danger of injury to her offspring. Fleas spread tapeworms also, and lice may cause anemia in both dam and puppies.

Many people are convinced that a bitch should never be bred at her first mating cycle, but there is no scientific support for such a belief. I have always mated bitches the first time they were in season and have yet to see any harmful results. A bitch does not come in heat until she is mature, full grown, and well able to look after a litter.

Your bitch should be bred as near her time of ovulation as possible, in order to insure subsequent pregnancy. This is most likely to be from the fourteenth to the sixteenth day of her period. Be sure you know the date of the first day. Do not rely on her showing blood at all. Instead, watch for swelling of the vulva and an increase in appetite. (See diagram on the opposite page.)

Be sure the dam is well fed but not fat. One of the better grades of dry dog food is probably the best choice if economy is any consideration; if not, good canned food or table scraps are satisfactory, provided they include enough calcium, phosphorus, iron, and vitamins. Too many table-scrap diets are low in calcium and iron. Milk will furnish calcium; meat, phosphorus and iron; vegetables, some of the essential vitamins. I have found that a little alfalfa-leaf meal of 20 per cent protein content or higher will do more to insure success in pregnancy than any other one ingredient of diet. Most dry food contains an ample amount of this.

How to Diagnose Pregnancy. A novice can do a lot of expecting and may even sell expected puppies on the basis of outward signs in the dam. He may then be disappointed when no puppies arrive. If a bitch is fertile and ovulates, it is to be expected that even though she is not bred she will behave like a pregnant bitch. There will be appetite increase, deposition of fat, increased weight, swelling of breasts, milk production, and often a tendency to want to mother. At the time when she would have produced her litter had she really been pregnant, she may act for all the world as though she were going to whelp. For a day or two she may refuse food, make a nest, and apparently experience every sensation of birth—without result. This is called a phantom or pseudo-pregnancy. It is entirely normal.

The dam may actually become pregnant and then resorb her fetuses—a not uncommon phenomenon. To be able to distinguish between a case of this sort and pseudo-pregnancy, it is helpful to know how to tell at an early stage if the dam is actually pregnant.

This is done by *palpation*, or feeling. Look on page 48 at the diagram of the female reproductive organs. Note how the lumps in the uterus lie. Unless your bitch is overly fat, you can feel these solid lumps along her uterus. If you have a keen sense of feeling, you can tell almost to the day how old they are. These lumps grow rapidly. In a forty-pound dog they feel as large as a pea at twenty-two days, as large as an English walnut at twenty-eight days, and as large as a small hen's egg at thirty-three days. After that they become so soft that palpation is difficult.

When you are sure you are not mistaking the lump—which consists of fetus, fetal membranes, placenta, uterine walls, abdominal walls, and skin—for a piece of feces, you can be certain that the bitch is pregnant. As you follow the development by making these gentle and frequent examinations, you may one day note that the lumps are smaller. If so, the dam is resorbing them; the uterus is practically digesting them back into the circulation.

Unless the litter is small, after thirty-five days there will be sufficient distention of the abdomen so that palpation will not be necessary; the condition will be obvious.

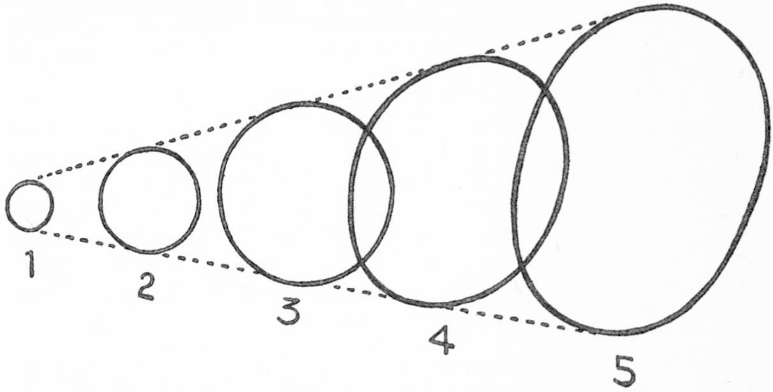

The size of the uterine lumps in a forty-pound bitch at various stages of pregnancy: (1) 22 days, (2) 25 days, (3) 28 days, (4) 31 days, (5) 34 days.

The time from fertilization of the ova until birth is sixty-one days. However, because mating so often takes place too early, the time is more often sixty-three days from the time of mating. The day before the dam whelps, her temperature usually drops one degree or thereabouts. Her actions, too, indicate that she is soon to whelp. She becomes restless, somewhat apprehensive, makes a nest or seems to be searching for a place to make one, often stops eating, and demonstrates in general the same behavior mentioned in the case of a phantom pregnancy.

The Whelping Bed. Be sure that everything is ready for the puppies. The dam's whelping box should be prepared with the proper bedding. The ideal whelping box is square. If the bitch is three feet long when she lies flat, the box should be four feet square. The sides should be a foot high.

The bedding should be of an absorbent material. Rye or oat straw and dehydrated sugar cane are all excellent. Whatever is used, be sure there is an ample amount of it. Fill the box with the material and then trample it down until it is saucer-shaped rather than flat. Those who have had little experience with bitches whelping often copy the whelping boxes built for sows. These have bars up a few inches from the side under which the pigs can roll if the mother tends to lie on them. However, bitches do not lie down in this fashion. A good mother hollows out a nest by walking around and around, pushing her puppies into a pile in the lowest part of the hollow. Then she lies down with all her teats available.

There are bitches which are so clever and petite that they can make a nest in a haymow barely large enough to turn around in and in it whelp and raise to weaning a large litter of puppies. The majority of house dogs, however, are incapable of such an expert and natural performance. If left to herself, every bitch will hollow out a nest in which the puppies tend to roll into a pile in the bottom, where they keep warm. If left on a flat floor, the puppies are more apt to be killed by their mother's lying on them.

The Birth of the Puppies. The puppies, in the uterus of their mother, may have caused the Y-shaped tube to grow from eight inches long on each side of the Y to perhaps three or four feet or even more in length. When birth commences, the cervix first relaxes. Waves of peristalsis, together with pressure from the abdominal muscles, crowd the puppies toward the pelvis. The uterus shortens, but its diameter does not decrease until the last puppy is out of that side. The bitch lies flat or curled up. When her efforts at expulsion have squeezed the first puppy into the pelvis, a certain amount of uterine fluid precedes it, and the odor makes her eager to lick it up. The sac surrounding the puppy may burst from the pressure, and she will endeavor to lick this fluid too, although most of it seeps into the bedding.

Little by little the puppy is moved through the pelvis until it slips out onto the bed. In her efforts to reach around to lick, the mother often helps push it out; nearly every bitch will be twisted around with her head close to her newborn puppy during the time it is being expelled. She will be eager to lick the puppy, but this is not wholly a demonstration of maternal affection. The puppy is entirely enclosed in a thin membrane called the fetal envelope, and running from the puppy's navel is a cord attached to the placenta, a liverlike piece of tissue about one quarter to one half inch thick. The mother eats these two structures and at first is usually much more interested in that activity than in cleaning the puppy. If the cord from the puppy's navel breaks off from the placenta during the process of birth, the placenta is usually expelled along with the next puppy. However, for safety's sake, it is wise for the owner to take hold of the delicate cord and gently pull until the placenta is detached and drawn out.

If necessary, you can help the bitch by taking hold of a partly expelled puppy and pulling. Pull firmly but gently. It is possible to break the puppy's neck or dislocate a leg by pulling too hard. Do not worry if the puppy comes tail first. A great many are born that way. It is a perfectly normal, not unusual, presentation.

Break the membrane if the mother fails to do it; otherwise the puppy will suffocate. Occasionally, when two or three puppies come along rapidly, the mother is so occupied with the first that the others die before she can give them the necessary attention.

When the membrane, almost a soft shell, is ruptured, it will fold back and hang from the navel, covering the umbilical cord, making it seem fatter. The cord can be cut by twisting it between the thumbnails or by using a pair of dull scissors to sever it an inch or two from the body. There is no need to tie off the umbilical cord. It dries up and drops off in two or three days.

One often reads the most ludicrous directions for helping bitches to whelp, especially those about being sterile in technique. Disinfect the scissors and hands, the directions warn, and tie the cord with sterile gauze. All these warnings are merely overzealous applications of the human birth technique. With dogs you need pay no attention to such nonsense. Every puppy is a bacterial flower garden almost as soon as he is born. He comes, bacteriologically speaking, into a filthy world. If his mother is left to herself, he may plop down in a manure pile; and even if he does, he'll live. You can be as sterile as you wish and in spite of your efforts the puppy will be an ideal breeding ground for bacteria. His mother's breasts and legs, his nest, his hair, and his intestine are teeming with them. Fortunately most of these bacteria will be benign, and nature has equipped the puppy to combat the others. The most important precaution for you to observe is to avoid handling puppies after you have been handling sick dogs. You have far more to fear from viruses and coccidiosis spread by flies than from contamination from well-washed hands or home instruments which are usually clean if not sterile.

One by one the puppies are pressed through the birth canal until the last pup and the last placenta have been expelled. Then, and not until then, will the bitch become relaxed and calm.

Using the method of palpation, it is possible to tell a great deal about birth just as it is possible to diagnose pregnancy. One fact that can be ascertained is when a Caesarean operation is necessary. By reaching up from underneath and placing the fingers on one side of the belly and the thumb on the other, you can clearly feel a puppy entering the pelvis. If you find that the puppy is in the birth position and the bitch is straining but accomplishing nothing, check the situation again in a few hours. If the puppy is in the same position, get the dam to your veterinarian. He may be able to extract the puppy with special forceps, or he may have to perform a Caesarean section.

Palpation can also be useful in determining whether or not the bitch has finished whelping. If you have not had practice in this technique, hold one of the newborn puppies in your fingers and then feel through the abdomen to see if there is a similar object contained within it. Some persons prefer to feel with both hands, keeping the finger tips of each opposite the other. This is particularly helpful in the case of large bitches.

Birth can take a few minutes for one or two puppies or perhaps twenty-four hours for a large litter. Regular injections of Pitocin, using one quarter c.c. to a forty-pound dog at three-hour intervals, may help a great deal if the bitch is slow in her delivery.

When you think the last puppy has been born, allow a few hours to pass before you let the mother out. The great pressure on her bladder and other organs has relaxed and she can and naturally does go a long while without elimination. If she refuses to leave her pups twelve or sixteen hours after birth, take her for a walk, unless she is in a pen where she can go out at will. If she is in a pen, she will wait until it is dark and very quiet before going out.

If the litter is a large one and all the puppies are to be raised by the mother, remove half the puppies by stealing them away without the dam's

Table X—Size of Litters by Breeds

	AVERAGE	LARGEST*
Hounds		
Bloodhound	9	17
Beagle	6	13
Foxhound	7	23
Basset	8	15
Dachshund	7	13
Otterhound	8	12
Bulldogs		
English	6	11
French	5	9
Boston	5	8
Bull terrier	7	13
Italian bulldog	12	22
Bird Dogs		
Setter	8	17
Pointer	7	13
Spaniel		
Cocker	5	12
Springer	7	13
Irish water	7	11
Retriever	7	13
Giants		
Great Dane	9	17
Newfoundland	8	15
Mastiff	8	21
St. Bernard	9	22
Great Pyrenees	9	16

	AVERAGE	LARGEST*
Sight Hounds		
Russian wolfhound	9	15
Scottish deerhound	8	15
Irish wolfhound	6	15
Greyhound	7	12
Whippet	5	11
Toys		
Italian greyhound	4	9
Chihuahua	3	11
Pug	6	11
Pomeranian	3	9
Pekinese	4	10
Toy poodle	4	7
Japanese spaniel	4	5
Toy terrier	4	7
Brussels griffon	4	8
Schipperke	5	11
Papillon	4	7
Miscellaneous		
Elkhounds	7	13
Samoyeds	7	13
Chow	5	9
Eskimo	7	11
Boxer	7	13
Dalmatian	7	13
Doberman pinscher	7	15

*Represents not the largest ever, but the largest ever to come to this author's attention. Knowledge of larger litters will be appreciated for the next edition of this book.

knowing what is being done. Stroke her head; and, as you cover her eyes with your hand, quickly take a puppy and place it behind you in a box. This can usually be done most easily while the bitch is giving her attention to the latest arrival. On the other hand, it is possible to wait until all the pups are born and then take half of them away. The mother cannot count and will be content with the puppies you leave, provided the absent ones are placed so far away that she cannot hear them.

The two groups of puppies can be switched for feeding every two or three hours for the first few days and every four hours for the next few. To have them grow satisfactorily, however, you must change them at not more than five-hour intervals.

A frequent question is whether or not a litter of puppies can have two fathers. Yes, a litter of pups can have two and sometimes three fathers. Some of the ova may have been fertilized by the sperm of one male; other ova by the sperm of a second male. The majority of the puppies are likely to resemble the male which mated with the bitch nearest the fourteenth day.

FEEDING

If the dam's milk is infected or insufficient, or if she is nervous and even seems afraid of her pups, it may be necessary to feed them from a bottle. Supplementary feeding may also be advisable if the dam has too large a litter.

Bitches' milk is naturally slightly acid. Many persons blame the death of puppies on acid milk, but they should look for other causes. If a formula is used as a substitute, do not try to modify cow's milk so that it approximates the chemical composition of human milk even though you have read that this should be done. Bitches' milk is not at all like human milk. It has more fat, less sugar, more protein, and more ash. Most of the old formulas advise adding lime water, glucose, or dextrose. These formulas, however, are modified in precisely the wrong direction, as you will see from the table below:

Table XI—Milk of

	BITCH	COW	HUMAN
Water	78.7	86.3	87.4
Protein	5.7	3.8	1.3
Sugar	3.1	4.7	7.0
Fat	11.2	4.0	3.5
Ash	1.3	0.7	0.2

There are specially prepared modified milks for puppies on the market today. If these are unavailable in your neighborhood, try one of the spray-dried baby milks. Mix one ounce with six ounces of water by volume and add one ounce of fresh coffee cream. This can make a stock solution which serves admirably, although it is high in sugar. Keep the solution refrigerated. It should be shaken and warmed before being fed to the puppies.

I have tried many feeding devices and find a small bottle with a small baby nipple best. If a 20-gauge hypodermic needle is inserted through the hub of the nipple next to the bottle's lip, the air can run in while the puppy is sucking and the nipple will not collapse.

The milk must be close to body temperature at first. Even five or six degrees of variation in either direction will inhibit sucking. Feed the puppies before returning them to their mother. At first puppies will take about one c.c. of milk for each ounce of weight. You can increase the amount proportionately as they grow. They must be nursed at least four times a day if they are to thrive, and five times a day is preferable.

If a foster mother must be used, a good way to introduce the new puppy to her is to spread some of her milk or vaginal secretions over the puppy and let her lick it clean. Then let the puppy nurse. Stay to watch the foster mother's actions toward it. If she refuses it, take a few of her pups away and leave the foster pup with them, returning the lot at intervals until she accepts the new one.

When puppies reach the age of three weeks their mother does something for them of which many persons strongly disapprove—she eats food, lets it partially digest, and then vomits it before them. That is their first natural food. The mother's actions are probably under hormone control. Do not be alarmed if you witness this phenomenon. Learn a lesson from it and start supplying the little pups with solid, easily digested food when they are three weeks old. There is at least one baby animal food on the market made especially for the specific requirements of explosively growing puppies just as the human baby foods are geared to the specifications of slow-growing children. If such food is not available, offer the pups a cooked meat and cereal food. Make a stew of such ingredients as protein, lots of vegetable matter, and fat. Let it cool and watch them eat it! The addition of such foods to the puppies' diets spares the mother the burden of furnishing huge amounts of milk, and she is thereby kept in good condition.

When weaning time arrives, at from six weeks onward, you will have eased the puppies off dependence on their dam, and her milk secretion will diminish naturally. But if you suddenly have to remove the puppies or lose them, she will still dry up in a natural way. You need not bind her breasts, rub them with camphorated oil, or massage or milk them. The udder will become inflamed. A hormone action stops milk secretion, and after a time the inflammation will gradually decrease. If you do rub the breasts with oil, the secretion will subside—but not because of the medication. I have tried massaging and oiling only one side of a heavy milk producer's udder and have found that both sides dry up at the same time.

If the puppies are orphans, remember to provide for their toilet facilities. They tend not to defecate or urinate until their mother laps them; this action stimulates their evacuations. Unless you arrange to produce a similar stimulation, they will soil their beds and each other. To enable the puppies to evacuate and keep clean, hold them over a small container and stroke their anuses and vulvas or penises with a soft brush or piece of cotton. This should be done shortly after they have been fed.

IMPORTANT POINTS OF GENERAL CARE

As the puppies grow older the bedding in the nest box can be leveled by bringing it down from the sides. This keeps the puppies in. Much of the bedding material will have to be changed soon after whelping is over because of the large amount of amniotic fluid which accompanies the birth of each puppy.

The floor of the bed is of great importance. If it is of concrete or rough wood, it should be covered with several thicknesses of burlap or cloth before the bedding is put down. If the rough surface is not covered, the pups will wear away their navels, infection will creep under the skin, and the puppies will die unless treated early.

Treatment consists of cleaning away the infected parts and injecting an antibiotic about the area. An antiseptic powder or ointment should be applied and worked under the skin, which should then be covered with a gauze pad bound in place by adhesive tape. It is best to keep the puppy under treatment isolated and carry it to the mother for nursing five or six times a day. The puppy should be treated until the skin has grown across and healed. Another method is to dissect the infected area away and suture the skin together. Healing may require five days or more.

As soon as puppies begin to crawl about, a pen must be made for them. They can use sand runs. Grass and concrete are the devil's own devices for spreading worm infestation. The best plan—one which has everything to recommend it and few drawbacks—is to provide a wire-bottom pen. A picture of its construction is shown. The wire for the bottom of the pen, one-inch square mesh, should be 9 or 11 gauge, preferably welded. Lighter netting soon breaks, unless the puppies are of a light breed. Smallish bitches can be kept in such a pen and allowed to whelp in the hutch.

When the puppies crawl out on the wire and defecate, there is no chance for contamination. If the droppings are removed from under the pens every few days, even flies cannot transmit infestations of embryonated worm eggs. The only serious objection to the use of such pens is that puppies raised in them often cannot successfully be introduced into homes with hot-air floor registers unless such registers are screened from the pups. Having trained themselves to defecate over the wire flooring in the pen, the puppies search tirelessly for a similar surface to use for the same purpose in the house. When a pup finds the furnace register, the owner often feels that the idea of a wire-bottom pen was all a mistake.

Raising puppies in cool or even cold weather is generally more successful than when it is too hot. When they are cold they will pile up to keep warm, and their mother is less likely to lie on them than she is if they have spread out to keep cool. The best temperature is that which will induce the puppies to remain piled together to keep warm.

If a little pup gets chilled—falls out of its box, for example—but is still alive when found, heat may revive it. Never give up. As it becomes more animated, let it suck some warm formula and watch the quick change.

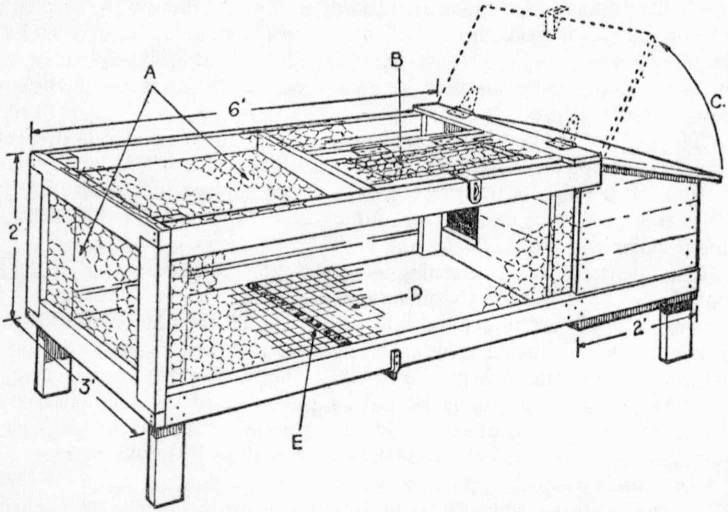

Details of construction of a wire-bottom pen. (A) Sides and top of 14- or 16-gauge, 1½-inch, hexagonal fox netting. (B) Door covered with same. (C) Hutch cover. (A piece of flat rubber can be tacked over the crack where the cover hinges.) (D) Wire bottom of 9- or 11-gauge, 1-inch-square mesh, preferably welded. (E) Angle-iron brace.

As little puppies grow, they occasionally twitch. You may see this jerking in one after another and think it means that they have fleas or are sick. It doesn't; instead it means that they are healthy and doing well. If they *fail* to twitch, they are unthrifty, possibly underfed, or anemic.

How early may little puppies be dewormed? Since they may be born with intestinal parasites, it pays to have fecal examinations made starting at three weeks of age. If they are infested, they can safely be dewormed with tetrachlorethylene at any age, *if they are empty*. The dose is 0.1 c.c. to each pound of body weight.

In the case of hookworms, owners are occasionally advised to build the puppies up before having them dewormed. Actually it is almost impossible to build puppies up in competition with a heavy worm infestation. It is also well to realize that, even if it could be done eventually, there usually is not time to build them up; they cannot be cleaned out too soon because of the anemia hookworms cause.

Puppies open their eyes on the tenth day after birth. The corners next to the eyes open first. If the puppy's eye bulges before it opens, use a toothpick and get the lids apart next to the nose. If you press the lump or bulge over the eye, a creamy pus will exude through the opening. Fill the opening with ophthalmic ointment squeezed from a tube and repeat this daily. You will probably save the eye by so doing. It may be opaque when it opens, but it will usually clear.

Always clip the sharp nails of puppies when they are a few weeks old, and keep them clipped. This may be done safely with the points of household shears, if you have no special clippers. If the nails are allowed to remain long, injury to the eyes of one or more puppies may result. Hundreds of puppies are rendered unsalable every year by failure of the owners to take this simple precaution.

15. General Diseases of Dogs

OUR love for our dogs and their unquestioning loyalty and devotion to us are so much a part of our lives that we all have moments when we think with dread of the time when old age, or accident, or disease may take them from us. Age we cannot control; an accident may strike the pet of the most careful owner; but diseases we *can* do something about. With sufficient knowledge of prevention and cure, we can both reduce the incidence of disease and limit the injury it does.

The early recognition of disease symptoms is, of course, closely linked with intelligent day-by-day care, the general principles of which we have considered in the earlier sections of this book. If you know the normal behavior of your dog—how he should and does act when he is in sound health—you will be able to judge more easily when he is suffering from one of the many maladies he may develop. To care for him intelligently you must know something about the most frequent of these ailments—their specific symptoms, cause, complications, and treatment.

There are two types of general diseases to which dogs are subject—those of virus origin and those resulting from bacterial infection. In this chapter we will consider the virus group first.

VIRUS DISEASES

Carré Distemper. This disease, so feared by dog owners and once the scourge of dogdom, is now rapidly dwindling in incidence. Still a menace in some parts of the world, in others it has been practically eliminated and is approaching the status of human smallpox in its infrequency. The control of distemper is an eloquent demonstration of the excellent results of co-operation between researchers, veterinarians, and dog owners.

Distemper is a disease of the epithelial tissue which covers the body, inside and out. All of the mucous membranes, such as the lining of the nose, the mouth, the tissue around the eyes, the intestinal lining, the internal genital organs and the bladder lining are attacked, as are the glands and those cells which secrete substances.

SYMPTOMS: Before we generalize about the disease and its spread, let us consider the symptoms.

The first noticeable indications are a loss of appetite and photophobia —that is, shunning of light. Dogs act as though the light hurt their eyes and made them smart. There may be nausea. Dogs of some breeds have running fits, others are giddy from the initial fever. After a few days the fits stop or the giddiness disappears—indeed there are usually only two or three days when these symptoms are apparent.

A dog will run a temperature of 101° for three or four days after the initial infection. On the fifth day the temperature rises to 104° or thereabouts. On the sixth it drops almost to normal. On the seventh it rises again to about 103° to 104° and, while varying considerably around those figures, remains high up.

Some dogs will die in the first two weeks of the disease, but most do not. That is why you sometimes hear experts say that distemper seldom kills a dog. The point they are making is that since the virus disappears from the blood after a few days, the dog no longer has "distemper." If he continues to be sick he is affected with some bacterial disease, called a secondary invader—that is, a new disease superimposed on the original virus disease.

The theory of some students is that several different diseases probably enter the tissue soon after it is weakened by the distemper virus. Others believe that the fact the virus is no longer present in the blood does not mean that it is gone from the body. In all probability the second theory is the more accurate because, as we shall see, the virus may manifest itself later on.

Once distemper becomes established—by the seventh day after infection—a dry hacking cough starts. This is not the moist, gagging cough of other diseases but an annoying cough indicating irritation of the tissues of the respiratory system. The nose begins to run with a thick, purulent, stringy discharge and, in some cases, appears to be completely sealed over. When the dog has sufficient ambition to snort out this mucus, it does not spray in fine droplets, but flies out in thick drops or strings and sticks to whatever it touches.

The eyes are generally as caked with mucus as the nose. It is often necessary to remove the pasty, crusty material and moisten the eyes each morning before the dog can see. Diarrhea is a persistent symptom. The infected intestinal wall cannot handle the food and discharges vile-smelling, dark, usually liquid feces with an odor that characterizes the distemper-infected dog. One who has nursed dogs through the disease seldom forgets this peculiar distemper odor.

Throughout the course of the disease the coat appears rough and unkempt. In some cases pimples may be found on the skin of the belly. As the disease wears on, with the secondary diseases which complicate it, dehydration often occurs. The skin can be pulled up in folds and does not snap back into place as healthy skin does, but remains in ridges which return to normal very slowly. The tongue usually is coated and sometimes ulcerated.

Carré distemper generally lasts a full four weeks. When complicated with certain diseases, it may be a three-month disease.

These are the symptoms which are obvious to the dog owner. Your veterinarian can find others of more certain diagnostic value.

The virus of distemper produces groupings within the cells known as inclusion bodies. If a dog in the neighborhood dies of the disease and the owner will allow a post-mortem examination, the doctor can section the brain, the lining of the bladder, or other tissue, and by proper staining can demonstrate the inclusions. Most of them are found in the cell substance and few within the nucleus. This is in contrast to rabies, which produces inclusion bodies in the nucleus, and both are in contrast to housedog disease, the virus of which produces no inclusion bodies.

COMPLICATIONS: The sequellae, as the doctor calls the complications and results of the disease, are many. Pneumonia is a frequent complication; enteritis (inflammation of the intestine) even more common. Encephalitis (inflammation of the brain) probably occurs in a quarter of all dogs which live long enough to be so affected. It may produce convulsions, chorea, or other symptoms. But this is the result of the virus attacking the brain and inflaming it, not the result of a secondary disease.

Some dogs are left deaf, blind, or with an impaired sense of smell. Of those which survive encephalitis, many are left with a chorea jerk in one or more muscles; some have complete reversals of personality.

HISTORY OF THE DISEASE: Before considering methods of infection, prevention, and treatment, let us look for a moment at the history of the disease.

Once a catchall term for sniffling diseases accompanied by a rise in temperature, it was used for most dog illnesses as was the term *malaise* in humans. Anything which indisposed a dog was likely to be called "distemper," and if the condition was not severe, the animal was said to have "just a slight touch of distemper." No one knows when the true disease first affected dogs, but it was long ago. Since it is known also to infect foxes, wolves, raccoons, mink, fitch, and other species, it may first have been a disease of wild animals.

The world-wide distribution of the disease has enabled scientists of many nations to study it. In recent years the old-fashioned "distemper" has been divided by scientists into many diseases—not all of them of virus origin—which produce symptoms of sniffling, temperature rise, and malaise. No longer do dogs have "just a touch"; such unspecific diagnosis is a thing of the past. A Frenchman named Carré isolated a virus which produced the most common disease in the distemper complex. An Italian, Puntoni, found that a vaccine could be made of dog brains which would immunize against the disease after a fashion. A French scientist, Lebailly, using dog spleens, gave us our first practical immunization method. Two Britons, Laidlaw and Dunkin, added the idea of giving a dose of live virus following the Lebailly method. The same two students discovered the value of antiserum for temporary prevention and cure and suggested giving dogs virus and serum simultaneously for permanent immunity. Working on the same problem, I showed that the Lebailly vaccine, if used fresh and in large enough amounts, was sufficient to insure immunity.

METHOD OF INFECTION: From infection with the virus until the appearance of the earliest symptoms, the incubation period is five days. During that time the disease is extremely contagious. It requires no more than the merest sniff of a sick dog's breath to infect a well dog. Once I saw what looked like a healthy dog owned by a neighbor approach a pen of my dogs, sniff noses with all six hounds, and then run off through the woods to his home. Two days later I heard that he was sick. Five days later all six of my hounds, when they came out to greet me, blinked at the light and were unsteady on their legs, as dogs with high fevers often are. The neighbor's dog had been incubating distemper and had infected my dogs before anyone knew he was sick.

Infection probably occurs chiefly through the nose, eyes, and mouth. Flies and other insects can spread it. Even worms may become infected from excreta, keep the virus alive in their bodies, and spread it when they crawl up out of the ground. Distemper is not confined to any one season of the year, nor does it exempt any age, sex, breed, or color of dog. One possible exception is the remarkable resistance of the pregnant bitch, who in some way is protected by her pregnancy to such an extent that one often hardly realizes she has the disease. If she does contract it toward the end of pregnancy, she may whelp her puppies and, in doing so, lose her protection and be as severely affected as any other dog.

It has often been suggested that dogs in fine physical condition are able to throw the disease off. This is doubtful. Whole kennels of dogs in top condition have been known to contract Carré distemper.

What proportion of dogs is generally saved? That depends on the breed. In some breeds, such as bull terriers, 90 per cent will survive. Other breeds, such as bloodhounds and great Danes, will show a 90 per cent mortality. It also depends on the strain of distemper. There may be more or less virulent strains. My own experience, year after year, has been with only one type—a very virulent one, until vaccination has almost put an end to it.

How long will the infection last in an area after a dog has died with the disease? Outside the body the Carré virus is generally short-lived. It may live for several days in insects, and dogs which eat them will be infected. We don't know whether the virus can be transmitted by fleas, but in all probability it can be. In extreme cold the virus may not die for a number of years. Heat kills it quickly. In moist stools in cool weather, it may live longer than in hot weather. But the old idea that a new dog may not be brought into a home for six months after the previous dog has died finds no support in modern research. In summer the safe period is probably nearer to a week.

This is a problem on which one dislikes to give advice. When one dog has had the disease, it is usually found in other dogs in the neighborhood, because it continues to pass from one to another. As new dogs are brought in, they may become infected and keep the virus alive. You may lose a dog and buy another which, unknown to you, promptly becomes infected from a neighbor's dog. In all probability you will assume that your pet caught it from your old dog's bed or the chair where he used to sleep.

Actually the persistence of the virus need not concern the owner greatly today, because a new dog may be brought into any home or neighborhood with little risk provided he has been properly vaccinated. It should be remembered, however, that this does *not* apply to the spread of housedog disease, which will be considered later.

IMMUNIZATION: Since true Carré distemper is such a loathsome disease, it behooves every dog owner to have his dogs properly protected against it. Even though in some sections the disease is dying out, immunization still remains the sensible, the sporting, the economical, and the humane thing to do. It is easy to accomplish. You may have the choice of several methods.

Lebailly Method: A dose of fresh vaccine. If the dose is large enough, it will produce lifelong immunity. This was proved by one of my own studies. By grading the size of the dose to the size of the dog, solid immunity could be established.

Laidlaw-Dunkin Method: A dose of vaccine followed in a week by a dose of living virus.

American Modification of Laidlaw-Dunkin Method: Two doses of vaccine, one two weeks after the other, followed in two weeks by a dose of living virus. The objection to both the second and third method is that the virus used at present in America is so often dead, and the small dose of vaccine is insufficient for even a moderately large dog. In England, where fresher biologics are used, this is a satisfactory method.

Serum and Virus Given Simultaneously: This is an excellent method, used widely in many parts of the world, but it also depends for its success on virile biologics.

The Green Method: This involves the use of a live virus made by passing the virus of Carré distemper through a number of ferrets. This passage modifies the virus to such an extent that when it is returned to a susceptible dog it produces such a mild disease that the dog shows but a slight indisposition. Here again, the method is excellent when the material is alive, but uncertain with improperly stored biologics.

Avianized Virus Method: Carré's virus has now been grown in hen's eggs and now after a hundred or more passages from one egg to another it will not produce Carré's disease in dogs but will quite definitely protect dogs against the disease when the egg tissues are made into vaccine and injected. The material is quick-frozen, dried in a vacuum, packed in ampoules from which most of the air is drawn, and in this form its keeping properties are greatly enhanced. The use of avianized live vaccine is rapidly replacing all other methods in many sections.

Since it has been shown that even very young puppies are not immune, wisdom dictates that at least one dose of immunity-producing biologic be given all dogs at an early age. Some veterinarians advise giving serum which, as you will remember, is made from blood and contains antibodies. Serum is all right; it protects for about ten or twelve days. But if serum is given it must be repeated at frequent intervals, which makes it expensive. Why not give vaccine which will induce almost permanent immunity within a week after it is administered? It costs no more initially, and in the long run very much less. Before we had means of effecting immunity against Carré's disease, I had over five hundred cases among my dogs. Since I started injecting my four-weeks-old puppies with vaccine and giving them another dose when they were nearly mature, I have not had a single case of Carré's disease in my own dogs—and my hunting dogs and bloodhounds go everywhere.

CAUSES OF FAILURE IN IMMUNIZATION: Even with our modern biologics, failures in immunization can occur. Here are the primary causes of unsatisfactory results:

Stale Biologics: In the United States there is so much old material used that it is amazing that immunization is even as successful as it is. You pay to have your dog immunized. It is only fair that you be shown the date on the small bottles of biologics which are used. Each ampoule of vaccine bears an expiration date of a year from the time the biologic was made. Live vaccines or virus bear a six months' expiration date. Generally it is not possible to get any fresher than one month old, because the sterility tests take approximately that long. Personally, I have little confidence in distemper biologics which are over four months old. Be sure that the biologics used on your dog are fresh.

Improper Storage: Some biologics are handled like groceries—left on radiators in post offices, put in postmen's automobiles where the heat may almost cook them in summer, sent from one storage to another until no good is left in them. Try to ascertain that the biologics used on your dogs have been shipped quickly and properly refrigerated.

Insufficient Doses: When a Pomeranian is given the same dose of vaccine as a St. Bernard, someone's reasoning is faulty. If a Pomeranian needs five c.c.s, a St. Bernard needs at least fifty c.c.s for permanent immunity.

Serum and Vaccine Given Too Closely: Serum has antibodies. It is the purpose of vaccine injections to make a dog's body produce antibodies. If antibodies are left over from the serum when vaccine is given, they neutralize the dead virus in the vaccine, and less immunity is produced than when no serum is used.

TREATMENT: Needless to say, the use and administration of biologics, as well as of prescription drugs, such as the sulfa drugs, penicillin, and streptomycin, will be left to your veterinarian. As a dog owner, you should understand that even though drugs are not effective against the distemper virus itself, they may often be useful to prevent or control the secondary diseases which follow it. Veterinarians may use large doses of serum to good effect, though certainly small doses are a waste of money. They may use the Green method with sick dogs, and much virtue is claimed for it. But whatever treatment is prescribed, the nursing may be left to you. Here are a few suggestions which may help you through what is at best a difficult period:

Keep your dog dry and out of drafts; keep his eyes and nose clean. Your veterinarian will give you ophthalmic ointment to keep his eyes from sticking together, and possibly some with a local anesthetic to take the sting out. He may recommend oily substances with menthol, eucalyptol, camphor in them, which you can rub on your dog so that the heat of his body will volatilize them and the fumes keep his head clear.

You may be given vitamin preparations to administer by mouth or even to inject, if you are handy with a syringe. You may be told to feed good wholesome foods, or to leave a pan of sour milk for him and let him drink it when he is hungry. Some recommend giving meat, egg yolk, buttered toast. Actually the kind of diet a dog gets makes little difference in the course of the disease. I have seen fully as many dogs recover which were left milk to drink as those stuffed with expensive foods—in fact, more.

If dehydration occurs, your veterinarian may come and administer infusions of salt solution and glucose with some vitamin and possibly amino acids added. If you leave your dog at his hospital, he may be able to relieve certain symptoms with still other treatments. Except for the expense, any dog will be better off in a good hospital if distemper strikes —and so will you, because caring for a distemper-sick dog is a difficult and often trying experience. I know, because I took care of hundreds before I became a veterinarian and have cared for quite a number since.

Housedog Disease. This is the most significant and widespread virus disease of dogs in the northern areas of the world and in the higher altitudes of the southern sections where it is cold. It is primarily a winter disease. To some degree, the curve of its incidence follows the curve of human colds. Although some sufferers can be found in any month of the summer, they are so rare as to be almost exceptions.

SYMPTOMS AND COMPLICATIONS: First reports of a mysterious new disease began about 1940 in America. It was at first identified as encephalitis, which is only one of its sequels, not the disease at all. I spent a considerable amount of time studying the symptoms of the new disease. After having watched over five hundred cases of distemper among my own experimental dogs and having learned to recognize its early symptoms, I noted in 1940 that the new disease was a mild one, causing some loss of appetite, sometimes loose stools, a gagging cough—all quite unlike the early symptoms of Carré distemper. The difference was startling. By keeping accurate records I found that sore throat was the real disease, that some dogs developed pneumonia following the virus infection, and that the virus sometimes invaded the brain and caused encephalitis, as in the case of Carré distemper.

Client after client brought his dog to me and said, "He has a bone stuck in his throat," or, "He has hair in his throat." What he really had was a congested throat with enough phlegm so that it annoyed him and he tried to raise it, often coughing up small spots which looked like whipped egg white.

The disease in itself is not very serious, but its complications are. Bacterial pneumonia often sets in. Encephalitis follows it more or less frequently depending on the age of the dog. Old dogs seldom die, but whole litters of young puppies may be killed by it. The incubation period has been found to be from five to eight days.

Although housedog disease resembles Carré distemper in certain ways, there are several significant differences besides those already mentioned. It is not nearly so severe. There is a scratchiness to the eyes but no true photophobia. The eyes may discharge slightly, but the nose seldom crusts over and there is no thick purulence to the nasal discharge. The temperature is quite constant—very close to 102.6°. Carré distemper, as we have seen, causes higher temperatures. If complications develop in housedog disease, the temperature may be over 103°. Treatment with sulfa drugs often reduces the fever to 102.6°, indicating a definite complication with bacterial disease. In England a *Beta hemolytic streptococcus* was found complicating the disease. An American study found a new unnamed bacterium of the *Shigella* group causing high mortality in young dogs. When and if a dog develops encephalitis, the temperature may act very strangely. Sometimes it rises to 109° and the dog will die. In other cases temperatures may stay around 103°; occasionally one will go subnormal.

Dogs lose their appetites to some degree, but not completely. There may be a looser stool than normal for a few days, but it has no nasty stench as it has in Carré distemper. The disease seems to last only a week to ten days, and after that the dogs may appear practically normal unless pneumonia sets in. If it does not, the average dog is practically well in two weeks.

If the virus reaches the brain, inflammation of that organ develops as a complication. The resulting encephalitis may manifest itself in any one of nine different ways: (1) Convulsions with stiffening of the muscles, grinding of the jaws, frothing, and possibly urinating and defecating. Running and yelping may precede the convulsions. (2) Chorea, generally preceded by moaning or crying, with indications of muscle pains. The jerking with almost clocklike regularity soon appears. It may not kill the dog but may gradually disappear after many months or even years. (3) Tics. This is much the same as chorea except that perhaps only one small muscle is affected. The dog may jerk his lip, blink his eye, or twitch his ear. These twitches, like chorea, never stop, night or day, during sleep or while awake. (4) Spastic paralysis. All the striped muscles of the body may become rigid and tense, so that if the dog lies down his legs stand out straight. (5) Flaccid paralysis. A limb may become so badly paralyzed that the dog may have no use of it, and it may hang flaccidly and limp. This paralysis may ascend until it kills the dog. (6) Disorientation. The dog may be so confused as not to know where he is, and he may wander aimlessly about, usually in circles. (7) Vertigo. If you place a dog with this type of encephalitis on the floor, he may roll in a corkscrew fashion all the way across the room to the wall. If you pick him up, his head leads his body in a corkscrew twist so that it is difficult to hold him. (8) Lethargic form, or sleeping sickness, as it might be called. The dog sleeps so soundly it is difficult to rouse him. He may get up, eat, drink, defecate and urinate, and go back to sleep. (9) Ophthalmia. Blindness may occur because of the part of the brain which controls vision being affected.

Usually during the time a dog has encephalitis he will continue to eat almost normally. Some will eat almost until they die. Occasionally one refuses food, but this is an exception.

What kinds of dogs are most likely to develop encephalitis? The pointed-nose breeds, such as German shepherds, farm shepherds, cocker spaniels, have a very high incidence. Boxers, St. Bernards, bulldogs, bull terriers, and other such wide-headed and less nervous types stand at the opposite extreme.

What effect does age have on the development of encephalitis? In general, the younger the puppy, the greater the possibility. In my experience, only 9 per cent of dogs over a year old developed encephalitis after the throat phase of the disease. Over 30 per cent of young dogs developed it, and in many cases whole litters perished. A considerable number of whole litters of boxer puppies gagged but failed to develop the brain inflammation. Breed seems to make a difference where puppies are concerned as well as in the case of mature dogs.

METHOD OF INFECTION: How do dogs catch housedog disease? Probably by droplet infection. As in distemper, merely smelling a sick dog's breath will infect a susceptible dog, and being in a room where a sick dog is gagging is almost certain to infect a well dog. Eating from pans used by sick dogs may be a means of infection. Contacting feces doubtless is another. Human hands can spread it.

There is more than a faint possibility that humans with a certain kind of sore throat and cold can infect a dog. Too many apartment-house dogs, which have never been near another dog but have been in contact with humans with colds, have become sick with housedog disease to discard this possibility. The evidence is such that this method of infection might almost be called a probability. Certainly the danger exists. On the other hand, we know of no case in which a dog has infected man.

TREATMENT: As we have seen, housedog disease in itself is not a serious ailment, but the pneumonia and encephalitis which may follow it can be dangerous to your dog. Pneumonia, a bacterial disease, may be quite effectively prevented by giving sulfa drugs or penicillin, but since housedog disease is a virus disease, there is as yet no certain means through medication of preventing it from reaching the brain and causing encephalitis.

Many investigators are now working on the disease. A vaccine has been developed which, as this is written, has given encouraging results. And a serum has been prepared which if given in liberal amounts during the gagging stage appears to cut down markedly the incidence of encephalitis. Your veterinarian should be consulted if your pet shows the symptoms we have listed. There is some evidence that greyhounds which raced following the throat phase of housedog disease tended to develop encephalitis in higher proportion than kennel mates which did not race. Again, there may be some danger in deworming a dog for a few weeks after the initial symptoms have appeared.

SUMMARY: We do not yet know by what name this disease will eventually be called. When I discovered it and wrote the first description of it, I found that it occurred more often among housedogs than among kennel and farm dogs. Housedog disease, therefore, seemed an appropriate name. Others have observed the encephalitis complication and some have called the original disease encephalitis, but as we saw in the case of Carré distemper and as we shall see in the case of rabies, and in hardpad disease, encephalitis occurs in or after all of these diseases.

Hardpad Disease. As this is written, the whole question of the diseases of the "distemper complex" is in a state of confusion—even among the experts. One group in America considers several of these diseases variants of Carré distemper. Others hold that many more true diseases will be isolated from those we now think are so few. Hardpad disease, first described by scientists in England, where Carré distemper is still common, appears to be distinct.

In contrast to housedog disease, which is a cold-weather ailment, hardpad comes at any season. The temperature during the disease proper remains close to 103.5° or 104°. The appetite does not disappear; rather, it remains poor, yet the dog eats without coaxing. The eyes and nose crust, but no long strings of mucus run from the nose, nor does light hurt the eyes. The stools remain fairly normal. No objectionable stench pervades the atmosphere in the dog's room.

The disease drags on, the foot pads slowly becoming hard like linoleum. Most pads become flattened, but some remain round. In the later stages, if recovery ensues, the pads peel off. If the virus invades the brain, the dog develops encephalitis, which usually manifests itself in convulsions, twitches, or both. Prognosis is unfavorable.

Rabies. Because of the many popular misconceptions concerning rabies, it seems advisable to consider a few general facts about the disease and its spread before taking up the specific symptoms.

CAUSE AND DISSEMINATION: Rabies is a virus disease, transmissible to almost all kinds of animals and many kinds of birds. Today, despite the fact that it could quite easily be eradicated, it is altogether too prevalent, and the dog is the principal agent of dissemination. It is believed that if we were to apply what we know about vaccination and restraint, the disease would disappear in a few years. Needless to say, every effort should be made to eradicate rabies, because of its danger to humans, if for no other reason.

Not all dogs bitten by a rabid dog develop rabies. Only about 15 per cent of the humans who took no treatments to protect themselves after being bitten developed the disease. In the past, when rabid wolves bit humans, a higher percentage died. Of dogs bitten by rabid dogs, 40 per cent die; with horses, the percentage is also 40; hogs, 30 per cent, and cattle, 30 per cent.

It is the saliva of the rabid dog which is dangerous. The bite drives the virus in the saliva deep into the tissues, where, being a neurotropic virus, it attaches itself to nerves and grows. It is not dangerous on the unbroken skin. When an animal is bitten, there is no certainty about how long the virus will take to grow up the nerves until it reaches the huge mass of nerve tissue represented by the brain. The position of the bite has some effect. If a dog is bitten on a back foot, the virus will have quite a distance to travel before it reaches the brain, while with a bite in the jaw the elapsed time would be much less. From 15 to 285 days are the extremes found in a study to determine how long it takes.

If the virus is able to attach itself to a nerve after the dog has been bitten, the dog has rabies. If the dog's body is capable of destroying the virus, the dog does not have rabies. The time which elapses until the virus grows to the brain is not an incubation period in the true sense.

What we think of as rabies is merely the manifestation of brain inflammation—encephalitis—and the dog may exhibit any of several typical forms of that malady. Thus present-day students of rabies have come to hold concepts of the disease completely different from those of our forefathers. Even the old name, hydrophobia, is no longer used. The conceptions of dumb and furious rabies have been dropped because the symptoms these terms describe are only two manifestations of encephalitis. In rabies, dogs do not have fits and then recover, as they may with housedog disease. Once the symptoms appear, it is a downhill drag until death ensues.

SYMPTOMS: The earliest sign may be what seems to be a perverted appetite, but this may be due to hunger coupled with such a dimming of the sense of taste that anything will be chewed and swallowed. Another sign may be restlessness, excitability, a desire to move which becomes accentuated as the virus grows in the brain. Complete character reversals are frequent. Some ugly dogs become docile, while some lovable, kindly dogs may become ferocious. As the disease progresses we find a whole range of symptoms from drowsiness to such violent reactions to exciting disturbances that the dog appears wild. A startled look haunts the eyes. Some dogs may be paralyzed and stupid and quiet, giving rise to the idea of "dumb rabies." Another dog may become fearless and run about, head down, biting anything which moves. Since its peripheral nerves are partially or completely paralyzed, the dog has little sense of feeling when bitten. In fights with dogs which refuse to run, the rabid dog can stand terrific punishment. When confined to a cage, it may break its teeth on the bars without apparent pain.

Probably the paralysis of the throat causes panic because the helpless feeling of not being able to swallow drives the animal wild and creates some pain. Rabid dogs do not have a phobia, or fear, of water; they simply cannot manage to swallow it, try as they may, and after many attempts to drink naturally they behave queerly toward it.

In the paralytic form, the lower jaw may hang; it is not held open by muscle power, but rather from want of it. The frothing from the mouth in some forms is well known to all who have heard about mad dogs. Indeed, the common conception of a mad dog is of an animal running about with froth drooling from his mouth. This misconception should be corrected. That type of behavior is far from being the typical form of rabies, and because this fact is not generally recognized, hundreds of people have died.

In all forms of rabies, once the severe encephalitis symptoms appear, death generally ensues in less than a week, sometimes in three days. The dog's bite can be infectious three days before anyone knows he is sick. One dog was found to have infected saliva eight days before he showed the typical symptoms.

Diagnosis beyond the suspicion created by the symptoms is possible only by microscopic and biologic means. In order to do this, the suspected dog must be destroyed and a portion of the brain examined for inclusion bodies.

I wish I had space to tell of the many cases I have seen of the encephalitis following housedog diseases and how exactly some followed the course of rabies encephalitis. Thousands of dogs which died of housedog disease have been suspected of having rabies. I myself have suspected at least a dozen to such an extent that I had the brains examined. One dog bent heavy wire in his cage front, snatched a one-inch-square stick out of my hand, chewed and swallowed some of it, ate the metal of a feed pan, ate the equivalent of a newspaper which was on the floor of his cage, and died stiffened out completely rigid. His brain was sectioned but showed no inclusion bodies, because housedog disease does not cause them. The next step in diagnosis was the injection of mice, and they, too, showed that the dog was not infected with rabies. If a dog dies in the early stages of rabies, no inclusion bodies have developed, so mouse tests are used as standard procedure in diagnosis. Mice are immune to housedog-disease virus but do, of course, react to rabies infections.

Table XII—Cases of Rabies Reported in 1951 in the United States (States not listed reported no rabies)

	IN ANIMALS	IN MAN		IN ANIMALS	IN MAN
Alabama	356	2	Montana	13	—
Arizona	14	—	Nebraska	43	—
Arkansas	165	1	New Mexico	4	—
California	54	—	New York	538	1
Colorado	5	—	North Carolina	255	2
Florida	65	—	North Dakota	106	—
Georgia	332	1	Ohio	198	1
Illinois	189	—	Oklahoma	125	—
Indiana	491	2	Pennsylvania	240	—
Iowa	410	1	South Carolina	356	—
Kansas	14	—	South Dakota	105	—
Kentucky	583	—	Tennessee	369	—
Louisiana	254	1	Texas	1235	1
Maine	1	—	Virginia	223	—
Maryland	1	—	Washington	21	—
Michigan	128	—	West Virginia	158	—
Minnesota	246	—	Wisconsin	37	—
Mississippi	166	—	Wyoming	1	—
Missouri	507	1			

Courtesy of U. S. Department of Agriculture.

PREVENTION AND CONTROL: Suppose you think your dog may be rabid, what should you do? Confine him in a veterinary hospital or dog pound. Give him time to develop characteristic symptoms. If he does have rabies, have him destroyed, have the brain examined, and put yourself in the hands of your doctor.

The questions are often asked: Why don't veterinarians try to cure dogs affected with rabies? If they can't drink, why aren't they given water by vein? Isn't there any serum for rabies? The answer to all these questions is that human beings don't want to handle rabid dogs, so practically nothing has been done in the way of cure.

Prevention is the keynote in rabies control. It can be made more effective by keeping all dogs under supervision and by rigid enforcement of the regulations requiring dog wardens to pick up all strays. Prevention consists of animal vaccination. These are made very inexpensive in some states. In areas completely free of the disease nothing need be done and this dread disease can be forgotten.

If there is a possibility that infected saliva or other excretion from a rabid dog has entered a cut or abrasion, a person can be given the famous Pasteur treatment, which, if taken in time, causes the human body to develop immunity in the blood, and the immune bodies in turn attack the virus growing on the nerves and destroy it.

What chance have you of owning a rabid dog? Having set down in some detail the dangers of this disease to man and his pets, and warned dog owners of the precautions to be taken, a more cheerful note may well be struck. The accompanying table shows the relative prevalence of the disease by states in the United States.

Of the 8,946 cases in animals, 6,949 were dogs, 393 were cats. Rabies was reported in the following wild animals: coyotes, foxes, rabbits, mice, gophers, squirrels, rats, skunks, wild cats, raccoons, opossums, and muskrats.

Infectious Hepatitis (Inflammation of the Liver). This virus disease has been recognized only recently. It is one we shall probably hear more about. It occurs in dogs of all ages but kills mostly the puppies.

SYMPTOMS: The symptoms vary, depending upon the extent of invasion of the different organs of the body. Generally the apparent symptoms of the disease last from two to four days. The dog loses interest in his surroundings, may crawl into dark places, has no interest in food but develops a great thirst. His head and neck may swell with edema of the tissues. There is vomiting and diarrhea. Some dogs groan with pain or discomfort. The temperature is elevated but falls to subnormal before death. Some dogs develop spasms of rigidity and trembling. The dog breathes rapidly and his heartbeat is increased. His eyes water profusely. If you open his mouth and lift the lips, they and the gums may appear blanched, indicating anemia. The tonsils are often swollen.

DAMAGE TO THE BODY: The changes in the body include a thickening and sponginess of the skin of the neck, shoulders, and chest, from the fluid which has accumulated in it, and perhaps a slight yellowing of the tissues. Some of the lymph nodes and the spleen may be enlarged, but this is not a constant finding. The fluid in the abdomen may be pink. The liver is often somewhat enlarged, with a dry surface, and sometimes small deposits of a fibrinous nature are found on the surface. On dissection and microscopic examination of the liver, a pathologist will observe inclusion bodies which are characteristic only of virus diseases. These are now thought to be identical with those of a disease of foxes called fox encephalitis, and it is quite probable they are one and the same disease.

TREATMENT: Serum is now available which is said by the producers to have protective and curative properties. Vaccine, too, is available.

Puppies may die so suddenly with the disease that the owner won't know they are sick; others may show only an indisposition for a day and die; a few slowly recover. Older dogs may have the disease and recover without ever being correctly diagnosed. Some doubtless are said to have "distemper."

The disease has been recognized by its symptoms since 1928 but was studied and named in 1947 in Sweden. It has been reported as one of the major virus diseases in England and in the United States in 1948 and 1949.

Canine Influenza. This ailment has the typical characteristics of a virus disease. It is an explosive sort of disease which has affected dogs only during years when influenza epidemics caused the sickness of thousands of humans. In the eastern part of the United States this was during the winters of 1935–36 to 1940–41. It has not been seen since. However, it may appear again.

SYMPTOMS: The first symptom is generally running fits. However, there is a distinct breed difference in manifestations of the fits. Beagles are most likely to exhibit them, and hounds of all sorts seem to be seriously affected, but it is rare to see an afflicted cocker spaniel have a fit.

The disease lasts five or six days and ends as abruptly as it started. Infected dogs act depressed, and some are prostrated. The appetite disappears. Eyes are moist and a slight nasal discharge is present. Victims want to be kept very quiet and warm. There appears to be a headache accompanying the disease, for dogs with canine influenza dislike to be touched near the head, eyeing the person handling them with a frightened look, as if ready to snap if the hand gets near the head. In the early stages sharp noises may cause a fit. Clapping the hands near the dog seems to hurt him.

The temperature curve follows a typical course. It rises to about 106° and remains high, between 105° and 106°, for five days, then drops nearly to normal, and the relief afforded the dog is very obvious. The nasal discharge clears; the appetite returns. In recent epidemics the only serious sequel was pneumonia, and this appeared in only a small proportion of the affected dogs.

PREVENTION AND TREATMENT: Recovery from canine influenza appears to produce lasting immunity. One of the interesting features is that such recovery affords no protection whatever against Carré distemper, yet dogs recovered from or vaccinated against distemper are just as immune to influenza as they are to Carré's disease.

The treatment is problematical. When the disease last appeared, sulfa drugs and antibiotics, such as penicillin, were not available. Probably the pneumonia which sometimes followed it can be prevented by their use, if the disease returns. Such fever-reducing drugs as "aspirin" appeared to afford considerable relief.

All dog owners should be on the alert for its reappearance.

BACTERIAL DISEASES

There are a few bacterial diseases which have a wide distribution throughout the body, rather than affecting only one or two of the organs. These are known as generalized diseases.

Leptospirosis. Of spirochetal origin, the bacterial agent which produces this disease is spread to dogs most frequently by dog urine. As yet

(1952) there is no known protective vaccination against the disease. Many cures have been reported, but none has stood up under further investigation. These include injections of live Carré virus and chloromycetin. In my own experience nothing except large amounts of blood from recovered dogs, given in early stages, has helped. Leptospirosis is also a disease of humans; in this form it is called Weil's disease, or Canicola disease.

SYMPTOMS AND DIAGNOSIS: The symptoms are similar in all species. The disease appears in two forms, the *canicola* and the *icterohemorrhagic* (jaundice-hemorrhages). The former is often inaccurately diagnosed since it presents particularly difficult diagnostic problems.

Both types produce a number of common symptoms which can be traced to the impairment of certain organs by the spirochetes. These are unsteady elevation of temperature, nausea, lassitude, loss of weight, loose stools, and stiffness. An almost constant symptom in both forms is the congestion of the tiny blood vessels in the whites of the eyes, which may be a coppery red. The canicola form shows a few additional symptoms. The dog generally dies quite emaciated, and the urine may range in color from orange to chocolate brown and may at times contain blood.

The second type (icterohemorrhagic) differs in the symptoms it produces in the manner implied by the name. There is bleeding in the intestines and gums, and sometimes tiny hemorrhages scattered throughout the body. The vomitus may show blood; the stools appear bloody.

A further diagnostic symptom is one which a disease of the liver would be expected to exhibit: namely, jaundice. The mucous membranes, skin, and whites of the eyes appear a more and more intense yellow as the disease progresses, until, at death, some tissues may be almost a canary yellow or orange. By the time the yellow has appeared, however, the disease has progressed so far that serious damage may have been done to the kidneys and liver. The difficulty of identifying the disease at an early stage makes it difficult to cure the first dog in an area to contract leptospirosis. By the time the diagnosis has been definitely established there is usually little hope. Even if the dog should survive, the damage that was done before the treatment was started will often make him an invalid for the remainder of his life.

Leptospirosis in a kennel or in a pair of dogs is a different matter. If one dog dies, diagnosis by post-mortem and bacterial examination is possible. Then, after the disease has been identified, treatment may be started immediately with those pets which have been infected a shorter time. When the disease is detected at an earlier stage, the dogs may—and usually do—recover if proper treatment is given. Urine analyses can be made on all as a helpful indication. Every dog not entirely well, particularly those that show indications of a fever, can be treated. If the temperature fluctuates markedly from very high to almost normal, it may add to one's suspicions, for leptospirosis does not cause a uniformly high fever even at the beginning.

Table XIII—Features of Distemper and Diseases Often Mistaken for It

	CARRÉ DISTEMPER	HOUSEDOG DISEASE	COCCIDIOSIS	PNEUMONIA	TONSILLITIS
Character	Disease of the skin, glands, and linings of the body	Pharyngolaryngo-tracheitis	Disease of intestinal lining	Disease of the lungs	Only tonsils and adjacent tissue involved
Cause	Virus of Carré	Virus	Protozoan	Bacteria	Virus
Temperature	103°–104°	102.6°	102°–103.5°	104°–106°	103°
Appetite	Nil	Poor unless encephalitis ensues, in which case excellent	Poor	Poor	Poor
Stools	Loose, evil-smelling, often bloody	Soft only	Watery at height of disease	Often unaffected	Usually unaffected
Nasal discharge	Gummy, ropy	Little or none	Slight	Some	None
Optic discharge	"Gummy" eyes	Slight, eyelids may appear "scratchy"	Often heavy	Sometimes severe	Quite runny
Photophobia	Decided	None	None	None	None
Throat	Tonsils swollen, throat and gums inflamed	Prinicpal affected area	Normal	Normal	Tonsils enlarged and deep red
Inclusion bodies	Yes	None	No	None	No
Duration	Short, but long (6 weeks) if secondary diseases are included	5 to 10 days unless brain is affected	3½ weeks	4 to 5 days with proper treatment	5 to 7 days
Immunity	Lifelong	Questionable	Lifelong, but a carrier	Lifelong for that type	Questionable
Encephalitis	Often	Often	Occasionally	No	No
Blood changes	Decided in secondary stages	No increase in white cells	Yes	Yes, white cell proliferation	No
Prognosis	Unfavorable	75% recovery	Favorable if prevented from reinfestation	Excellent with proper treatment	Favorable
Season	Any	Cold seasons	Warm weather for	Any	Any

Table XIII—Cont'd

	HARD PAD	STREPTOCOCCIC INFECTION	INFLUENZA	INFECTIOUS HEPATITIS
Character	General debility and footpad hardening	Chiefly a throat disease	High febrile disease	Liver disease
Cause	Virus	Several types of "streps"	Virus	Virus
Temperature	103°–104°	104°–106°	105° plus	105°
Appetite	Very poor	Poor	Very poor	Poor
Stools	Normal	Loose at first	Loose	Loose
Nasal discharge	Some	Slight	Slight	Some
Optic discharge	Some	Slight	Thick	Some
Photophobia	None	None	Marked	None
Throat		Intensely red; glands under ears swollen	Normal	Normal
Inclusion bodies	Yes?	No	No	Yes
Duration	5 weeks	Five days if treated	1 week	Several weeks
Immunity	Lifelong	Lifelong	Questionable	Lifelong
Encephalitis		No	No	Lifelong
Blood changes	Common	Yes	Not studied	
Prognosis	Unfavorable	Favorable if treated; poor if neglected	Favorable	Unfavorable in puppies
Season	Any	Any	Cold	Any

METHOD OF INFECTION: As we have indicated, the disease is most frequently spread by rat urine. Almost all recorded cases—and they are sporadic—can be traced to garbage or bones which have been left where rats had access to them.

TREATMENT: Penicillin has been found to be useful when given in heavy doses, but it should be administered as early as possible. The mortality is high, but some dogs do recover with no aftereffects. Laboratory tests with the serum from infected dogs, mixed with colored spirochetes, cause clumping of the bacteria and show whether or not a dog has recovered. These tests have demonstrated that a fairly large percentage of dogs have at some time had leptospirosis, which may have been diagnosed as distemper or some other disease. From my own experience, it would seem that the difficulty in diagnosing this disease and the harmlessness of penicillin injections warrant their use whenever suspicion points to the possibility of leptospirosis.

Tuberculosis. We do not know how many dogs are tubercular. Certainly the number varies in different parts of the world. There are three types of the disease: human, bovine (cattle), and avian (bird). Dogs may contract either the human or the bovine, the former being three times as prevalent as the latter.

Doubtless dogs with lung tuberculosis cough T.B. germs. Yet, so far as I have been able to find out, no human being—man, woman, or child—has been reported as having contracted the disease from a dog. Yet the possibility does exist, and it hardly seems sensible to allow children to fondle tubercular animals. That dogs have contracted the disease from humans can hardly be doubted.

Tuberculosis in a dog is seldom recognized. The symptoms are not distinctive. Coughing may be characteristic of many diseases, and so may loss of weight with fair appetite. Very few dogs which, on post-mortem, showed tubercular lesions were known by their owners to have the disease, and many passed as well dogs but not exactly thrifty. The post-mortem examinations which revealed lesions showed them principally in the lungs.

Any dog suspected of being tubercular can be tested very easily by injecting a tiny amount of tuberculin into the skin and observing the reaction seventy-two hours later. A reaction may be any sort of enlargement at the site of the injection—an even lump or a thickening of the skin over a considerable area.

There is at present no cure for tubercular animals. If a dog is found to react, it would seem best to have him destroyed, unless, with the remarkable progress of pharmacology, some means is found to cure the disease.

Tetanus (Lockjaw). Few known poisons are so deadly as that produced by lockjaw germs. Before discussing the peculiarities of the bacterium which causes tetanus, let us consider some of the symptoms.

SYMPTOMS: Growing in a sealed-over wound, forming a minute pocket, yet giving off their deadly toxin, these germs produce a stiffness in the dog, due to muscle contraction, which is generally diagnostic. The gait is stiff, the head tends to be extended too far in front, the tail is held out stiffly behind, the ears are hard and cocked, not hanging pendulously as they should in the case of a lop-eared dog.

All the reflexes are sharpened. Any noise causes a quicker response than normal. The facial expression shows pain and anxiety. Occasionally, with tetanus, dog owners may suspect their dogs of being rabid.

Locking of the jaw muscles is not a universal feature. In fact, some dogs have only parts of their bodies affected and their jaws not at all. But once the jaw muscles have contracted so that the dog can neither eat nor drink, he is helpless without heroic treatment.

METHOD OF INFECTION: When a dog becomes infected with a spore of the bacterium *Clostridium tetanii,* it does not necessarily mean he will have lockjaw. In fact, the germs are exceedingly common over the earth's surface and often grow outside of animal bodies. They are found in soil, around manure piles, and also in many unsuspected places as well. An interesting fact about them is that they grow when oxygen is excluded from their environment. They do not grow in an open wound to which air has access. But with other bacteria in a deep wound they thrive. The other types of bacteria exhaust the oxygen supply and render the environment propitious.

PREVENTION AND TREATMENT: Prevention consists in having every dog with a puncture or bullet wound given antitoxin and the wound cleaned. In treatment very large doses of antitoxin are injected and the source of infection is thoroughly disinfected. Antitoxin is a chemical antidote for the toxin. When used in large enough amounts, it "knocks out" the toxin, as bacteriologists say.

Supportive treatment of relaxing the muscles by drugs which the veterinarian can give is helpful. Then, too, if the dog's jaws are affected, he must be fed by vein or rectum until his jaw muscles are sufficiently relaxed to allow him to eat.

The treatment of tetanus requires extreme patience, but it is often rewarded by the joy which comes in watching a dog recover when there had appeared to be little hope.

16. The Reproductive and Urinary Systems

FEMALE REPRODUCTIVE AILMENTS

THE female organs of reproduction are, from the outside in, the vulva, clitoris, vagina, cervix, uterus, Fallopian tubes, ovaries; and, on the belly, the udder, which includes the mammary glands with their accessories. The udder is actually a group of skin glands, and its ailments are considered here only because they are so closely tied in with the reproductive processes.

The reproductive system is subject to many ills, but those most obvious to the layman are growths, unnatural discharges, irregular heat periods, infertility, and insufficient milk production. In addition there are many disorders and infections which, though not evident from the outside, can cause infertility and even death.

Ovarian Ailments. A bitch's ovaries, as we learned in Chapter 2, are about as large as pea beans and are surrounded by capsules on the outside of which the Fallopian tubes twist along and end in spongy-looking organs —fimbriae.

CYSTS are not found in young bitches (up to six or eight months old, let us say), but in older animals they are the most frequent ovarian ailment in my experience, which includes the removal of at least ten thousand pairs of ovaries and uteri in spaying operations.

These cysts do not grow out of the ovaries proper but from the tissue connected with them. They may be as large as pigeon eggs but more often are half an inch across or smaller. Many exploratory operations to determine the cause of sterility have been performed, and when cysts were discovered, it was found that merely rupturing them resulted in the bitch's coming in heat promptly and producing sizable litters.

Cysts around the ovaries do not always produce complete sterility, and they usually affect the general health very little. For example, there is the case of Mary, the most prolific bitch I have ever heard of. She produced an average of sixteen puppies per litter for eight litters. Then came three litters of five, four, and five puppies. It was found that her drop in fecundity was due to cysts about both ovaries. She had shown no signs of ill health, and if an exploratory operation had not been performed we never should have known that she had cysts.

Tumors of bitches' ovaries are rare. In a study of approximately seven hundred cases of neoplasms we found no ovarian tumors.

Uterine Ailments. Most of the troubles of the reproductive tract are centered in the uterus, and usually these conditions are not apparent unless one is watching carefully for them. Three principal types of ailment occur: those connected with the process of birth; those due to infection not associated with pregnancy; and growths.

PERITONITIS AND RETAINED PLACENTAE. Bitches may die of peritonitis a few days after whelping a litter, frequently because of failure to expel a dead puppy. Often puppies die in the uterus, decompose, and poison the mother, who cannot give birth to them. The mother dog may have received a blow which killed one or more of the unborn litter. A disease she may have contracted can kill her puppies. Occasionally one huge puppy will block the birth canal and cause complications of this type.

As frequent a cause of death as any in this general category is the retained placenta. This large lump of decaying tissue may cause the uterus around it to die too. When that happens the uterus ruptures and the putrescent material runs into the abdomen; peritonitis develops and the bitch dies.

There is doubtless some dietary connection with the inability to pass the puppies and placentae properly. Bitches on inadequate diets have such complications much more frequently than those on complete, wholesome diets. My own nutritional studies indicate that when a known complete and balanced diet was fed, retention of placentae was extremely rare. But among the dogs owned by my clients it is a common difficulty. Many of the animals have been fed the old meat-and-dog-biscuit or kibble diet; others have been given inadequate assortments of table scraps.

Following birth it is important to see that all of the afterbirths are out. A wise dog owner who has time will sit with the bitch and, as each puppy is born, catch the cord and hold it, exerting a slight pull until the placenta comes out. The bitch may be allowed to eat it without harm and perhaps with some benefit to her. She always will if she is left alone. If there are not as many placentae passed as there are puppies, the veterinarian can inject one of several drugs—usually Pitocin or Pituitrin—which will help speed up the muscular contractions in the uterus and help to force out any afterbirths that remain. Sometimes high douches will remove the placenta, and quite often, as the uterus shrinks and shortens, the doctor can feel the retained placenta in the uterus through the abdominal walls, insert a special pair of long forceps into the uterus, and remove it.

Retention of placentae interferes with milk secretion, raises the temperature, produces a foul smell and a long, continued discharge from the uterus. It also interferes with future pregnancies and, because of the general debilitating effect on the mother, prevents the proper development of the puppies. When bitches which have retained placentae recover, it is not unusual to find blackened areas in the uterine wall, if not ruptured uteri. It has been observed that those which do recover are generally the ones that have a healthy thirst even though they do not eat during their illnesses.

MONSTERS. The production of so-called monsters—puppies of odd forms or immensely oversized—frequently causes death or requires Caesarean sections. Among the monsters are great headless lumps covered with hair, two-headed puppies, greatly oversized abnormal pups. Sometimes a puppy will die before birth, become contaminated by bacteria, possibly of blood origin, and blow up with gas to many times its normal size so that the mother cannot possibly pass it. Others become distended with fluid, as in dropsy. All such dystocias, or interferences with normal birth, require veterinary service—the prompter the better.

RESTRICTED PELVIS. Bitches whose pelves have been broken and in healing have become constricted cannot have normal births. They should not be bred except in some very unusual cases.

TWISTED UTERUS. Occasionally the uterus becomes twisted. Once in a while a puppy manages to get down one horn of the uterus and up the other, so that he is part way in each and his back is toward the body of the uterus. Manipulation can generally effect a normal delivery, but by herself the mother may not be able to expel a live puppy.

GIANT PUPPIES. It has been observed that matings of large males with small females may produce puppies so large that they cannot be delivered normally. A good deal more research on this subject is needed. It may be that the dam has more effect on birth size than we yet know. I have mated, artificially, a 120-pound St. Bernard and a 30-pound French bulldog bitch; a 55-pound German shepherd with a 22-pound poodle; a 90-pound bloodhound with a 33-pound basset hound, and made many other such crosses. In all cases the puppies were whelped without difficulty.

GROWTHS. There are a number of growths which develop in the uterus. Some of these are relatively harmless, but there are others which cause the organ to fill with pus. Some types develop rapidly, and with these it is often impossible to save the bitch. Growths, especially those in the pelvis, have been known to cause difficult birth.

INFECTIONS (METRITIS, ENDOMETRITIS, PYOMETRIA). When you see the word *metritis,* remember that it means inflammation of the whole uterus. *Endometritis* means inflammation of the lining of the uterus. *Pyometria* means pus in the uterus.

The first two, metritis and endometritis, are evidenced by a swelling throughout the whole reproductive tract. Even the vulva shows it. These conditions are more or less tied up with the aftermath of birth but also occur following an accident such as gunshot wound, or some other type of injury which can cause the uterus to become inflamed.

Pyometria is different. It occurs in between mating cycles. The small, resting uterus—normally no larger in diameter than a soda straw, but with thicker walls—fills with germs which proliferate in enormous numbers, causing pus formation until the uterus is distended to seemingly incredible proportions. I have removed a uterus from a German shepherd that was two and a quarter inches in diameter and three and a half feet long in each horn. The amazing thing is that an animal could carry this amount of pus and live. The kidneys, which have heroically tried to handle the toxin, are usually damaged materially.

With infections of this sort the abdomen becomes distended, the temperature is generally fairly high, and the bitch often has a great thirst. A reddish discharge from the vulva with a fetid, sickish-sweet odor continues as a constant symptom, often being sufficiently copious to wet the tail and hind legs and attract flies in warm weather. Some species of flies will lay eggs in the moist hair, and maggots develop. The vulva is somewhat larger than normal. The bitch loses her appetite, becomes thin and somewhat potbellied, weak and often tottery in gait, with a general unthrifty appearance.

When this condition develops it is best to have the uterus and ovaries removed, unless the bitch is especially valuable as a breeder. An infusion of saline and glucose following the operation materially increases the chances of success, and few bitches die when the whole uterus is removed, unless it is ruptured and the pus has escaped into the abdomen.

In the case of valuable bitches whose germ plasm is worth perpetuating, it is possible to give Pituitrin to open the cervix, make an incision in the abdomen wide enough so that a hand may be admitted to act as a guide, insert a large catheter through the cervix, and then drain the pus out of the uterus. If a long-acting anesthesia is used, the drain may be kept in until the uterus has reduced considerably. Then a bland antiseptic, such as propylene glycol with sulfathiazole, is introduced to flush the uterus, and more allowed to remain in and trickle out by itself. A further injection of posterior pituitary extract can be given and further flushing done before the abdomen is closed. If a subsequent rise in temperature indicates a recurrence of infection, the process may be repeated before the uterus has become distended again. In this way a cure may be effected. Obviously, however, the treatment is difficult and expensive and is justified only to save exceptional bitches for future breeding.

Vaginal Ailments. Compared with the uterus, the vagina gives little trouble. Most of its ills are those connected with the mating cycle. Within it are the cervix—actually a part of the uterus—the hymen, and the external urethral opening and clitoris.

RESISTANT HYMEN. Before copulation can be completed, it is sometimes necessary to insert an instrument to break the hymen. This is not often present in bitches, but in certain strains it is a constant feature. If a male cannot insert his penis far enough to become tied, an examination should be made. About two inches inside the vagina an up-and-down web of tissue across the middle can be felt and ruptured by cutting. I have seen these strings so tough that they would have prevented a bitch from ever mating unless they were broken surgically.

CLITORIS ENLARGEMENT. The clitoris enlarges greatly during the mating cycle. Some bitches develop such huge ones that the dog's penis cannot push it out of the way. It may stick out of the vulva and show as a red knob. It may lead to a prolapse of the vagina, so that a red bunch as large as an average-sized tomato protrudes from the vulva, cutting off the urethra and causing death. It should be replaced by strong, patient squeezing, to remove the edema, and then sewed in by lacing stitches through the skin back and forth across the vulva, leaving room for the urine to pass.

Such a condition may cause sloughing of the lining of the vagina, at least in spots, and the inflammation often makes fertile mating impossible. If it occurs during one mating cycle, it is generally repeated at every subsequent one.

INFLAMMATION AND INJURIES. Inflammation of the vagina is usually accompanied by similar inflammation of the vulva, which becomes unduly red, much as it does when the bitch is "in heat." In ordinary vaginitis there is a discharge of a whitish nature, a good deal of licking by the bitch, and straining to urinate because the inflammation partially closes the urethral orifice. Urination probably causes a burning sensation, so that only small amounts are voided.

Vaginal infection may be caused by injuries to the vulva. Curious children have been known to insert sharp objects into the vaginas of bitches. Bullet wounds cause trouble. Bird shot sometimes penetrates the skin and lodges in the vaginal lining, where it sets up severe irritation until it is removed. The vulva is also subject to neoplasms. Barbed-wire cuts are not uncommon. There may be damage from biting wounds when bitches fight with other dogs, or from automobile accidents.

With adequate surgery, such injuries may be repaired quite easily, often with only local anesthesia.

Mammary Gland Ailments. In my experience there are only three general types of ailments which affect the mammary glands of bitches: growths, injuries, and the ills associated with reproduction.

GROWTHS. Of the growths, the most common are those known as adenocarcinomas. This form of cancer is definitely known to be associated with the activities of the ovaries because spayed bitches do not develop it. It is often said that cancer of the udder is caused by the production of milk and the "drying off" process. It is true that when a bitch has ceased to give milk after weaning puppies a lump can sometimes be felt in the udder. Possibly there is activity in the breast tissue which encourages development of the tumor. But it is also a fact that the bitch would not have developed it had she been spayed. Moreover, even after these tumors are removed from a bitch, more may grow in new places. But if she is spayed, no new ones develop. If your veterinarian advises spaying your bitch, even though she is not young, you will be wise to trust his judgment. He knows his business. There are drugs he can inject which will cause such tumors to disappear—heptaldehyde and testosterone, for example—but both present difficulties. Spaying is usually preferable.

Other types of tumors also grow on breasts, but they are rare and you are not likely to see one. Needless to say, a growth anywhere should have prompt attention, and this is especially important in the case of growths in the udder.

INJURIES. The udder is especially vulnerable to injury, particularly during lactation, when it is enlarged. Next to the feet, it is the most likely part of the dog to be torn or cut. Bitches frequently rip their udders on barbed-wire fences as they crawl between the strands or cut their udders on glass or other sharp objects when they crawl under fences.

Such injuries must be sutured carefully after the tissue has been cleaned. Active udders become infected easily. If the blood supply of this glandular substance is cut, it may die and slough out. In that case it is better to leave the wound open and allow the bitch to lick it until she has removed all the dead tissue, after which it may be sutured to promote quicker healing and result in a smaller scar.

A bad bruise of the gland may cause outpouring of blood into a section of the udder. Bacteria may creep up through the teat and cause infection. Abscesses may form. They must be opened and flushed with antiseptics, a job for the doctor or for a layman with an exceptional "touch" and sense for animal care.

PSEUDO-PREGNANCY. The question most often asked the veterinarian about any phase of udder trouble is: "Doctor, my dog's breasts are all swollen. What can be the matter?" Usually nothing is the matter. She was in heat two months ago and wasn't mated. All bitches which ovulate develop so-called phantom or pseudo-pregnancies. If they do not, they failed to ovulate. So this condition is the normal one. If your bitch comes in season and fails to develop swelling of the breasts later, then you should consult your veterinarian.

CAKED BREASTS. Swollen breasts after weaning result in congestion, which is nothing to be alarmed about. That is nature's way of shutting off the milk flow. Rubbing with softening remedies actually accomplishes no useful purpose. It is probably best to leave the breasts alone; eventually they will get soft. This advice applies, of course, only when there is no infection; if that occurs, your veterinarian had best be consulted.

INFECTION. Udder infection sometimes gets in through nipples, or it may be in the breast before weaning. Such infection is called *mastitis,* whether it occurs before or after weaning. Udder infection is one of the chief causes of puppy death. Uninformed dog owners often say their puppies died of acid milk, but normal bitches' milk *is* acid. The puppies either died of infection which might have been contracted from infected milk, or from starvation.

When an udder is infected for some time, sections involving several nipples may be put out of commission. At subsequent lactation periods, only part of the udder will be useful to the puppies. But even with fewer teats, the mother will produce almost as much milk as if she had her whole complement functioning.

MALE REPRODUCTIVE AILMENTS

It has been my experience that more male dogs are sterile than unspayed females. That is not surprising when we consider the delicate mechanism of the reproductive tract (page 49). Neoplasms of the testicles are common. The pathway traveled by the sperm offers many chances for infection, and the accessory organs along the way may also cause trouble.

Testicular Ailments. GROWTHS. In a study I once made of neoplasms in dogs, about 8 per cent were in the testicles. A high percentage of old dogs are so affected. When a growth occurs in one testicle, the other generally atrophies. When the testicle with the growth is removed, the shrunken testicle usually increases to normal again, and there may be further production of sperm.

Some tumors, notably those which do not invade the testicle itself but grow on the side of it, may cause the dog to take on female characteristics. He develops enlarged nipples, does not lift his hind leg when urinating, and has no interest in mating with bitches.

INJURIES. The testicles are frequently damaged by accidents and fights. The sheath may be torn away and require extensive suturing. I have known cases in which the scrotum was frozen to a rock. The dog may sit on a very cold surface until numbness sets in, and when he stands up the outside layers of the skin can literally be torn off. The sheath often thickens from injuries and infections, but it is fairly easily treated with medicated salve.

INFLAMMATION. Orchitis means inflammation of one or both of the testicles. You can often tell that a dog feels pain in the testicles by the way he moves about. He walks with his hind legs spread slightly, giving a stiffness to his gait. If an infection sets in, the testicle may have to be opened and drained. The scrotum may also be infected. All injuries and abscesses in this area are extremely painful to the dog, and any pain-deadening agent is a humane adjunct to treatment. Your veterinarian can give you effective drugs, if he is available, but in the absence of something better, aspirin or even paregoric will ease the pain.

CRYPTORCHIDISM. In cryptorchidism a testicle is retained in the abdomen or in the abdominal ring between the layers of muscle through which it normally descends. If the dog is a young puppy, it can often be brought down by doses of A-P-L (anterior-pituitary-like) hormone. But in older dogs surgery is recommended as the best treatment. Retained testicles may cause undependable dispositions in dogs and, if they are kept in for many years, tend to become cancerous. The operation for testicles retained in the abdomen is equivalent in risk to the ordinary spaying operation.

Prostate Ailments. ENLARGEMENT AND INFECTION. As dogs grow older their prostate glands tend to enlarge. This is an ill which may be caused by infection, by a hormonal action, or by growths. Prostatic enlargement causes such a lump in the pelvis that it may give the dog a sensation of stool in the colon and cause him to strain a great deal in an attempt to relieve himself. As we have seen, this enlargement of the prostate is often a cause of perineal hernias. It is also a cause of constipation, because it blocks the passage of large, firm stools, permitting only very soft stools to pass over it.

An infection produces pus along the tube which conducts the sperm. Each emission of semen shows myriads of pus cells mixed with the sperm, and such semen generally is incapable of effecting fertilization with the eggs. This is one of the most common causes of male infertility.

In stud dogs the use of antibiotics, such as penicillin or streptomycin, helps materially. I have restored fertility to many studs in this way. In the case of dogs whose germ plasm is of no great value, two methods of reducing the prostate are useful: castration and feeding of stilbestrol, the synthetic female sex hormone. Either method effects a cure but also causes sterility.

ABSCESSES AND GROWTHS. Abscesses are not infrequently found in dogs' prostates. A veterinarian can sometimes drain them by introducing large, sharp, hollow needles through the abdomen and guiding them with a finger inserted in the rectum. Malignant growths have been reported only rarely in dog's prostates.

Penis Ailments. The most frequent ailment of the penis is injury from tears, gunshot, and dog bites. Neoplasms also cause considerable trouble.

INJURIES. When the penis is injured it takes a considerable time to heal, because the tissue is spongy and because the sheath prevents air from reaching the wound. Clotting does not occur easily, and the blood may continue to trickle out for some time. The bulb at the back of the penis, when injured by a dog bite, can cause considerable blood loss. I have seen a dog whose penis was pierced by a 22-caliber bullet bleed to such an extent that he was too weak to walk.

An injury of this type is usually best left to the veterinarian, who will place sutures so as to check the blood flow.

GROWTHS. There is one form of tumor, probably mistakenly called lymposarcoma, which may be contracted by copulation. It grows on the penis, and mere contact will infect a bitch, which in turn can infect other dogs. It transplants readily and I have made four transplants to study it. I have removed several types of malignant growths from the sheaths of dogs but none from the penis except the one mentioned above. When this growth has to be removed the dog is practically valueless as a stud thereafter, unless only a very small area is affected.

DRIPS AND INFLAMMATION. All dogs constantly drip smegma, a greenish-yellow or creamy yellow discharge from their sheaths which they themselves customarily clean. This drip comes from the space between the sheath and penis, which constitutes a deep pocket. There is nothing abnormal about it. However, some dogs which fail to keep themselves clean become objectionable because of it.

Douching this pocket with a mild antiseptic under fairly strong pressure will do a lot to reduce the amount of drip. If there is inflammation, the condition is known as *balanitis*.

PHIMOSIS, PARAPHIMOSIS, AND SWELLING. **Phimosis** is a condition in which the opening of the sheath is too small for the penis to pass through at the time of copulation. It can be remedied by a simple operation.

Paraphimosis occurs often in puppies about the time of adolescence. The penis protrudes through the sheath, swells, and then cannot be withdrawn to its natural cover.

An irritation in the penis sometimes causes it to swell within the sheath, which cannot stretch to the full size of a distended penis. This creates great pressure and attending pain. The dog evidences his discomfort by running around and frequently sitting and licking his penis.

The best treatment for either condition is to get the dog's interest turned in some other direction. Taking him for a walk, soaking him in cold water, brushing him with a stiff brush, mentioning a ride in the car if he has learned to like it, or even saying, "Where's kitty?" to a dog that knows what it means may effect an almost instant reduction in the size of the penis. Even then, however, the pain from the distention diminishes only gradually.

DISEASES OF THE URINARY TRACT

The blood-filtering mechanism of the kidneys, with their complex system of tubules, is subject to a number of ills. The whole system may be thrown out of balance or there may be a failure of one or more of the parts—in the ureters, the bladder, or the urethra. In addition to the damage done by these primary failures, infections or defects in these organs directly affect the functioning of other parts of the body and sometimes are instrumental in causing other diseases.

There are certain outward symptoms indicative of kidney disturbances which you can and should recognize. If you are aware of them you will be able to have your dog treated while the disease is in an early stage before it has done irreparable damage. The final, definite diagnosis of the specific ailment, however, will usually be made by your veterinarian. A urine analysis is generally necessary, for only an examination with a microscope will reveal that the tubules have shed their lining, that the urine contains crystals or bacteria, or that a number of other conditions indicative of a particular disease are present. Nevertheless, early recognition of the common symptoms discussed in this chapter is important, for these outward signs are usually first indications of trouble and as such are the basis for further examination.

KIDNEY AILMENTS

Inflammation. The scientific name for this ailment is nephritis. Inflammation of the kidneys may be recognized by excessive thirst, some fever, and sometimes by pain indicated when pressure is applied over the kidney. If the thirst is great, the urine may be very thin. Albumin may be present in the urine, but this can be determined only by testing. There may be nausea, occasioned by a rise in the uric-acid and waste-product content of the blood; weak and rapid pulse; blurring of the eyes; lessened appetite; and a stiff gait.

When the attack first begins the dog loses his appetite and thirst. His urine will then be thicker than normal, highly colored, perhaps orange or red from blood. It may even appear opaque from pus. When a dog suffers pain from this trouble he frequently passes only a small amount of urine at a time, even though there may be a considerable amount in his bladder. In a severe case the dog may be dizzy, stagger, have convulsions, and eventually go into a coma.

In some cases these acute symptoms terminate not in death but in a chronic state. Often dogs cured by proper medication can be kept in good condition by proper diet. One fact is strongly in the dog's favor: the kidneys normally do not use their entire filtering mechanism all the time. Consequently only a comparatively small part may be damaged, and when the condition is corrected the balance of the organ may still be able to function.

In its most severe form nephritis may cause the kidneys to enlarge—even to double their size—or it may cause them to shrink until the organs are only half their normal size.

Nephritis is caused by bacterial infection of the kidneys, by food toxins, or by poisons. It may also be brought on by blows over these organs. Bacteria carried in the blood become lodged in the tiny tubules and grow, causing destruction of all or part of one or both kidneys.

The tiny, delicate tubules are especially vulnerable to poisons and often become useless after an attempt to filter out an overload of these toxic substances. In many instances all organs of a dog except the kidneys may recover from a heavy dose of poison.

Kidney inflammation often follows an attack of some disease elsewhere in the body and apparently is due to the tax placed upon the kidneys in trying to eliminate the toxins caused by the bacteria producing the disease. A bitch whose uterus is infected very often suffers severely damaged kidneys. After a serious attack of blood poisoning or peritonitis, a dog may be affected in the same way.

The symptoms which we have listed could, of course, be indicative of other diseases. One easy test which anyone can make will help to establish a fairly accurate diagnosis: Catch some of the dog's urine. A male's can be obtained by taking him for a walk and catching some urine when he sprinkles on a tree. When a female squats to urinate it is a simple matter to catch some urine by slipping a small flat dish under her. Fill a pyrex test tube three quarters full of the urine and, holding it by the bottom with the top inch of the urine over a flame, allow it to come to a boil.

When the kidneys are damaged they are unable to handle the albumin as they should and the excess will be found in a soluble form in the urine. In this form it is colorless. Everyone knows what happens to egg white when it is boiled. The same thing happens to the albumin in the urine—it turns white and thus becomes visible. You may see it as a white cloud or it may be so heavy as to look like egg white boiled. The proper evaluation of the condition should be left to your veterinarian, as should the treatment. The layman can be misled by the precipitate, which may be mineral in origin. To distinguish between the two, your doctor will add a few drops of acetic acid to the urine. The acid will cause the phosphates to disappear, but if the white precipitate is albumin, it remains.

TREATMENT: Obviously, if a dog can't handle albumin properly, large amounts should not be fed. The dog with chronic kidney disease needs a small amount of adequate protein in order to live. This he can get in whole milk and good quality meal-type dog foods. Avoid meat, organs like liver and kidneys, poultry, fish, eggs, cheese, skim milk, navy and lima beans, and all high protein foods. Feed a diet of cereals, vegetables, fruits, some fat, and whole milk. Doughnuts, ice cream, some candy are good for him. A dog properly fed can survive in spite of chronic kidney disease for a long time. But let him have a big meal of meat and you are likely to find him having a convulsion or possibly in a coma.

Permanently damaged kidneys cannot adequately filter the wastes out of the blood. Consequently one often finds weak hearts associated with kidney trouble. With these two organs functioning improperly, fluids naturally accumulate in the body. The heart loses the strength it once had to force the blood through the circulatory system and back again, so some stagnates along the way. The abdomen is the easiest place for it to filter out, so we frequently find large amounts of fluid accumulating in that cavity. I have taken as much as a gallon out of a twenty-pound Boston terrier. The legs often stock up, as does the skin and tissue under the belly. If you pinch this tissue it causes the dog no pain but leaves a pit, indicating edema.

If water is withheld, the dog may be forced to absorb much of this fluid back into his circulation. The treatment is rigorous. The dog's great thirst drives him to beg for water or milk, and his owner generally gives in. The patient is then ready for tapping again, and even that may be useless. I have seen a number of young dogs with severe dropsy which recovered without additional treatment after a few tappings, but in old dogs it usually brings only temporary relief.

Kidney Stones. When a dog occasionally passes small amounts of blood in the urine, there is a good chance he may have stones in a kidney, especially if it is demonstrated that his bladder and urethra are clear. Even though kidney stones are found much less frequently than bladder stones, post-mortem examinations show them more often than most people suppose. In the majority of cases the dogs' owners had no suspicion of their presence.

In acute cases dogs affected may show great pain, walk with arched backs, cry or whine. These are not diagnostic symptoms, however, because they can indicate many other disabilities. But even if X ray fails to show the stone and the pain appears to be intense, a veterinary surgeon may decide that the symptoms are sufficiently specific to justify opening the abdomen to remove the stone.

Of all the cases with which I have dealt, most were brought to me by owners after the dogs had been exercising violently—jumping, swimming, retrieving. It would appear that the exercise had altered the position of the stone and produced the spasm of pain and/or the blood in the urine. Unless the attacks are severe or frequent, an operation is not advisable. One of my own coon hounds lived to be eleven years old and always had a kidney stone. He suffered mild attacks and passed blood only after he had been hunting.

Uremia. Many an old dog dies because his kidneys fail to function as they should. Eventually the whole chemistry of the body is disturbed by an excess amount of uric acid in the blood. Such a condition is called uremia. It is a kind of blood poisoning—not the bacterial sort, but poisoning nevertheless, since it is a toxic condition. Younger dogs may die from the same condition, possibly due to other causes, such as long retention of urine because of stones in the bladder or a ruptured bladder.

The poisoning or toxemia associated with uremia produces nausea. After a few days the dog will vomit anything he eats, including water, and he may evince a great thirst or none at all. Some dogs act dizzy; some become blind; some have convulsions, and some end in comas. Often an old dog exhibits all these conditions.

TREATMENT: The most effective treatment consists of infusions of sodium lactate and glucose. Another method of treatment is to feed glucose, six to eight tablespoonfuls a day for a forty-pound dog. Bicarbonate of soda is often given by mouth.

BLADDER AILMENTS

When distended, a dog's bladder occupies a considerable area in the abdomen. It has a capacity far greater than that of many other species. Perhaps because of its size, a dog's bladder seems particularly vulnerable to injury. Dogs that are struck by automobiles—especially those that have just been let out of the house to relieve themselves—often have their bladders ruptured. The bladder is frequently punctured by gunshots, ruptured by kicks or blows, and sometimes even by falls.

A normal bladder shrinks to a very small organ after urination. Its walls are thin and pliable. When it is inflamed, however, it feels thick and hard. This fact sometimes leads to errors in diagnosis. For example, a bladder filled with stones also has greatly inflamed walls and is likely to give one the impression that the stones within are larger than they actually are.

Ruptured Bladder. A dog with a ruptured bladder soon exhales the odor of urine on his breath; his temperature falls; he collapses and, unless drastically treated, dies in a short time. If an injured dog is brought to the veterinarian in time, he can operate and may be able to save him. I have sutured a number of ruptured bladders. After flushing out the abdomen, I leave a catheter in the urethra so that the urine will drain away as fast as it enters, give infusions with glucose and sodium lactate, and administer sulfa drugs or antibiotics.

Bladder Infection. This is common. Dogs, especially bitches, may go about urinating far more frequently than normal, as if they felt a burning. They may even cry as they urinate. The condition is called cystitis. Occasionally a little blood may follow the urine; the temperature may rise a degree or two. When a dog has been affected for several days, the urine may appear stringy or cloudy from pus and blood. Males show similar symptoms and may stand for long periods with one hind leg lifted and only drops of urine produced.

It is not safe, however, to assume that because you see these symptoms your pet is necessarily affected with cystitis; he may have stones. It is best to consult your veterinarian in such cases and have him make the necessary tests.

Twisted Bladder. In a perineal hernia, the bladder sometimes twists about and moves out through the hernia under the skin. It fills with urine, and unless it is tapped and replaced, the dog dies. This is also a matter for your veterinarian.

Stones in the Bladder and Urethra. A great deal can be told about the bladder by palpation (feeling) by a skillful and experienced practitioner. The layman ordinarily cannot diagnose ailments by this method, although occasionally one does—for example, the dog owner who brought me his pet, saying that he had felt bladder stones "like gravel which crunches together." As it happened, the stones were a variety which were not visible by X ray; but they could be felt and I was able to remove them.

When a dog owner sees some of the stones which his veterinarian has removed from his pet's bladder, he often can scarcely believe his eyes. "How did they ever get there?" he asks, or he may say, "I never knew him to eat stones." A stone that was eaten couldn't possibly get into the bladder. It would pass through the alimentary canal. Stones are slow accumulations of mineral matter in the urine around initial crystals which formed and in some way failed to pass out with the urine. Not all bladder stones are of the same composition. Some, as we have indicated, fail to show in X-ray photography, while some types appear as distinct as do bones.

Stones are found in all sizes, from tiny crystals to huge accretions as large as hen's eggs. Often one finds a bladder filled with assorted sizes, from fine gravel up to huge stones. The surface of the stones varies too. Most are smooth from constant rubbing, but occasionally a stone may be as rough as coarse sandpaper and more or less adherent to the bladder wall, the inner surface of which has become pitted to correspond with the irregularities of the stone.

Weight alone would make such a load of stones uncomfortable and probably somewhat painful. More serious, of course, is the fact that they irritate the bladder, causing it to bleed. They afford a perfect environment for bacteria to multiply among them. But the worst feature is the tendency of the small stones to work into the urethra. At the point where the urethra joins the bladder, a small stone can easily form a plug. The most common place for a stoppage is just behind the bone in the penis. There the urethra runs through the bone, and a stone which could pass down the elastic urethra cannot pass through this rigid bone and so lodges behind it.

TREATMENT: Dogs thus affected try to urinate but usually cannot pass more than a few drops at a time. Often large numbers of stones, one behind the other, form in a line in the urethra and have to be removed surgically. The cystoscope, with its tiny crushing device at the tip, which can be used for similar difficulties in human beings, cannot be used with most house dogs since the bone in the penis is too small to permit its passage. The only way to remove large stones is by surgery followed by bladder antiseptics. When the operation is performed by a skillful surgeon the mortality is low, but if the dog is nursed at home, close supervision and faithful medication are essential. If your doctor gives you sulfa drugs to administer and the dog vomits them, report to him promptly. If you can't make your pet swallow the prescribed medicine, let the doctor know. Don't take your dog home to treat unless you will be able to follow the veterinarian's directions implicitly.

In females, as well as in males, bladder stones become lodged in the urethra, but females usually pass them, upon occasion accompanied by pain. It is sometimes possible to massage them out by inserting the finger in the vagina. In some cases your veterinarian will be able to dilate the urethra while the dog is anesthetized and catch hold of the stones with the tip of long slender forceps and so remove them. Failing this, he can operate.

Urinary Incontinence. This is usually called "dribbling." While it is a common complaint of older spayed bitches, this disagreeable characteristic occurs at all ages and in both sexes. It should not be confused with the reaction so common in some dogs of squatting and wetting, or wetting without squatting, from the joy of seeing a familiar person or from fear or excitement. These are nervous reactions based largely on heredity. Here we are discussing disease or disability. Some male dogs, some unspayed females, and many which have been spayed are unable to retain a full bladder of urine. The sphincter muscle is weak, and as soon as the bladder begins to stretch, urine leaks from the urethra.

TREATMENT: Bladder irritations, as well as weak sphincters, may be the cause. Stones, infections, adhesions can also produce the same result. To effect a cure, one must be certain first of the cause. Drugs are used for infections; surgery for stones; and a simple expedient is helpful for spayed bitches—administering female sex hormone as a substitute for the natural secretion of the missing ovaries. This is done by adding stilbestrol, an inexpensive synthetic hormone, to the diet. The amount required is a matter of experimentation with every bitch; what is sufficient for one may be inadequate for another. Generally a 5-mgm. dose is given every other day at first and then 1 mgm. daily or every other day until continence is established. Thereafter less frequent doses are effective. The size of the dog and the degree of relaxation of the sphincter determine the size of the dose.

Bladder Tumors. The formation of tumors in the bladder is extremely rare in dogs and is a matter for surgery after diagnosis has been established.

Bladder Worms. There are also bladder worms of two sorts, *Capillaria plica* and *Dioctophyme renalis.* Both are such curiosities in dogs as to warrant no more than a mention.

Diabetes. Diabetes is discussed in this section not because it is in any way connected with the urinary tract but simply because urine analysis is the standard test for its presence.

There are two forms of diabetes, both of which cause excessive urination: *diabetes mellitus* (which means honey diabetes and is also called sugar diabetes), and *diabetes insipidus,* also called incipient diabetes. In the former, the urine is heavy and contains far too much sugar. In the latter, it is so thin it is almost water. Urine is tested with a delicate hydrometer, an instrument which indicates the specific gravity of any fluid in relation to that of pure water. A fluid which registers 1.00 is exactly as heavy as water. Normal urine tests about 1.025. If urine tests 1.010, the difference is enough to make one suspicious of incipient diabetes, but if it floats high to 1.040, the urine has an excess of substances other than the water and this may point to sugar diabetes. Your veterinarian can make the tests to determine the cause. The table shown below will help you to understand his findings.

Table XIV

	ORGAN AFFECTED	SPECIFIC GRAVITY	SUGAR TEST	BOILING TEST	APPETITE	INDICATED DIET
Diabetes mellitus (Sugar diabetes)	Pancreas	Higher than water	Sugar	Normal	Normal	Low sugar and starch
Diabetes insipidus (Incipient diabetes)	Pituitary gland	Like water	Negative	Normal	Ravenous	Normal
Nephritis (Kidney disease)	Kidneys	Normal	Negative	Albumin	Normal or depressed	Low protein

Sugar diabetes is caused by a shortage or complete absence of the secretion of the isles of Langerhans in the pancreas. Affected dogs are unable to store sugar in the liver and become sick if they eat large quantities of carbohydrates or sugar. They need proteins and fat, with a minimum of carbohydrates. This, as you will remember, is the opposite of the diet needed by dogs with kidney disease. Incipient diabetes, on the other hand, is caused by a deficiency in the pituitary gland and has no connection with food.

Dogs with both types of diabetes drink and urinate copiously and usually have voracious appetites. They slowly waste away in spite of their heavy food consumption. In the incipient form, one frequently finds the hair thinning out, starting about the head and hind legs.

TREATMENT: Tests which your doctor will make are quite positive in their diagnostic properties. To be doubly sure, he may try protamine zinc insulin on a dog diagnosed as having sugar diabetes. This should bring about a cessation of symptoms for twelve to eighteen hours. If he is reasonably sure of incipient diabetes, your veterinarian can inject posterior pituitary hormone. It will supply the needed chemical to restore the normal functions for many hours. In either event the thirst diminishes. Having thus identified the disease beyond doubt, the doctor and the dog owner must decide whether the daily or twice-daily injections are worth the trouble and the cost. In my opinion there are many cases where they are, either because of the value of the dog or because of one's attachment to him. The owner himself must always be the final judge of the amount of time and money he can devote to the care of a dog afflicted with diabetes.

17. The Digestive Tract

In this chapter we shall group all ailments which occur anywhere in the digestive tract, from the dog's lips to his anus, starting at the mouth.

CAUSES AND PREVENTION OF BAD TEETH

Dental Cavities. Dogs, even when fed inadequate diets, are almost completely free from dental cavities. One study which went into the matter very carefully found only 5.8 per cent of all the teeth examined to have cavities. Many of these were in teeth that were already so loose and had such badly receded gums that they were practically useless to the dogs.

The kind of cavity dogs' teeth develop is not the painful variety which humans may have. When the grinding tips of front and canine teeth wear away, small cavities appear which are no more than we often have in our own front and "eye" teeth. These spots are not the result of decay, but rather areas where the hard enamel has been worn off and the pulp of the tooth exposed.

It is strange how few dogs are found with imperfect teeth as the result of inadequate diets during their growing periods. Dogs allowed to run wild on the "root, hog, or die" basis, though they may appear emaciated and undernourished, usually have fine teeth. "As clean as a hound's tooth" is an accurate simile, and the teeth of "pot lickers" as well as of well-fed hounds are usually healthy. As a matter of fact, bad teeth are found more frequently in pampered pets. Why?

Dogs allowed to run wild can nearly always find old or fresh bones, and though their diets are otherwise inadequate, the bones supply enough of the minerals necessary for fine tooth development, principally calcium and phosphorus. The worst teeth I have known have been in dogs raised in kennels or homes where dog biscuits, cod-liver oil, and meat were fed exclusively. Pet dog owners are more likely to forget to furnish calcium than they are phosphorus. It is a rare thing to find poor teeth in dogs fed entirely on the meal-type dog foods, since these foods usually contain a considerable amount of dried ground bone, an excellent source of the necessary minerals. As it happens, bone meal is about the least expensive ingredient than can be added to dog food, so it is never stinted. It is unfortunate that comparatively few one-dog owners have learned the value of these excellent foods because they mistakenly depend on their dog's appetite to dictate what he will or will not eat and make little effort to train him to eat what is good for him.

It is impossible to generalize about the effect of canned foods on dogs' teeth. Dogs fed certain types of inadequate canned foods often have deplorable teeth, while those fed other brands, in the manufacture of which careful biological research has ensured the foods' completeness, will have beautiful teeth.

The quality of a dog's teeth is very little affected by the consistency of the food he eats. As we have said, teeth are made from the food the animal assimilates, not by rubbing them on the outside. Whether a food is soft or hard is unimportant, so long as it contains a sufficient amount of the necessary elements. From the nutritional standpoint, hard foods may be either good or bad. The only special advantage that firm, resistant foods have is that they help to clean the teeth. Spoiled pet dogs which dictate to their owners what they are going to eat choose mushy foods and meat (to say nothing of candy and ice cream) and therefore have heavy tartar deposits.

If every dog owner would give his pet a nice flat beef rib bone occasionally and let the dog chew it in a spot where it could not be contaminated by worm eggs, he would be sure that the dog, in crunching through the bone, would keep his teeth sparkling white and at the same time get the minerals necessary to keep them sound. Many owners feed big round knucklebones. Rib bones do a vastly better job as toothbrushes, because with them the teeth punch through the bone and are scraped to the roots, whereas with knucklebones only the edges of the teeth are polished. However, this should not be construed to mean that bones are essential for the development of sound teeth. Dogs fed meal-type foods reach old age with perfect teeth so long as the tartar is chipped off occasionally. A bone is merely a convenient toothbrush to clean off the tartar. But if the dog already has bad teeth, he won't chew the bone vigorously enough to benefit him because it hurts. And if he is eating a constipating diet, bones will make him more constipated. In that case it may be necessary to alter the diet and give some graham crackers to help prevent constipation.

Pitted Teeth. Some dogs go through life with teeth pitted from diseases they had at teething time. There is nothing which can be done for this condition. However, such teeth are almost as serviceable as unpitted teeth and rarely cause any difficulty.

Abscesses. Abscesses at the ends of roots are common. Regression of the gums may leave the teeth with the appearance of having been pushed out of their sockets and yet the roots may be solidly set. In time, however, this condition leads to a gradual loosening of the teeth. Bacteria have easy access to the roots and penetrate deeper and deeper, causing greater and greater regression of the gums. This is particularly true of the narrow teeth with two roots which are found behind the big canine teeth—premolars, they are called, but dentists refer to them as bicuspids. These are usually the first teeth to become loose and require extraction.

Tartar. Inadequate diets are the greatest enemy of dogs' teeth. Tartar accumulation is possibly the second. When tartar collects in heavy deposits next to the gums, it tends to push against the gums and thus causes irritation and recession.

Owners often delay taking their dogs to the veterinarian until there is as much as a quarter of an inch of tartar on the back teeth and the canines are heavily encrusted. By this time the dog's breath is usually vile. More than one pet owner has asked me to pull all his dog's teeth because they looked so horrible. In such cases I simply anesthetize the poor dog, clean every jot of tartar off, and when the master returns to claim his pet, show him an animal with a beautiful mouthful of teeth. The removal of tartar is a job that can be done by any dog owner who is handy in such matters and not too squeamish. A special dental tartar scraper is all the equipment that is necessary. But your veterinarian usually will be able to remove all the tartar more quickly and with less discomfort to the owner and the pet.

Worn and Broken Teeth. Broken teeth are commonly the result of accidents. Another and very common source of difficulty is the delight some dogs take in carrying and retrieving heavy or hard articles. Your dog may bring you stones and tease you to throw them for retrieving. Other pups seem to prefer a piece of metal pipe. If you encourage the habit, such dogs' teeth may eventually be worn off nearly to the gum. I have examined many dogs which had several teeth missing because the rocks they had caught in the air had broken them off.

Hunting dogs that love to dig have notoriously bad teeth. Terriers and hounds, farm dogs, and country dogs which dig out woodchucks, badgers, raccoons, possums, and the like will tear at roots covered with sand, chew on rocks which bar the way. The teeth of older dogs of this kind—especially their front teeth—may be almost entirely worn away.

MOUTH, TONGUE, AND SALIVARY GLAND DISORDERS

Foreign Bodies in the Mouth. Dogs frequently get bones or sticks wedged across the top of the mouth so tightly that proper forceps and considerable strength are necessary to dislodge them. Bone chips forced between the teeth sometimes cause gum ulceration. It is not uncommon to find a dog unable to close his mouth and, upon examination, discover that a tooth has been driven through the center of a short ham bone in such a way that the bone has become a long cap protruding above the tooth. The bone is often so firmly lodged that a good deal of strength is required to pull it off.

Tumors in the Mouth. There are two quite common forms of growths in the mouth—gingavomas and papillomas. Both are fairly common in dogs (see page 158).

Plugged Ducts. Into the mouth of the dog empty three sets of salivary glands through little tubes called ducts. We have considered the functions of these glands in Chapter 2.

The ducts may become plugged by bacteria, and sometimes even by foreign bodies such as stones, with the result that the saliva can't get out. The sight or smell of food causes the production of saliva and the gland is distended. If it is squeezed, the pressure will sometimes push the obstruction into the mouth. If this does not work, an incision through the skin must be made by the veterinarian and the thick, viscous, syrupy fluid drained out. A puncture in the wrong place might sever the big jugular vein, so this is a matter for one who knows anatomy. After proper medication, the duct is freed, the incision heals, and the gland functions normally.

COMPLICATIONS: If for any reason this treatment fails, the usual consequence is a fistula. The constant production of saliva forces a sac to form. The lining of the sac is often composed of the secreting variety of cells, so that it fills and heals as often as it is emptied. In such cases it is necessary to cut the lining out. This is an unpleasant piece of surgery because of the proximity of the blood vessels and nerve, necessitating great care to avoid the severance of an essential blood vessel. Some of these sacs will not only involve the gland but push forward into the mouth. They sometimes peel out smoothly, but often they require extremely careful dissection.

Salivary Gland Infection. The salivary glands sometimes become infected with various kinds of organisms. Mumps in the parotid glands occasionally occurs, but with antibiotics and sulfas the dog is soon cured. The parotid glands may also swell from collars which are too tight and squeeze them. Kicks, shot wounds, traffic accidents may damage them, but such traumas are rare.

Tongue Injuries. The tongue also is subject to its share of maladies, most of which are caused by injuries, though occasionally mouth infections and tumors will cause it to swell. In my experience the most common injuries to the tongue are bites, usually inflicted by the dog's own teeth as the result of traffic accidents, kicks, or blows. I have seen a few dogs which have had their tongues bitten and even partially amputated by other dogs, or by cats, raccoons, or rats. On a hot day a dog pants with his tongue lolling far out and hanging down between his teeth, so that a blow from underneath can cause serious injury. However, an accident of this sort usually results in a straight cut which bleeds little.

On two occasions I have removed elastic bands which had become embedded in the dogs' tongues. Not infrequently needles and fishhooks are found in or through the tongue. Needles are usually embedded in the back of the tongue, while fishhooks are more often found piercing the front, thin part.

All such foreign bodies cause great discomfort to the dog, and considerable saliva is usually discharged. He may roll about, poking his face here and there against the ground, but he will generally paw violently at his face with one or both paws. Such actions in themselves should indicate what the trouble is, but I have known many an owner to rush his pet to the veterinarian believing that the dog was strangling or even that he had rabies.

Injuries to the tongue may cause parts of it to die and slough away. The dead area is gangrenous and the odor is extremely obnoxious. Early action by your doctor will help to lessen the amount which has to be removed.

Poison Injury to Mouth, Tongue, and Tissues. Animals are too often badly burned by caustics, acids, and concentrated chemicals which sadistic human beings give them disguised in food. Other dogs may pick up poisons from garbage pails or eat poison intended for pests. If the dog is known to have eaten anything of a poisonous nature, the promptest action is necessary (see Chapter 6).

AILMENTS OF THE THROAT

Pharyngitis and Laryngitis. These are the general terms used to designate inflammation of the pharynx and larynx. They are applied to a number of conditions. Viruses of distemper, housedog disease, and bacterial agents, such as streptococcal diseases, will all inflame the throat, including the tonsils and the surrounding glands. The small lymph nodes and the salivary glands may also become inflamed. When these glands are felt between the finger and thumb, they may appear to be round instead of flat, as they normally are.

Coughing induced by any of these conditions tends to irritate these areas just as it does in humans. The tonsils and epiglottis take a great deal of strain. They may be found so greatly enlarged that they look like little roosters' combs protruding from their clefts and almost touching across the back of the throat. It is no wonder that dogs with chronically enlarged tonsils vomit frequently, even though they may not run temperatures. They must feel as we would if we were to tickle our own throats with a feather.

But merely finding redness instead of the proper pink color, or small deep red areas perhaps only as large as pinheads, or enlarged tonsils is not a diagnosis. It does not tell you *why* there is such inflammation. To determine the basic cause, one must have a complete knowledge of other symptoms, temperature, and history. The treatment depends on an accurate identification of the disease which is causing the symptoms in evidence. Chronically enlarged tonsils can be removed safely; tonsils enlarged from upper respiratory diseases may not be removed so safely, since the surgery may give viruses and bacteria which are confined ordinarily to the mucous layer of tissue access to the blood stream, where they may do further and more serious damage.

Your veterinarian will prescribe drugs if he is sure that the condition is of bacterial origin or if it is necessary to prevent bacteria from developing in the tissue damaged by viruses. But he cannot *cure* true virus diseases by any known drugs. Don't expect him to, any more than you would expect your doctor to cure your cold or influenza. In both cases, however, some alleviation or easing is possible.

Paralysis of the Pharynx. There are times when the pharynx becomes paralyzed, as in rabies, or after injuries to nerves during surgery, or as a complication after housedog disease, which may cause the nerves on one side of the area to twitch and thus interfere with normal functioning. For paralysis of this kind no treatment is effective.

Growths in the Pharynx. Occasionally growths of one sort or another can be found in the pharynx. The most common I have found are polyps. These are generally more or less like toadstools with a pedicle attached to the tissues from which they grow. Several times I have located them growing above the soft palate. Such polyps have been reported as large as four inches across. Even the small ones the size of shoe buttons cause irritation and, to a greater or less degree, interfere with the normal functioning of the pharynx. They usually harbor bacteria and cause a fetid, objectionable odor on the dog's breath. Other growths may be extensions of growths in adjacent organs and nerves. Since they may be benign or highly malignant, your veterinarian should be consulted in all such cases.

ESOPHAGEAL INJURIES

The esophagus—the gullet, as it is often called—is the tube which leaves the pharynx parallel with the windpipe and down which—and sometimes up which—food passes.

The esophagus is subject to a number of ills, all of which cause the dog to show difficulty in swallowing and often in retaining food. Vomiting after eating may be a symptom of such difficulty, as well as of a number of other maladies.

Among the many causes of trouble in the esophagus are abrasions, corrosion, local infections, and inflammation due to more generalized infections. We also find ruptures, fistulas, and foreign bodies as well as esophageal worms, to say nothing of growths which can and do occur here as frequently as almost anywhere else in the body.

Very sharp objects may scrape, cut, or otherwise lacerate the lining of the esophagus or even cut through it. Needles and pins may penetrate it. I have seen a case in which a bullet passed directly through the esophagus without killing the dog. However, the wound caused a stricture in the tube so that the dog had trouble swallowing anything but food in small pieces. Caustics, acids, and corrosive drugs inflict great damage to the gullet if they are consumed in sufficient quantity, but such damage is rare compared with other troubles.

When the esophagus is injured but the animal can still swallow, the general treatment consists for the most part in providing easily swallowed liquids. If it is impossible for the dog to swallow, it is necessary to prevent dehydration by rectal applications of water. When administered in this way, water is almost as quickly absorbed by the intestines as when taken by mouth.

There are times when the gentle application of a stomach tube down which liquids can be poured is of special value. In difficult cases veterinarians administer saline solutions made to approximate blood, and add vitamins, amino acids, and glucose, all by vein. A week of such treatment while the patient's gullet is healing is very worth while. Often the stomach and intestines and other organs are also injured, so that such infusions are a "must" if the dog is to survive.

Rupture and Enlargement. A section of the esophagus may be ruptured so that a small pocket forms. The pocket fills with food and decomposition occurs. Gradually the tear lengthens, letting more and more food out into the pocket until a protuberance like a bird's crop is formed. This crop or diverticulum, as veterinarians call it, has no elastic tissue to force its contents back into the gullet, so the collection remains for long periods, gradually spilling out by the pressure of the surrounding muscles. The break or tear seldom occurs in the neck but usually where the esophagus runs through the chest cavity.

Enlargement of the gullet without an actual break in the wall is also fairly common. The effect is similar to the formation of a pocket, with vomiting after eating. Affected dogs get thin because of failure to retain food. They do not handle mushy food as well as chunks of meat.

In diagnosing the condition, your veterinarian will usually X-ray the throat after the dog has been fed bismuth. The enlargement or pocket can then be seen clearly along the route of the esophagus.

When the diverticulum occurs in the neck, it may be felt with the fingers. In that case surgery offers a comparatively simple cure. But when the pocket occurs in the chest, surgery presents problems which many veterinarians are not equipped to handle. A dog's chest may not be opened without collapse of the lungs, unless some artificial "breathing" mechanism is applied to the windpipe.

Damage from Acids, Caustics, Cuts, et cetera. When the esophagus has been burned by acid, or cut and scratched by glass or another sharp body, the treatment which it needs is rest, so that it can heal. Many laymen, not realizing how long a dog can go without food, try to force him to eat. This is a great mistake. Milk, broth, and foods that trickle down the gullet with as little irritation as possible are best for him.

Foreign Bodies in the Esophagus. The esophagus has a tough lining, but sharp objects occasionally penetrate it. Such objects as pins, wires, and needles manage at times to stick through and require surgical removal. Your veterinarian can locate them with his X ray, look down the gullet through a metal tube with a silvery lining, and then with a long pair of forceps extract the foreign object.

Sometimes a dog swallows a lump of food which sticks in the esophagus, not by adhesion but because of a stricture caused by some previous injury. The lump may be a large piece of stringy meat. A small end may by-pass the stricture, but the bulk may be unable to do so. The dog may not be able to regurgitate it. He can't swallow anything, and appears apprehensive and uneasy. He may paw at the side of his head or hold his head stretched forward abnormally. In fact, he may be mistaken for a rabid dog. And sad to say, many a truly rabid dog appears to have something stuck in his throat. There is a saying in all areas where rabies has been prevalent: "Beware of a dog with a bone stuck in his throat." It is usually not a bone!

Fistulas. These passages from the gullet out through the skin are easily detected. They may follow the path of a sharp object which worked out through the neck. Because of the constant mucous discharge, the hole sometimes fails to heal and forms a tube which must be dissected out. When the dog swallows, a little moisture works out along the fistula and is evident on the neck. Laymen will mistakenly insert disinfectants into these fistulas, not realizing that they connect with the gullet and that the disinfectant will flow down into the stomach. The removal of a fistula is a job for your veterinarian.

Tumors. These can be surgically removed, but the outcome is not favorable. The tumors caused by esophageal worms recede almost to normal when the worms are killed but interfere greatly with swallowing while they are alive. Here again your veterinarian can advise you.

STOMACH AILMENTS

The stomach is susceptible to many of the same injuries as is the gullet. After all, it is in a sense only an enlargement of the gullet and intestinal tract. It has a valve on each end and certain specialized functions, as we have seen.

Poisons, corrosives, and acids which might pass so rapidly down the esophagus as to damage it little or not at all can lie in the stomach for long enough to produce dire results. Sharp objects can penetrate its thin walls easily; gas formation, if the gas is unable to escape, can balloon it so that its walls are stretched sometimes permanently. Parasites live in it. Hot or cold foods affect it. Grass, straw, hay, pine needles, hair, cloth waste, coarse shavings—all kinds of foreign bodies may irritate its delicate lining or form impactions. Stomach ulcers may occur on its inner surface. Infectious diseases may inflame it and retard its functions. Accidents may rupture it, especially if it is full of food; it may be punctured by bullets or sharp objects. Abnormal growths may appear on either of its surfaces. Adhesions may cause the intestines to cling to it. How can a layman recognize such conditions? What can he do to alleviate them? Should he consult his veterinarian?

We have considered the question of recognition and treatment of poisons in Chapter 6. Now let us consider the causes and care of some of the other common difficulties.

Penetration by Sharp Objects. When a dog shows pain and vomits blood you should consider the possibility of stomach punctures by sharp objects. If you have reason to suspect that the animal has swallowed such an object, you may be able to force him to regurgitate it by administering hydrogen peroxide (page 126). If this fails, prompt veterinary treatment—usually surgery—is necessary. X ray shows some objects very clearly.

Some laymen expect that bones will cause such penetrations, and they often do, but in general the stomach fluids soften bones and blunt their sharp points quickly, so that they are harmless. It is not uncommon to find bones in the stools of dogs, or sharp bone chips in the rectum. All these are simply evidences of indigestion. There is little chemical action on the lime in bones once they have left the stomach. The acids, coupled with the protein-digesting enzyme, do a very thorough job on most bones. Note the gray, crumbly, constipated stools of bone-fed dogs whose stomachs are in healthy condition. The bones have been digested but they are constipating, which is a good reason for not feeding too many. If whole bones are found instead of the calcareous (containing lime) feces, it is an indication of stomach trouble.

Foreign Material Causing Impactions. Mature dogs with impactions —masses of material than cannot be assimilated—generally show considerable pain, sometimes vomit, and lie around without showing much interest in what goes on about them. The condition is not always easy to detect. One more or less constant symptom is the tenseness of the abdominal muscles. This is a symptom of nearly all pain in and about the stomach. Occasionally dogs will assume a position of standing on their hind legs with their chests resting on the floor.

Puppies with foreign bodies in the stomach react similarly. They may be so tense that one cannot feel the abdominal contents properly. When an emetic is given, the stomach empties and the abdominal muscles relax with the disappearance of the pain.

X ray may be helpful in revealing foreign bodies in the stomach, though it often fails to show such things as wood, glass, grass, or cigar butts.

When dogs eat pieces of meat or bones while lying on straw or bedding, very often the bedding sticks to the food and is swallowed. But dogs also eat such stuff all by itself and apparently from choice. It is more or less to be expected that a dog will nibble at grass and sometimes vomit within an hour after eating it—or even within a few minutes. But there are dogs which eat great quantities of grass—eat and eat until the mass in their stomachs cannot move one way or the other. Dogs sometimes develop a passion for pine needles. I have known them to stand up on their hind legs to eat needles off the trees.

Dogs eating garbage, especially from restaurant pails or barrels, often consume quantities of bologna, cellophane wrappings, paper, and other indigestible residue. Material of this sort forms a large lump in the stomach. In the Whitney Veterinary Clinic we have seen impactions containing twigs, cinders, hay, leaves all intertwined and causing great distress to the dogs. It is not uncommon for dogs to swallow women's stockings and other material of the sort.

But puppies take the prize for the oddities they will swallow. We have removed a ten-inch bone knitting needle from a ten-weeks-old cocker spaniel's throat; spark plugs from a puppy's stomach; metal jacks; golf balls partly chewed; rubber balls; a child's watch; dice, stones, cinders, coal of all sizes; steel wool, cigar butts, and glass, to mention only a few.

The treatment of such impactions had best be left to your veterinarian. If he is not available, or if you live too far away from one, first empty the stomach by the hydrogen-peroxide method (page 126). Occasionally, when long objects have been swallowed, one end will still be in sight and the object can be pulled out. Emptying an impaction of vegetable matter can frequently be accomplished with repeated large doses of mineral oil. If a tablespoonful is given twice a day it not only helps the mass to untangle, but lubricates the scratchy material as it passes through the intestines. We have recovered as much as two quarts of pine needles from a large dog, wads and wads of hay and straw, as well as rope, cloth, and quantities of sticks and bones.

There are impactions which only surgery can relieve, foreign bodies which cannot be extracted in any other way. Needles and wire may penetrate the stomach, work through the liver and diaphragm, scratch the heart, and kill the dog unless quickly removed. X ray is, of course, invaluable in such cases.

Ruptured Stomachs. These usually cause death, though prompt attention may save your pet. If your dog has been run over, kicked by a horse, fallen from a high place after he has eaten—rush him to the veterinarian. It is possible to open the abdomen, thoroughly wash the contents out, suture the stomach, suture the abdomen, and save the dog. The peritoneal cavity of a dog is quite resistant to infection, or saving him would be impossible because of peritonitis.

Ground Glass Fallacy. Frequently an owner will tell us that his dog was poisoned by someone who fed him ground glass. In recent years experiments have been undertaken to determine how much ground glass animals can pass through the intestinal tract without its causing death. (If you notice, the glass is always "ground." Naturally a dog will not swallow large pieces without chewing.) Dogs and hogs were found to be able to manage large quantities of ground glass and be not much the worse for the experience. So don't blame ground glass for your dog's death without careful investigation. I have never seen a death caused by it.

Inflammation of the Stomach. Several diseases cause inflammation of the stomach, as we have seen in our considerations of Carré distemper, leptospirosis, and food-poisoning organisms. The digestive function is so badly impaired as to make one wonder whether the force feeding recommended by many throughout these diseases is advisable. Some who have studied the problem—myself included—believe that it is better to let the digestive tract rest and feed by vein if feeding is necessary.

Diarrheas. These may originate in the stomach and follow down through the intestines. They will be discussed when we consider the intestinal ailments.

Stomach Parasites. These are easily destroyed, as we have seen on pages 110–16.

Bloat. A condition which kills a great many dogs of the large breeds, especially great Danes, St. Bernards, and bloodhounds, is "the bloat." One will see his dog eat a satisfactory meal, appear to feel perfectly well, and be dead three hours later. The pressure generated in the stomach by the formation of gas by bacteria becomes too great for the organs to endure. The stomach distends like a balloon, and even the skin becomes so taut from the expansion that it resounds like a drum if you snap it with your finger. The gas presses the diaphragm forward against the heart and lungs. Besides the pressure, there seems to be a bacterial toxin developed.

For some reason the bloat seems usually to take the best dogs. It has been my own misfortune over the years to lose many bloodhounds, and always it was the best dog that died. Such experiences have led me to feed my dogs the first thing in the morning because a dog does not bloat on an empty stomach, and those I lost all died at night.

TREATMENT: Since it is not always possible to obtain the services of a veterinarian in such an emergency, what can the dog owner do to save his pet? Assuming that you find him in the early stages, before the condition is hopeless, try first to run a stomach tube into the gullet and down into the stomach. Failing this, do not become terrified, but find some small hollow metal tube which you can sharpen on one end to make a large hypodermic needle. Be bold. Stick it through the skin and into the stomach three or four inches and allow the gas to escape. The best place to make this puncture is just behind the ribs on the right side of the dog. The gas will escape with a hissing sound, but the food in the stomach may plug the improvised "needle." Push a wire through to unplug it. On one occasion I could find nothing on the spot from which to fashion a needle but an umbrella rib. I used a broom straw as an "unplugger" or stylet, as the doctor would call it. It saved the dog. Once the gas is out enough to permit the dog to swallow, give a stimulant. Coffee is excellent. The caffeine gives a quick lift which lasts. Alcoholic "stimulants" produce depressions, as has already been pointed out. Two cupfuls of coffee for a large dog is not too much. Half a cup is a good dose for a cocker spaniel.

After administering the stimulant, treat the dog for shock (see page 135). Pay close attention to see that he doesn't bloat again. Veterinarians can give injections of drugs, like apomorphine, which cause the dog to vomit, if they get on the case early enough. Or Lentin may be administered; this is a double-acting drug, causing vomiting and speeding peristalsis, thus eliminating gas rapidly along the intestinal route. The veterinarian can give stimulants by injection, too, and possibly pass a stomach tube and apply drugs to stop further bacterial action on the food.

AFTEREFFECTS: A dog saved from bloating usually has little appetite for some time. The stomach and sometimes areas in the small intestine, too, have been so badly stretched that it is not uncommon to find brownish blood in the stool for several days. There are cases on record in which the stomach never did return to normal and post-mortem examination years later revealed a thin-walled, greatly enlarged organ.

Secretory Deficiencies. Certain of the small breeds, such as Boston terriers, French bulldogs, and some cocker spaniels, and a few of the larger breeds, such as bulldogs, often have secretory deficiencies which prevent their handling certain kinds of foods. One Boston terrier owner always spread newspapers on the floor where he fed his dogs, since he expected them to eat and regurgitate their food two or three times before they could get it to stay down. This was due in part to improper preparation of the food and was cured by allowing the food to soak well before feeding and by the addition of a little hydrochloric acid to each batch of food. When the gastric juice is inadequate in volume and in acid, such care in the preparation of food is well worth while. If the food is mixed with water in which a tablespoonful of hydrochloric acid is added to each quart, some dogs will no longer vomit.

There are dogs which will lose a meal that contains fatty ingredients; others will regurgitate a meal containing ground meat but will retain the same amount of meat if it is fed in chunks. Usually the dogs which vomit easily are those which are naturally nervous. It is not necessarily a stomach defect but possibly an endocrine disturbance which causes this disagreeable characteristic.

Growths in the Stomach. These occur, but they are rare. They are matters for surgery after diagnosis has been established. It is possible to remove parts of the stomach and have a dog live. In fact, dogs can live even after the whole stomach has been removed, provided especially prepared food is fed at frequent intervals.

INTESTINAL AILMENTS

The same kinds of troubles may occur in a dog's intestines as those we find afflicting the gullet and stomach. The intestinal lining, however, is so delicate, studded as it is with microscopic villi, that it requires less irritation to damage it. The dog's intestine is approximately five times his length, and in that ten or fifteen feet a great many things can happen.

Evidence of pain, excretion of foul feces, vomiting, temperature are all symptoms of enteritis—inflammation of the intestinal lining—but it is not always easy to put one's finger on the exact diagnosis or cause.

From a study of the feces, however, one can tell a number of things about the condition of the intestine. Feces may be residue of food. If they are, then one can tell whether the food is being properly digested. Feces may also be only wastes from the intestines, stomach, and liver. Or feces may be—and usually are—a mixture of the two.

If we find undigested bones, pieces of meat, food ingredients in their original form, we know something is wrong. If, by using a microscope, we find worm eggs, then we know the dog has worms. Or if tapeworm segments stick to the feces, we know tapeworms are present. If a microscopic examination shows pieces of intestinal lining, some part of the intestine has been injured or corroded and has sloughed off. This is, needless to say, an indication of serious trouble.

If we find brown, partly digested blood, we know an injury exists well up in the intestine; whereas if the blood is bright red, it obviously came from down in the lower part, probably from the colon. If the stool is especially evil-smelling, gray, and sticky, we can be sure insufficient bile is being secreted by the liver or that the bile duct is plugged, and we look for the trouble outside of the intestines.

Besides being subject to the infectious inflammatory diseases, the intestines are subject to the same kinds of injuries as is the stomach. Infection of the intestinal lining is called *enteritis*. In general the same poisons and corrosives, sharp objects, and foreign bodies can cause damage, and the intestine is much more subject to injuries since it harbors most of the worms, coccidia, putrefactive bacteria, noxious gases, toxins, and waste materials. One finds more bone and wire punctures and stoppages due to stones, clinkers, and other foreign objects in the intestines than in the stomach. It is not uncommon to find upon post-mortem examination that the intestine has been punctured by wires and similar sharp objects and that peritonitis has set in.

Occasionally, but rarely, the intestines of dogs twist and knot so as to preclude the passage of food. Sometimes a dog will have a hernia and a loop of intestine will pass into it, become filled with stool, and become useless (see pages 338–340).

In one four-months-old puppy a peculiar lump developed just beside the loin and a fetid odor rose from the ooze which seeped from the opening in the lump. The tip of a wire could be felt at this point. When I pulled it out, it turned out to be an eight-inch piece of wire used to seal freight cars. The pup had eaten the wire and passed it into the intestines, where it had made a fistula through the skin. Yet the dog had never missed a meal. The intestines become more amazing as one understands them better.

In bitches whose uteri have ruptured during whelping, peritonitis often causes intestines and uterus to adhere in a mass that makes the doctor suspect a neoplasm. The dog may live with no treatment whatever—so long as she drinks plenty of water or is given it intravenously.

Foods following intestinal damage must be soft; not bone or bran, which can scratch the soft intestinal lining. Bone chips also irritate it. Meat, cheese, milk are largely digested and have but little residue. Boiled milk, hard-boiled eggs, and soda crackers all tend to be constipating and can be given when there is diarrhea but should be avoided if the stools are hard. Glucose, in the form of corn syrup or as dextrose powder dissolved in water or milk, makes excellent food and is quickly assimilated. It is incomplete, to be sure, but is valuable both as a form of energy and because of its tendency to prevent dehydration. Dogs often can retain it when they regurgitate any other food.

Injury from Poison. This subject has been covered in Chapter 6.

Intestinal Tumors. Sometimes one finds persistent bleeding from the bowels. It often occurs in dogs which may appear perfectly well and without pain. One might suspect hookworms, but if they were present the dog would probably be anemic and debilitated, since such a large number are required to cause bloody stools.

In many cases the blood is found to be coming from a tumor or growth. It may be an involvement of the intestine or a polypoid growth which protrudes into the intestine as a ball held by a stem, something like a toadstool. The constant passage of food keeps it raw and bleeding and may cause constipation. The veterinarian may be able to feel the growth, but in some cases only an exploratory operation may reveal it, since X rays do not show it.

Intussusceptions. Another cause of bleeding is a telescoping of the bowel. A fold of intestines slides inside the adjacent intestine and is gradually forced farther and farther along until perhaps ten or twelve inches has become invaginated. This really means that three times that much of the intestine is involved, as can be easily understood. A ten-inch intussusception involves thirty inches of intestine. The invaginated part dies from pressure and because its blood supply is shut off. Food cannot move through it, nor moisture.

Once suspicion points to this condition, detection is not difficult, because a long, swollen section with an abrupt beginning can generally be felt quite easily through the abdominal wall. Usually the dog so affected vomits everything he eats. He becomes dehydrated, his temperature rises, his expression and attitude show pain. A day or two after the condition has become established, the fecal material begins to appear watery and to have an acrid odor. Usually this watery secretion turns reddish from the blood exuded by the entombed intestine, whose lower end is free.

The causes are not well understood. I reported a case in which a mother dog and six puppies all developed the ailment and died. No one had the faintest suspicion that they were so affected until the third had died. The mother was operated on, but three more intussusceptions developed. It has been said that giving strong purgatives tends to produce intussusceptions, but these particular dogs had not been dewormed recently. Foreign bodies which stick to the intestinal lining are often implicated. And growths, like large polyps, sometimes move downward, dragging the intestine after them in a fold.

Surgery is the one treatment for this condition. A piece of intestine has to be removed, together with the blood supply to the section. It is true, however, that there have been cases in which intussusceptions have just started and been detected by feeling, and surgery has been averted by manipulation, which has worked the fold out and prevented its further development.

Intestinal Parasites. Intestinal parasites cause bloody stools and diarrhea. Probably because of their toxins, even roundworms cause profuse diarrhea in puppies. Hookworms, which are like little leeches, draw large amounts of blood, living on the serum and letting the red cells loose in the intestine. They are the worst kind of worm when it comes to the production of bloody stools. Coccidia are protozoa which, because of their great numbers and consequent damage to the intestinal wall, produce bloody diarrhea. Such forms are easy to cure by the simple procedures of eliminating worms and waiting for the body to build up its immunity against coccidia.

Constipation. In ordinary constipation the stools are so hard that they are difficult for the dog to pass and straining at stool is often apparent. The feces may drop out in balls so hard that it is difficult to crush them. Or they may not come out at all. In such cases a dam of large diameter is formed, and if the residue of more food remains behind the lump, it may build up in extreme cases to an accumulation a foot long and two or three inches in diameter. This may stay for a week or more until softer food residue attempts to go on past it, in which case the dog drips a few drops of foul-smelling excretion when he attempts to defecate. Such a huge lump can cause the dog's death. By damming the feces, the stoppage at the very least causes autointoxication and puts a strain on all the organs concerned in toxin elimination. The intestinal wall may die, perforate, and allow stools to seep into the abdomen, causing death by peritonitis.

A surprising number of people seem to be unable to tell when their dog is constipated. It is not unusual for an owner to treat a dog for constipation because he has seen him straining. But straining at stool is not necessarily an indication of constipation. The dog also does that in diarrhea.

Constipation is difficult evacuation—difficult usually because the fecal mass is too large or too hard to pass the anus, because its consistency is such that it causes pain, or because of ineffectual peristalsis, weakness in the muscles which effect evacuation. Unless the dog is greatly overweight, an impacted mass in the rectum may easily be felt through the abdominal walls.

One of the most common victims of constipation is the overfat, underexercised city dog. For this condition there is little excuse. It is caused more frequently than not by feeding an unbalanced mixture of dog biscuits, meat, and bones. Biscuits are usually made principally of second-grade white flour. Meat has very little residue. Bones have a dry mineral residue. When the three are fed together without other material, the stools resemble a kind of modified concrete.

Enlargement of the prostate gland frequently causes constipation when the diet is not regulated accordingly. The prostate, being just below the rectum in front of the pelvis, when enlarged will present a formidable obstruction which leaves a very small space for the passage of the feces through the rectum.

A dog whose pelvis has been broken and has healed in a partially collapsed position is likely to be constipated again and again. Such a dog may have no more than half the natural pelvic orifice through which the stool can pass. Special attention must be given to his diet.

As a matter of fact, diet is related to all forms of constipation. If owners would simply feed properly, their dogs' bowels could be easily regulated, unless actually affected by a growth. Too often, however, owners are willing to resort to drugs rather than take the trouble to regulate the dog's diet to relieve constipation. The addition of an item of food or the elimination of one is usually all that is needed. Certain types of food cause increased laxation: the coarse, raw fibers in bran or alfalfa meal; milk sugar in skim milk, buttermilk, or whey; raw egg white; and fruits such as pears, apples, and peaches. Other foods are constipating: bones; muscle meat; hard-boiled eggs; boiled white rice; barley water; and dog biscuits. If a dog's diet is regulated to include the proper amounts of the right types of food, constipation can easily be prevented or relieved.

Cure for the temporary condition is to give enemas, and if they do not enable the dog to expel the mass, the veterinarian will have to crush it with the aid of instruments until it is small enough to pass out—a disagreeable experience for any dog.

Accidents. The intestines are less often affected by accidents than are the other organs. It is not often that crushed or ruptured intestines are found in a post-mortem examination of even an animal that has been run over by a vehicle. The liver and spleen may be split open and mashed, and the pelvis broken in many places, but unless the intestines are filled with a constipated mass they are usually unharmed.

It is true, however, that they are often punctured by bullets or bird shot, but sharp objects which penetrate the abdomen generally push the intestines aside. It is amazing how resistant they are. I once had the job of replacing a yard of intestine in the intestinal cavity of a dog which had received a four-inch tear in the abdomen. The intestine had worked out and had been dragged through dirt and hemlock needles in the woods. The owner brought his pet in, wrapped in a blanket, with little hope that anything could be done. The dog was anesthetized, the intestines were washed, and the soil and needles flushed out of the abdomen. After the intestine was replaced, the wall was sutured and the dog recovered.

Bullet wounds made by large-caliber bullets may need suturing. They nearly always result in adhesions, which often interfere with intestinal motility. The difficulty is in knowing whether a bullet which went through the abdomen actually penetrated any part of the intestine. Your veterinarian can help you to determine this. If it is established that the intestine has been punctured by the bullet, the veterinarian may open the abdomen and make the necessary repairs. If food has not already worked out and caused extensive peritonitis, the dog can often be saved.

RECTAL AND ANAL AILMENTS

At the lower end of the intestine the rectum and anus are subject to a number of ills, some of which we have already considered. Specific to this area we find foreign bodies, hemorrhoids, fissure, tumors, and anal-gland accumulation.

Foreign Bodies. Foreign bodies in the rectum may cause a dog to strain and cry and then stop straining, as in severe constipation. In fact, the presence of such bodies is often the start of genuine constipation. Bones are the most common obstruction. Their sharp edges cut and cause great pain, especially when the dog strains. Pins and needles, embedded in the fecal mass or lodged across the rectum, produce a similar effect. A thread hanging from the dog's anus is an object of suspicion—there may be a needle at the other end.

To remove foreign bodies, enemas should first be given, to soften the stool and loosen the objects from the fecal mass. After this has been done, the injection of mineral oil with a small ball syringe makes their passage less painful. The veterinarian can use a forceps to extract them. When a needle becomes lodged at right angles to the passage, it is best removed by cutting it in the middle and pulling out the separate pieces.

Hemorrhoids. These are swollen veins protruding into the rectum and even out through the anus. When present they cause itching and, especially after defecation, may be the source of considerable pain. Hemorrhoids are comparatively uncommon in dogs. Even after they appear they draw back again without treatment and do not remain a permanent annoyance to the dog. Many types disappear when a laxative diet is fed, but persistent hemorrhoids must be removed surgically.

Fissures. These are cracks in the anus. Cuts by bone chips, too great expansion of the anus in passing large lumps of stool, and wounds make tears which do not heal because of the constant irritation of defecation.

The best method of promoting natural healing seems to be to encourage a soft stool by the use of laxative foods and mineral oil and then to maintain it for several weeks until the healing is complete and scar tissue has sufficiently strengthened the tear.

Anal Tumors. These are among the most common which dogs have and among the most malignant. If you see even a small lump developing in the anus, have it removed. The veterinarian will take it out, removing a little extra tissue to be sure of getting all of it. But despite his best effort, a bud may already have started growing, perhaps on the other side of the anus. By removing every lump while it is small, it is possible to add years to the dog's life. Too many owners wait until it is too late.

Accumulation in the Anal Glands. Ailments of the anal glands, also called pouches (see pictures), are among the most common troubles with dogs. The normal secretion of these small glands is a yellowish liquid which is expressed by muscles when the dog is frightened. If too much secretion accumulates in the glands, the dog often sits down and drags himself along in order to force the liquid out. This puts pressure on the glands, and the fluid oozes out and is wiped on the ground, the rug, or wherever he performs.

If the dog is unable to squeeze the fluid out, the glands swell with the accumulation and then become thick with bacterial growth. It may be thick, black, and sticky or thin, yellow, and filled with curds, or gray and dry, or brown, thick, almost like feces. The glands, instead of being of any use as secretory organs, become pouches causing trouble. I have expressed more than a tablespoonful of vile-smelling, thickish fluid from a Newfoundland dog and as much as a teaspoonful from a cocker spaniel.

It is difficult to say how much harm is done by the accumulation which develops in anal pouches. The fact that many dogs seem to take a new lease on life after the material is expressed may be coincidental. That some paralyzed dogs seem to recover quickly may also be coincidental. It hardly seems possible, however, that such vile material could be retained in these glands without some of their toxins becoming absorbed to the detriment of the dog.

Expressing the gland contents is so simple that anyone can do it if he is not too squeamish. First locate the glands. They feel like small or large lumps in the skin, one on each side and below the anus. Spread a piece of absorbent cotton over the hand which will cover the anus. Squeezing with the thumb and second finger behind and slightly below the glands forces the liquid or gummy contents out of the ducts through the mouth of the anus onto the cotton.

But be sure that the cotton is held over the anus. If you neglect this, the stuff may spurt and soil you badly. The odor is extremely obnoxious and stays in cloth for a long while.

Fat dogs are difficult to treat because it is so hard to feel the glands; in such cases a veterinarian had best be employed to do the job. In some cases he may have to insert one finger inside the anus and squeeze from both sides.

Once thoroughly cleaned out, and kept cleaned out, the glands shrink considerably, so that the dog no longer drags his rear along the ground—an activity which, incidentally, is your best indication that his glands need cleaning.

Abscesses in the Anal Glands. There are occasions when the accumulation of debris in an anal gland becomes infected with such bacteria that an abscess forms. First evidence is the dog's constant licking of the spot. It becomes red, distended, and smooth with a soft center. It is too sore for the dog to sit and drag himself. Some dogs run about uneasily, as if unable to have a comfortable moment.

If the abscess is untreated and ruptures of its own accord, a large, slow-healing opening is left which discharges for days and occasions incessant licking. The dog is likely to leave a spot everywhere he sits. But when the abscess is opened surgically and flushed out deeply every day, it will usually heal rapidly and leave no scar.

There are cases where the anal glands become so troublesome they had best be dissected out by your veterinarian, who can do it with one of several ingenious methods. This ends the nuisance permanently.

LIVER AILMENTS

A dog's liver is less affected by disease and injury than other organs of its body. In the first place, though it is larger in proportion than the livers of many other species, it is quite well protected by its location. Moreover, it repairs itself after many abuses. Few dogs actually die of liver trouble, but there are a few liver ailments of some importance which a layman can frequently recognize. Along with liver disorders we include those of the gall bladder, that little balloon in which bile is stored as it is manufactured by the liver.

One of the most obvious signs that all is not well with the liver is the yellow pigment seen in the whites of a dog's eyes, in his skin, his gums, and mucous membranes. When these turn yellow the dog does not have a *disease* called jaundice; he has a *condition* called jaundice. The disease which causes the condition is not always apparent. It might be leptospirosis, or a stoppage of the bile duct, or a tumor.

Jaundice, with or without a pasty gray stool, is a warning sign. It should give any dog owner cause for concern and send him hurrying to the veterinarian.

Hepatitis. When the liver is enlarged, some of it pushes behind the protection of the ribs and can be felt easily. Liver damage from any cause which produces enlargement may be permanent or only temporary. Even though the liver does reduce in size to normal, it still may not be able to function normally.

Obstructive Jaundice. Any condition which prevents bile from escaping into the intestine may be said to be responsible for its becoming absorbed in the blood and turning the tissues of the body yellow. The urine, too, becomes orange. The stools, without bile mixed with them, become gray and sticky.

Obstructive jaundice is caused in dogs by roundworms which get into the bile duct and plug it, by inflammation of the duct, by stones in the gall bladder which block the exit, or by cancer or growths which press against the duct or gall bladder.

Your veterinarian should be consulted. When the difficulty is caused by a simple plugging of the gall bladder, two household substances will cause it to discharge its contents—fat and any magnesium salt (Epsom salts, milk of magnesia, et cetera). Clients have brought their pets to me after mistakenly removing all the fat they could from the dogs' diets. Jaundice has developed. One good meal with considerable fat has brought relief. And a teaspoonful of Epsom salts sometimes brings good results. The stimulus of the fat or magnesium salt caused such an outpouring from the gall gladder that the stoppage was removed.

Gallstones. These have been reported but they occur rarely in dogs. If the diagnosis is gallstones, feeding fat or giving magnesium salts may be unwise. Your veterinarian had best prescribe the treatment.

Infections. Another cause of jaundice, not of liver origin, is the breaking down of red blood cells, as in leptospirosis (see page 263), a disease which also damages the liver. Still another is *infectious hepatitis* (see page 260).

Toxins. Poisoning often injures the liver and indirectly causes jaundice. If tetrachlorethylene is given to kill worms when the stomach and intestines contain fat, the drug gains entrance to the blood by way of the fat in which it is soluble and may damage the liver seriously.

Poisoning with such metals as mercury, arsenic, phosphorus, or thallium may, in time, cause a reduction from normal in the size of the liver.

In such cases the only symptoms may be grayish stools and general debility.

Growths. Tumors are often found in dogs' livers at post-mortem. Livers are found greatly enlarged (hypertrophied) and occasionally are filled with connective tissue (cirrhosis). Abscesses may form when bacteria invade the liver and multiply.

Fatty Livers. These occur in enormously overfat housedogs. Fat cells become interspersed among the liver cells, but how much this interferes with their function is not known. It is impossible to feel the liver or any of the organs in such a dog because of the surplus fat all over and inside of the abdomen. Weight reduction removes fat from the liver as it does elsewhere about the body.

Injuries. The liver may be pierced or cut by sharp objects which work through the stomach wall. Being run over, falling from heights, receiving blows may cause the liver to rupture.

Again let me urge you to consult your veterinarian if you have any reason to believe that liver trouble is present. Watch for the telltale symptoms—jaundice and gray, sticky stools, sometimes accompanied by debility.

18. Parasites

There are so many misconceptions about parasites—the damage they do and the symptoms indicating their presence—that it is perhaps best to begin by pointing out a few of the things they do *not* cause. In Chapter 4 we considered the life histories and cycles of the important parasites. The facts presented there should make you suspicious of the suggestions of uninformed neighbors and friends who will almost invariably insist that your dog, if he is out of sorts for any reason whatever, needs deworming—or "worming," as they usually put it. Perhaps he does. And then again, perhaps he doesn't. A well-meaning neighbor's diagnosis is rarely conclusive. A simple test will shed light on the question—and you can make that test with a thermometer. Intestinal worms, external parasites, or heartworms do not cause the temperature to rise. Don't deworm your dog simply because he shows signs of not feeling well, especially if he has a fever. Find out first what is wrong. It will only complicate matters to dose your dog with something he doesn't need just because a friend's dog benefited by deworming.

If your dog rides around on his hind quarters, pulling his body with his front legs, don't accept some volunteer adviser's word for it that this is a sure sign of worms. It is not. The chances are good that he is trying to express the accumulation in the anal glands.

When your dog has a cough, that in itself is not necessarily a sign that he has worms. Nor is it when he scratches, or becomes bald, or eats odd foods, even sticks and stones, or has a bad disposition, or whines, or deposits loose stools, or vomits, or has fits, or likes garbage. Any of these symptoms *might* be an indication of worms but probably is not.

ROUNDWORMS

In puppies these worms cause potbellies, unthriftiness, diarrhea, anemia, often subnormal temperature, dull coat. When only a few worms are harbored, the symptoms are, of course, less noticeable and may consist only of a general unthriftiness, in spite of a fair appetite. In older dogs their ravages are much less severe. Perhaps the most serious injury done by roundworms is to the lungs. Dogs often develop verminous pneumonia as a result of the damage inflicted by large numbers of larvae boring from the blood vessels to the air sacs and causing irritation as they work up the bronchi and trachea to the throat.

Prevention: This consists in deworming the bitch before breeding, keeping her off soil and out of quarters which are contaminated with roundworm eggs, and washing her teats before the puppies nurse, if there is any chance that she has been where roundworm eggs are present. When the puppies are walking, they too must be kept out of infected quarters. Bones and food which can be dragged around in filth are common sources of infestation.

Treatment: With puppies, a fecal examination should always be made before treatment. If worms are present, the puppies should be put on absolute starvation for twenty hours and then dosed with tetrachlorethylene in capsule form, using one tenth c.c. to each pound of weight of the puppy. An hour later milk of magnesia may be given, and food two hours after that.

Let me again stress the *necessity* of a twenty-hour starvation period. If the puppies have even a teaspoonful of milk in their stomachs or intestines, the drug may kill them. In spite of the obvious danger involved, I have found that for small puppies tetrachlorethylene is much safer than either N butyl chloride or wormseed oil.

In adult dogs, N butyl chloride is safe and effective but has no advantage over tetrachlorethylene, except that it is less toxic if food has been taken unknown to the dog's owner. The dose for N butyl chloride is one c.c. for each ten pounds of the dog's weight. Tetrachlorethylene can be used at the same level, provided the dog has been starved for twenty-four hours. N butyl chloride can be followed by any safe physic, but when tetrachlorethylene is used no oily physic can be safely administered. This drug has an affinity for fat, which is absorbed along with the drug and may cause great damage to the liver. When the stomach and intestines are free of fat, however, quite large doses of tetrachlorethylene may be given without danger.

The treatment had best be repeated in two weeks to destroy the worms which come over from the lungs. Obviously those in the blood won't be reached by the drug.

Here is a trick which often comes in handy if you are deworming a number of dogs: smell the breath of every dog half an hour after dosing to be sure he has retained the capsules containing the drug. An etherlike odor should be plainly detectable in the breath. If you find a capsule on the floor of a cage in which the five puppies you have just dewormed are confined, all you need do to ascertain which pup lost the capsule is to smell their breaths.

Table XV—Estimated Probability of Intestinal Parasite Infestation at Any Age by Per Cent*

				TAPEWORMS		COCCIDIOSIS		
AGE	ROUNDWORMS	HOOKWORMS	WHIPWORMS	FLEA-HOST	RABBIT-HOST	RIVOLTA	BIGEMINA	FELIS
0–3 weeks	40	20	0	3	0	0	0	8
4–11 weeks	50	20	5	9	1	9	1	7
12–23 weeks	42	20	10	10	1	6	1	5
24–51 weeks	27	20	25	14	1	3	2	3
1 year	17	20	28	14	3	2	3	3
2 years	16	20	30	14	5	2	1	2
3 years	15	20	30	14	4	2	1	1
4 years	14	20	30	14	4	2	1	1
5 years	13	20	30	14	3	2	0	1
6 years	12	20	30	14	2	2	0	1
7 years	11	20	30	14	1	1	0	0
8 years	10	20	30	14	0	1	0	0
9 years	9	20	30	14	0	1	0	0
10–15 years	8	20	30	14	0	1	0	0

*Based on a study by the author of four thousand fecal examinations of Connecticut dogs.

Occasionally puppies are so filled with roundworms that even tetrachlorethylene prostrates them. If that happens, you should get them warm and keep them warm until the physic has moved the worms down into the colon. Then a mild enema with a bulb syringe will usually bring relief. The number of worms which can be removed from a dog which reacts so severely—even a six-weeks-old puppy—is often incredible.

Some owners ask at how young an age a puppy can have roundworms and how young they can safely be dewormed. I have kept a careful record of the age of infested dogs and have found a high percentage of three-weeks-old puppies with worms. These, of course, had been contracted before birth. It proved safe to deworm the youngest infested puppy. In my opinion it is safer to deworm them at the first sign of worms than to wait until they are two or three weeks older and sicker and then do it; they will stand it much better.

HOOKWORMS

The principal damage done by hookworms is the anemia they produce in young dogs and puppies. As dogs grow older and are subjected to repeated infestations, they develop partial immunity.

Infested puppies first suffer from lung damage similar to that caused by roundworms. The next result is anemia. One glance at the gums will reveal the puppy's condition. There are many other variable symptoms. The puppy may have fits; diarrhea may become persistent and the appetite picky; sometimes the legs will swell. He may moan; usually he remains lying down, as if even standing were an effort. He will lose weight, breathe more rapidly than a normal pup, and there is usually an acrid odor due to the water discharge which coats his anus and the surrounding hair together with part of his tail.

Older dogs often have fits when first heavily infested. They, too, lose their appetites, develop anemia, become sluggish, have a hangdog appearance, and develop a generally unthrifty look. If proper food is not provided, even older dogs may die—because the best efforts of their red-blood-cell-building mechanism is insufficient to make up for the loss caused by the hookworm infestation.

Prevention: Prevention is the same as that indicated for roundworms, but in the case of hookworms, diet is more important. Iron and copper are essential and the protein fed to the animal must be of good quality.

Treatment: Treatment is the same for hookworms as for roundworms so far as drugs are concerned. But supportive treatment is advisable. Food of high quality helps the dog to recover quickly. Transfusions often work wonders, once the worms are gone, or even before, in very anemic dogs.

Dog breeders often say it is better to build up an infested dog before he is dewormed. This seems to me to be a great mistake, because I have always found that a dog can't be built up as fast as his blood is being thinned by the worms, except by transfusion. The promptest possible action in getting rid of the worms is best if the dog is to be saved.

Having rid the dog of his pests, a diet rich in copper should be provided. Some liver is excellent. Meat has iron. Good-quality dog foods all have sufficient for ordinary requirements, but if a small pinch of ferrous sulphate or ferric and ammonium citrate is added to the diet daily, the redness will come back into the gums and the dog's energy return more rapidly.

One treatment is not sufficient to completely rid a dog of hookworms any more than it is enough to eliminate all roundworms. A second treatment two weeks after the first will kill the worms which were blood-living larvae when the first treatment was given. If the dog picks up another infestation, it will go much less severely with him than the first, and each subsequent infestation will build up a degree of immunity.

WHIPWORMS

These worms live in the intestine, but because most dogs have been dewormed, and since ordinary worm medicines kill whipworms also, they are found in greatest abundance in the cecum, that neat little hideaway where they can easily escape the poisonous effects of ordinary drugs.

A mild infestation of whipworms produces no more indication of their presence than alternating soft and firm stools. Severe infestations produce fits even in old dogs. Though the worms do not suck blood as do hookworms, they elaborate toxins which cause anemia. Loss of appetite, unthrifty coat, some eye discharge are all symptoms.

Prevention: All feces should be removed promptly and the sand in the kennel runs changed. If a house dog has the habit of defecating in any one small area, the top two inches of dirt should be dug up and replaced with uncontaminated sand.

Some of the worst cases of repeated whipworm infestation have been in dogs which used a part of a cellar to defecate in. Even though the feces are removed, there is bound to be a soft residue which sticks to the concrete floor. The furnace heat incubates the eggs. Then the dog drags a bone or dog biscuit about, manages to infect it with whipworm eggs, and thus becomes infested by eating the biscuit or lapping and chewing on the bone.

Even scrubbing concrete with soap and water will not remove all the eggs. No better means of disinfecting it has been found than the use of a flame torch. It is possible to obtain one which will burn the residue and heat the surface sufficiently to destroy all worm eggs in a few minutes. Such a torch or burner must be used with great care in a cellar, of course, but outside it may be easily applied with ordinary precaution. Around a kennel where fairly large areas of concrete require disinfection a flame torch is practically indispensable. If you do not have access to one, and your cellar floor is infected, a plumber's blowtorch may be used, though it takes longer. However, the time and effort spent will be amply repaid, as it will prevent your dog from continually harboring whipworms.

Treatment: Ten years ago the usual method in treating dogs for whipworms was the removal of the cecum—an expensive surgical procedure. Today we have several effective means which are much less drastic. One is the administration of large doses of N butyl chloride. Three times the dose ordinarily recommended for other pests will usually remove 90 per cent or more of the whipworms. Twenty-four-hour starvation is essential. Thus the stomach and intestines are empty and the drug is not diluted or rendered dangerous to your pet as it is when any food remains in the system. To use it successfully against whipworms, a dose of some antiemetic must be given before the N butyl chloride.

A second method—which is definitely dangerous in some cases—is the use of ordinary hydrogen peroxide as an enema. The drugstore strength is diluted with an equal volume of water, and after the dog is empty and has had a laxative to clear out his bowels, the peroxide is given rectally. The anus is held about the tube for a minute or two until the drug soon fills the cecum as well as the colon and kills the worms. No more certain killer of all of the intestinal parasites has been discovered, but its use is hazardous. The intestinal tract can be damaged mechanically since a 1½ per cent solution of hydrogen peroxide gives off five times its volume of oxygen. The gas released in this manner may balloon a part of the intestine and cause hemorrhages.

In using this treatment on hundreds of dogs I have seen at least 25 per cent of them develop some blood in the stools. But every parasite the solution touched was killed, and its use has rid dogs of whipworms when no other treatment had previously been successful. It is most effective, but it should be used only as a last resort. The amount to use is about two ounces of the 1½ per cent solution for each ten pounds of body weight of the dog.

Even tetrachlorethylene, calomel, and other worm killers will destroy whipworms if they touch them. The trick is to be sure they do, and N butyl chloride and hydrogen peroxide, administered wisely and expertly, seem to accomplish this best.

TAPEWORMS

Tapeworm infestation, also called teniasis, is a disease just as is any one of the ailments caused by bacteria, though its effects need not be serious.

In small numbers tapeworms produce few ill effects, but when large numbers infest a dog they can make him a sick animal. He will show symptoms of nervousness, restlessness, and sometimes irritability. Because human beings are thought to have an increased appetite when they harbor tapeworms (it is doubtful if they really do), dogs also are generally expected to be hungrier. But they are not. Actually dogs usually lose their desire for food to some extent when they are infested with tapeworms. Owners constantly bring their pets to our hospital and tell us that the dogs must have tapeworms because their appetites are so enormous. Usually these prove to be thrifty puppies, not sick dogs.

Tapeworms can cause such loss of condition that the dog has convulsions; his coat may become thin, his digestion be disturbed. There is often a marked tendency to vomit small amounts—enough to be a source of worry as well as a nuisance in a house dog. Occasionally, segments of the worms lodge in the anal glands and cause irritation, so that the dog pulls himself along on his rear quarters.

Detection of segments of tapeworms in the dog's stool is the most certain method of determining the presence of the pest. A fecal examination may be made, but in the case of the flea-host worm it is not conclusive even when done by a thoroughly competent technician. They tend to retain their eggs, and the examination of any particular stool may not show evidence of infestation even when the worms are present.

Prevention: While it is obviously impossible to avoid all contact between a dog and any potential tapeworm host, the owner should try to reduce such contact to a minimum. The animal should never be fed any raw rabbit and whenever possible should be prevented from catching and eating them. It is also wise to see that all beef, pork, and fish fed to the dog is well cooked. Both the dog and his quarters should be well dusted with flea powder in order to reduce to a minimum his chances of catching and swallowing an insect host. If a dog has been infested, the kennel and the rugs and furniture in rooms he has been in should be thoroughly gone over with an efficient vacuum cleaner to remove all dried worm segments. It is also necessary to burn or bury the feces for a time to eliminate the chance of reinfestation.

Treatment: Arecolene hydrobromide, the drug most frequently used to eliminate tapeworms, is available in any drugstore, or your veterinarian may supply you with it. He may also give you Nemural or Teneathane or some newer drug. Arecolene is a wonderfully efficient drug in the removal of tapeworms. The chart shows the dosage by weight of dog. Be sure he is starved for fifteen to eighteen hours before dosing. The effect is unusually rapid, and generally a dog will have passed all of his tapeworms within forty-five minutes.

HEARTWORMS

This infestation is one of the most difficult to treat, and when heartworms are suspected the care should be left to the veterinarian.

Imagine a dog's heart stuffed with dozens of worms about twelve inches long and a sixteenth of an inch in diameter! Naturally the animal lacks endurance, becomes fatigued easily, stopping to gasp for breath, the mucous membranes turning blue as they do from asphyxiation. If you put a leash on his collar and let him tug even a little, he will cough—one of the symptoms which should arouse suspicion if you live in a heartworm section. Some infested dogs cough at frequent intervals even when standing free. Poor circulation resulting from heartworm infestation may cause dropsy of the abdomen and swelling in the legs. Some dogs become nervous, and occasionally convulsions have been known to occur in heavily infested dogs.

Prevention: Since heartworms are transmitted principally by the bite of infected mosquitoes, prevention consists simply in keeping mosquitoes away from your dogs, or vice versa. Obviously this is a difficult and sometimes impossible task, even with DDT and other insecticides available to keep dogs free of body insects. Unfortunately no other effective method can be recommended.

Treatment: As we have said, the cure is up to your veterinarian. He will be able to detect the larvae in the blood and may treat your dog with an antimony drug, such as Fuadin, or a newer drug, Caracide. Because of the necessity for drastic means, the dog may die from the treatment, though, happily, most dogs recover. If the heart is badly stuffed with the worms and too large a number are killed by the drug at once, they form a plug in the pulmonary artery leading to the lungs, and the dog cannot survive. Many judiciously measured injections in a series, or oral doses, depending on the drug used, are necessary. The larvae are killed first, thus cutting down on the spread of the infestation. Obviously no infested dog should be kept around healthy dogs as a source of reinfestation.

Since it is dangerous to kill the adult worms if the infestation is very heavy, it is sometimes advisable to let them be and concentrate on killing the larvae only. The question then arises, "How long will the worms live in the heart?" No one knows. It has, however, been demonstrated that the larvae may live in dogs for as long as two and a half years—and possibly longer. Consequently the treatment must be continued for a considerable length of time if it is to be effective.

TRICHINOSIS

You will recall that trichina is carried in the flesh of infested animals. Since an infestation is difficult to diagnose in a live animal, not many cases have been reported which could definitely be identified as trichinosis. Most of those which have been detected occurred when both the dog and his owner had a meal from the same undercooked pork. In a number of cases both had eaten undercooked bear meat. In these instances the owner has reported that his dog apparently experienced the same symptoms. Usually a domestic pet is not known to have had trichinosis until a post-mortem reveals it. It is amazing, however, what a large proportion of both dogs and cats are found to have had an undetected infestation. One study showed that 8 per cent of those examined were infested.

When the cysts are forming in the muscles of the dog, there is pain and stiffness, depending in severity upon how many trichinae there are present. The animal have have a fever, loose stools, loss of appetite, some grunting when he has to move. It is difficult to get him to show the reactions of a normal dog in play or in any activity in which exertion is required.

Since there is no remedy for trichinosis, don't feed pets raw or undercooked pork. Hunters should not feed raw bear meat, raw raccoon, or the raw flesh of any other meat-eating animal. Never allow a dog to eat dead rats or mice which have been living on garbage. Garbage-fed hogs which die should be buried deeply, after first being covered with quicklime, to prevent dogs or wild animals from eating them.

ESOPHAGEAL WORMS

Here, again, is a parasitic disease which is not always easily diagnosed.

Dogs infested with these worms exhibit the symptoms of coughing and vomiting. The tumorlike pockets or pouches in the gullet, with many worms protruding, cause irritation. Sometimes one or more such tumors may be felt in the gullet behind the windpipe. Considerable damage to blood vessels is believed to result from the migration of the larvae in reaching their resting and living place in the esophagus. Dogs often lose weight, and their frequent gagging and coughing is racking to the dogs and a source of worry to their owners.

The intermediate host for esophageal worms is the dung beetle. Therefore, keeping dogs clean and removing stools frequently will do much to prevent infestation.

Treatment: Hydrogen peroxide in 1½ per cent solution—half drugstore strength—poured into the dog's mouth or cupped lips, and allowed to trickle down his throat, kills these parasites. This medication should be given on an empty stomach. The dog will vomit, and as the drug comes up it strikes the worms a second time, often carrying some out with the vomitus. There is no simpler or more effective method of which I know.

FLUKE DISEASE

When dogs eat raw fish in which the cysts of flukes are present, they become infected, and in a week the flukes are mature and are laying eggs. Salmon poisoning, one of the fluke diseases, is serious in the Pacific Northwest and southwestern Canada.

The symptoms are somewhat like distemper, except that the temperature is much higher—106° to 107°. The dog shows great thirst, refuses food, has an eye discharge. In some dogs it causes a swelling of the face. After a day of high fever the temperature drops and the stools become liquid and bloody. This and the effects on the organs cause emaciation and dehydration. In six to eight days the temperature falls below normal, and the dog soon dies. The mortality is high—75 per cent of untreated dogs die. Study has convinced students that the presence of the flukes in themselves is not the cause of the disease, but rather that a bacterium associated with flukes is the actual agent of infection.

Other fluke diseases, such as heart disease and lung disease, are serious in their localities, but these are prevalent chiefly in Asia and the Philippine Islands. The invasion of the lungs produces coughing and pneumonia symptoms, while the heart is weakened to the point of inefficiency and even death by the presence of the parasites in large numbers.

With one or two exceptions, the avoidance of feeding uncooked fish is the important precaution in the prevention of flukes of most varieties. If dogs can't get raw salmon they are spared salmon poisoning. If they are not fed raw fish of any sort, they will not contract fluke diseases generally.

Among the fluke diseases, only salmon poisoning in dogs can be treated. According to investigators, treatment with sulfa drugs is very effective.

PROTOZOAN DISEASES

Animal parasites of the lowest order—usually very small and single-celled—belong to the class called protozoa. But tiny and lowly though they are, serious diseases are attributable to them. Coccidiosis and piroplasmosis are the most important protozoa diseases.

COCCIDIOSIS

This disease (pronounced cock-sid-e-osis) affects dogs of all ages. It is self-limiting and usually passes with no treatment just about as quickly as with any treatment which has been devised to date. Any dog, once recovered, will never again have the disease caused by that particular species of coccidium, but can be infested by one of the other species. However, once immune, a dog is a carrier all the rest of his life, and eggs (oocysts) can occasionally be found in fecal examinations.

Puppies are usually quite severely affected, while mature dogs may show no symptoms other than impairment of appetite and loose stools. Symptoms to be watched for are loose stools, often with bloody color, maturating eyes, elevated temperature (about 103°), loss of appetite, general unthriftiness. In severe cases, weakness and depression are apparent as well as emaciation.

Coccidiosis is a disease not easily differentiated by external symptoms from Carré distemper. Often miscroscopic investigation is necessary to establish the diagnosis. Puppies affected during the teething period (from three and a half to five months) may be left with pitted teeth, as they are from Carré distemper or housedog disease.

When nursing puppies are infected they seem to have light cases. It strikes them much harder after they have been weaned. Whether this is the result of changing from a diet rich in fat to one with a very low level, as is so often done, or whether the mother's milk possesses some antibody, or the puppies possess some maternal immunity, we cannot say positively. It is known, however, that puppies weaned onto a high fat diet come through the disease with less loss of condition and weight than those on a low fat diet.

Puppies can contract the disease from their mothers' breasts. They also pick it up from infected quarters. Coccidiosis has been called the "pet-shop disease," because where puppies are placed together indiscriminately there is likely to be one or more infected, and, not being housebroken, they drop stools into which other pups are bound to walk. Infection is a certainty in that case. When direct contact is not responsible for infection, flies are usually to blame. Even in kennels where the environment is immaculate, where puppies are raised in wire-bottom cages, we find coccidiosis occurring regularly so long as other dogs in the kennel are infected.

Prevention: By thoroughly screening pens and cages and by thoroughly cleaning one's own hands and feet, it is possible to raise pups in kennels and to keep them free from the disease. But it is difficult to realize that what we can't see may be present, and here we are dealing with organisms only a few sizes larger than bacteria.

Comes the question: Do we want to raise puppies free from the disease? Most parents are not greatly disturbed when their children contract one of the so-called children's diseases. They feel that it is best that the children be immunized early rather than be subject to these diseases later, when they may be more difficult to deal with. I am happy when my dogs have coccidiosis and recover. They will, in all probability, have it anyway, so perhaps we should not complain of the loose stools indicative of the disease. The danger is that the puppies might have more than coccidiosis. When several diseases strike at once, puppies may not recover. If they have to have it, it is better for them to have passed the young puppy stage, for when they are a little older they will throw off coccidiosis quite easily.

From the life history of the infecting organism (page 92), it becomes obvious to us that for a puppy or a dog to have the lightest case it is essential that he get as few infestations, one heaped on the other, as possible. The first is bad enough, but if every day he is exposed to new eggs in large numbers he has far less chance of recovery.

The wire-bottom pen is the best possible insurance against heavy reinfestation. If it is screened on the outside down to the ground, flies cannot continue to carry eggs from feces to food dishes or lips.

Treatment: Almost all cases of coccidiosis that are treated are already on the way to recovery, since the whole duration of the disease is only about three weeks. Let's assume your puppy shows definite signs of sickness. His eyes maturate; he has a fever of 103°; his stools are watery. You may reasonably think he has coccidiosis. Your veterinarian makes a fecal examination and finds thousands of coccidia eggs. By that time the pup is right at the height of the disease. If you give him brick dust, cobwebs, sulfa drugs, vinegar and molasses, or any other remedy, he will probably recover—but not because of the treatment. He is getting well anyway. As one scientist has said, "Coccidiosis is the disease about which more foolish cures have been reported than any other disease of animals." Every so often a study reports a new cure, but usually the investigation has been made without untreated controls for comparison. However, some promising treatments are now under scientific investigation and your veterinarian will tell you about them if they prove satisfactory.

Feeding good wholesome food with rich milk and fat up to 25 per cent of the diet is a good treatment. The addition of a heaping teaspoonful of bone ash, mixed with the food, for a puppy the size of a five-weeks-old cocker spaniel is helpful. A tablespoonful a day is the dose for a large breed puppy. Remember that bone ash is not bone meal or steamed bone. It is an entirely different product obtainable through your veterinarian or druggist.

Immaculate cleanliness is as important as anything. If the pup uses paper for defecating purposes, destroy the stool before he can walk in it. Prevent reinfection and his chance of recovery is better than 90 per cent.

PIROPLASMOSIS

This protozoan disease is more prevalent in some sections than in others. There are places where dog owners have never heard of piroplasmosis because apparently it doesn't exist in that particular locality. There are other areas where it is present, though rare, and still dog owners have never heard of it. In the southern part of the United States—especially Florida—it is a serious disease. The British Isles have been practically free from it. Some sections of South America report it. Wherever ticks are prevalent, the protozoan organism causing piroplasmosis may be present.

The protozoan causing the disease is known as *Piroplasma canis*. It is so tiny it can and does live in the red blood cells. From one dog to the next, the transfer is made by ticks, especially the brown dog tick.

Piroplasmosis can be very serious when it is acute. When it is chronic it may simply keep a dog feeling miserable for a long while and afford a splendid opportunity for ticks to replenish their supply of the infecting organism and spread it. In other words, the chronic cases are carriers.

In the acute form it is most difficult to distinguish the outward symptoms from those of Carré distemper. The dog's temperature rises; the haws under his eyes look redder than usual; his pulse and respiration both increase; his appetite diminishes; his urine may be reddish brown. But, *unlike* distemper, and *like* leptospirosis, about half the afflicted dogs develop jaundice. Unless given adequate treatment, mortality is high.

In chronic cases the mucous membranes, such as the haw of the eye, gums, and lips, all become pale instead of red; the temperature rises and falls intermittently; the dog's appetite is poor and picky; he refuses to play, preferring to lie about. He seldom develops jaundice.

How can you be sure that your pet has this particular infection? First, your veterinarian, becoming suspicious because of the reddish-brown urine, can detect the organism easily in the red cells in a small sample of blood he takes. All he has to do is stain the cells on his microscope slide with methylene blue after he has properly prepared it, and there they are —little irregular-shaped bodies in the blood cells.

Diagnosing the chronic form is not too easy, so in kennels the veterinarian draws a little blood from valuable suspected dogs and injects it into one or two susceptible puppies. If the dog has the disease, the doctor will find the organism in the blood of the puppies in from four to seven days. Then he can cure both the adult dog and the puppies.

The best *prevention* is to keep the dog free from ticks.

The *treatment* is by a series of injections of various new drugs. It had best be left to your veterinarian, who will tell you what needs to be done and how you can co-operate.

19. Lungs, Heart, and Blood

THE RESPIRATORY SYSTEM

THE RESPIRATORY system is composed of the nose, the windpipe, or trachea, the bronchial tubes into which the trachea divides, and the lungs themselves. Like other parts of the body, each of these is subject to disease.

The Nose. When an animal's nose is moist, with a clean, watery moisture, it is a sign of good health. This moisture is one means of temperature regulation. The moisture of the nose is evaporated by the air passing through it, and thus the nose is kept cold. On very cold days the dog's nose is dry. When he curls up he puts his nose down between his legs. A dog which has just uncurled from resting or sleeping in this position has a warm nose.

The noses of trailing breeds sometimes crack deeply; often they become worn and the lips wear off until they are raw. Medication is impossible because the dog licks medicine off as soon as it is applied. He heals himself, and medication is unnecessary except in deep cracks where his tongue does not reach.

Noses which change color with the seasons are not abnormal. Such variations seem to be characteristic of certain breeds. Irish setters may have black noses at one season and liver-colored noses at another. Cats as well as dogs may show this variation, having bright pink noses which become white and turn back to pink again without treatment. The reasons for these color changes in noses have not been definitely established. Some believe that the sun darkens noses; others hold the contrary view, feeling that the sun bleaches them.

COLDS. It was once commonly believed that colds, in dogs as well as in humans, were in some way the result of drafts, dust, exposure, overwork, et cetera. In recent years, however, that belief has been supplanted by the theory that colds are caused by infection. Anything which lowers the body's resistance sharply may contribute to the likelihood of infection, but it is not in itself the *cause* of it.

There is apparently no canine disease like a human "cold," or coryza, which is confined strictly to the nose. In dogs, so-called sniffles are incidental symptoms of many generalized diseases. It seems probable that one type of "cold" may be transmitted to dogs by humans, but if it is, it is considerably modified in the exchange. Dogs do not exhibit the typical symptoms of a cold. The nearest thing to a human cold that dogs have is housedog disease.

Chronic catarrh may last for many weeks following Carré distemper but usually clears in time. Doses of sulfa drugs or antibiotics hasten recovery.

SNEEZING AND NOSEBLEED. There are many reasons why dogs sneeze. The causes range from inhalation of toxins or caustic and acid dusts to nose worms. Sneezing ceases when the offending material or parasite is finally removed and the mucous membrane restored to normal.

Nosebleed can be both the cause and effect of sneezing. It is frequently produced by long, continued, and violent sneezing. Many dogs sneeze so violently that they bump their noses on the floor or ground sharply enough to cause bleeding from the injury. Nosebleed may also be due to tumors.

In mild cases of sneezing or nosebleed, administration of a sedative drug, such as Nembutal or phenobarbital, will allow the dog to rest and promote healing. Stopping the sneezing permits clots to form. The use of ice packs is helpful. Injecting ice water or drugs directly into the nasal passages, however, is likely to cause worse sneezing. If nosebleed cannot be controlled by any of these methods, your veterinarian can use blood-stopping (hemostatic) injections of adrenalin or other solutions in conjunction with sedatives.

Nose worms, whose presence is usually discovered only when the veterinarian finds their eggs, are difficult to dislodge. He will do it by anesthetizing the dog and running hydrogen peroxide (one half drugstore strength) from inside the throat out through the nose by use of a bent tube.

The Trachea. TRACHEITIS AND BRONCHITIS. Tracheitis, or inflammation of the windpipe, and bronchitis, inflammation of the bronchial tubes, often occur at the same time. Their general symptom is coughing. This may be a dry cough, a phlegmy cough, or a mild, annoying cough such as humans often suffer during the resolution stage of coryza or "colds." In some cases the coughing may be so paroxysmal that it causes vomiting, and it is not unusual for a constant irritating cough to cause bleeding from the lining of the windpipe.

When inflammation is intense, shortness of breath is another symptom; the air tubes may become so constricted that the normal flow of air is retarded. Moreover, a considerable amount of mucus is discharged and this further interferes with normal breathing. Coughing is partly an attempt to rid the system of this phlegm.

The inflammation is usually symptomatic of some other disease, since tracheitis and bronchitis are seldom disease entities in themselves. Treatment of the cough in such cases usually involves the elimination of the underlying disease of which this inflammation is a part. Consequently, the first step must be an exact determination of the cause of the inflammation, since this will in turn determine the most effective treatment. There are several viruses which inflame these tissues; certain biologics may be helpful in combating them.

If the inflammation is due to irritating smoke, gas, or dust which was inhaled, it may be found advisable to prevent coughing to allow healing. Often there is the problem of deciding whether the cough produces the irritation or vice versa. If the cough is productive, i.e., raises phlegm which had best be removed, it would seem inadvisable to administer drugs which help to stop the coughing. But if a nagging cough merely irritates the membranes without serving a useful purpose, a drug like codeine may be used for relief. A dog's coughing sometimes troubles the owner more than the dog, and in such cases stopping the cough is almost essential. Terpin hydrate is sometimes mixed with codeine in solution because of its action in loosening phlegm. A mixture of these drugs, sold in every drugstore, is frequently prescribed by veterinarians. Some coughs are cured by the simple expedient of using sedatives to give the involved organs as much rest as possible.

The Lungs. PNEUMONIA. Dogs may contract many types of pneumonia—bronchopneumonia, lobar pneumonia, verminous pneumonia, traumatic pneumonia, inhalation pneumonia, and double pneumonia. The owner, however, need not concern himself with learning to distinguish between these types. It is sufficient if he is able to recognize the symptoms common to all kinds of pneumonia—the fever, the shallow breathing, and the loss of appetite. Mucus may be discharged from the dog's nose, but this does not always occur. The chief distinguishing feature is the vibrating, grating sound in the dog's chest. As soon as these symptoms are observed, the dog should be taken to the veterinarian.

Treatment consists of killing the germs that cause the disease and maintaining the patient in a comfortable environment. Pneumonia germs are almost always present in a dog; pneumonia is an opportunistic disease which develops when the system is run down or when the guards against disease are off duty. (It is not necessarily contagious.) Therefore it is apparent that the dog must be restored to good health principally by improving his general physical condition. He should be encouraged to eat by being fed the foods he likes best. If it is cold where he is kept, it is wise to cover his chest with a pneumonia jacket, which can be made by winding layers of warm blanket material or cotton batting about his chest and holding it in place with strips of cloth. Some owners sew old sweaters on their dogs. For larger dogs, a discarded man's vest makes an excellent cover. The vest is put on with the row of buttons on the dog's back and the part underneath the dog pinned and sewed to take out the fullness.

For a few years after their discovery, sulfa drugs—sulfathiazole, sulfadiazine, and sulfapyridine—were the main weapons used against pneumonia. Given in four or five doses a day at the rate of one grain to the pound per day, they greatly reduced the pneumonia death rate. Penicillin and other antibiotics are more frequently prescribed today. If these drugs are used in time, dogs usually recover within five days or less. Penicillin is used in a slowly absorbed base, so that one injection a day suffices. Because of the addition of procaine, there is almost no pain in its administration. Aureomycin given by mouth may supplant it, however, especially for home medication.

Treatment is started as early as possible. Since the dog's body is no longer called upon to do all the work of combating the invading pneumococci, or other germs, which cause the disease, it is not necessary to wait for the crisis, which was once a crucial time in pneumonia medication.

In an advanced case, in which the lungs are badly congested, the use of an oxygen tent may be necessary to save the dog's life. Your veterinarian will decide if such treatment is needed.

Verminous pneumonia is common in puppies. The puppy always has it in some degree when the larvae of roundworms and hookworms are tunneling in the lungs. This type of pneumonia disappears with the elimination of the larval invasion. However, since there is always the possibility of bacterial pneumonia getting a foothold in the injured tissue, a few days' dosage of penicillin may be advisable. Vitamin A therapy is also worth while at such times. A few drops of percomorph oil or a c.c. of carotene in oil, given daily, are to be recommended.

Inhalation pneumonia. This type of pneumonia is due to contamination of the lungs with dust, gases, and oily vapors which injure the delicate membranes. Treatment can do little more than prevent bacterial invasion. Penicillin or sulfa drugs keep these organisms from taking hold and allow the injured tissue time to regenerate.

Another form of inhalation pneumonia is that caused by improper medication. When an owner pours mineral oil, castor oil, or drugs in an oily base indiscriminately into the back of a pet's mouth, the dog can easily suck some of the liquid into the windpipe. When oil or other material difficult to expel stays in the lungs, gangrene may result and putrefactive bacteria multiply, causing death. This is avoided by always using the lip-pocket method of medication.

City dogs inhale so much dust that their lungs often show black mottling effects from it. Dogs kept about dusty factories and plants where stone dust fills the air may be victims of silicosis; the lungs become impregnated with the fine powder which stays in the tissue.

EDEMA OF THE LUNGS. When the body is stocked with dropsical fluid, the lungs may also fill up and develop edema. Shortness of breath is a symptom of this condition. Besides the pressure from abdominal distention, the fluid in the lungs themselves puts a burden on the respiratory system and demands drastic withdrawal of fluids from the body with drugs like caffeine (see Dropsy). Withholding water from the sufferer until most of the surplus fluid has been withdrawn from the tissues is also imperative.

EMPHYSEMA. As an aftermath of diseases of the lungs—and from other unknown causes—sections of the honeycomb lung tissue break down, allowing large pockets to form. These pockets often collect mucus. When many such pockets are present, a great deal of the lung tissue is useless and the dog has to breathe faster and deeper to aerate his blood. This is the disease which in horses is commonly known as the *heaves*. The symptoms are similar in both species.

There is no cure, but temporary alleviation of symptoms is possible. Every horse dealer knows the miraculous effect of doses of Fowler's solution and belladonna, and thousands of horses have been traded to unsuspecting victims who could see or hear no unsoundness. The same drugs will often relieve a dog for a few hours. The atropine in belladonna dries up the fluid in the pockets, and the arsenic in the Fowler's solution acts as a stimulant. This treatment, however, should never be considered more than temporary relief; it is certainly not a cure.

PLEURISY. After pneumonia, when bacteria may have worked through the pleura or coating of the lungs, there may be infection across the chest cavity to the pleura on the rib side. In such cases the two surfaces may adhere to each other in spots when healing is completed. While the inflammation is present, an exceedingly painful pleurisy can result.

Areas of the chest cavity may become filled with fluid which the veterinarian may have to tap and draw off. There may be areas of fluid which prevent heart and lung sounds from passing clearly. When these areas are tapped with the fingers, a dull thud is heard instead of a hollow, healthy resonance. In "dry" pleurisy a sharp, sandpapery, grating sound is produced with every inspiration and expiration. Treatment for pleurisy is the same as for pneumonia.

HYDROTHORAX. Hydrothorax, or fluid in the chest cavity, follows lung infections, growths, or accidents. Treating it is a task for your veterinarian. The symptoms are shallowness in the dog's breathing and, frequently, bluing of the tongue and gums, resulting from the dog's inability to obtain sufficient oxygen. Your veterinarian may draw the fluid off by tapping.

TUMORS. Tumors in the chest cavity are not uncommon. They are difficult to diagnose but may be suspected when the dog loses weight too rapidly, has shortness of breath, and develops an abnormal spring of ribs. Tumors sometimes occur in the lungs themselves. This type often sends out buds (metastases) which grow in other parts of the body. Colonies from one type often appear in the skin. The conscientious owner will have every growth examined in a competent laboratory.

THE CIRCULATORY SYSTEM

The Heart. The heart has many diseases. The dog owner will learn to recognize some of the more common conditions; others he will not be able to diagnose or treat. Valve dysfunction, due to several causes, is one general class. Inflammation of the pericardium is another. The pericardium, you will remember, is a kind of unattached skin or bag about the heart, formed by the pleura. The area between the heart and the pericardium may become infected and distended with fluid. The heart muscle itself may become infected (*myocarditis*) or dilated. Its walls can stretch until the heart becomes two or three times as large as when normal. Occasionally a heart is ruptured as a result of an accident.

LEAKY VALVES. The hissing sound characteristic of leaky valves can be clearly heard if you listen with your ear against the dog's chest, close to the heart. A person with a keen sense of touch may even feel leaky valves through his finger tips when picking up a dog, if his hand supports the dog under the heart. Leaky valves may sometimes produce such potent vibrations that no one can fail to feel them.

You should learn to listen to the heartbeat and interpret what you hear. If you hear the heartbeat skip every fifth or sixth beat, there is nothing abnormal about it. An abnormal heart beats steadily without skipping. The rate of the heartbeat varies with the state of excitement, physical condition, outside temperature, physical exertion, and the size of the dog. When the dog is at rest and fully composed there will be a normal pulse rate of 100 or more in a small dog and perhaps 75 or 80 in a large dog. There is no standard pulse, as in humans, whose normal pulse rate is about 72.

For all of their inefficiency, leaky valves seem not to shorten a dog's life appreciably. There is no known treatment or cure, nor has the cause been definitely established. A generalized bacterial disease which produces "vegetative growths" on the valves is often blamed.

GENERAL WEAKNESS. This can often be recognized by the dog's sluggishness, shortness of breath, loss of vigor and ability to sustain exertion, blueness of tongue and gums after exertion, and a weak, thready, feeble pulse which can be felt on the inside of the dog's hind legs close up to the crotch. Dropsy is sometimes present. Fainting spells may even occur. A dog that has always bounded up the stairs ahead of you may be so seriously affected that he will wait for you to carry him up.

Stimulants like caffeine and digitalis, or some derivative such as digitalein or digitoxin, can be used. Once digitalis is started under your veterinarian's direction, the dog must have his dosage every day.

ENLARGEMENT. A dog with an enlarged heart may seem perfectly healthy when at rest around the house, but he cannot endure continued exertion. The condition seems to develop in young dogs that are overworked. If the strain is too great for the heart muscle, it stretches and stays stretched. Its elasticity is lost. Naturally, if it occupies a larger space in the chest, it can be heard with the ear over this large area. There is a very noticeable contrast between the sound of a normal heart and that of an enlarged one. Enlarged heart conditions may be found in sled dogs broken too early and used on heavy loads, in field-trial coon dogs, and even in setters and pointers. The heart cannot be reduced to normal, nor will it ever become strong enough to allow the dog to indulge in what would have been his normal activities.

RUPTURE OF THE HEART. This condition is usually associated with accidents. Not infrequently the heart is ruptured by a broken rib which jabs a hole in it. The dog does not always die quickly. If the pericardium is not broken, the blood fills the space between the heart and the pericardium and expands that membrane. If the pericardium is broken, the blood runs out into the chest cavity. It may take several hours before death comes. When it does occur, the dog dies of apoplexy, perhaps very suddenly. Usually the owner has no idea of the cause of death unless a post-mortem examination is made. There is no treatment.

The Blood Vessels. Dogs have many of the same blood-vessel diseases found in man. Of these, the pet owner usually is able to recognize only hemorrhages which we have already discussed in the chapter on first aid, and a few others. Yet there are two common conditions which anyone can easily learn to recognize. These are embolisms and strokes.

Following surgical operations, blood clots have been known to loosen, be carried through the circulatory system until they reach a junction in an artery, and then plug this junction. All the area fed by that artery will then be without a blood supply unless other collateral arteries can supply it. If not, gangrene sets in. When the area is near the surface, the gangrene may work out through the skin, but when it is in a muscle it may cause great pain and eventually death.

A stroke, or apoplexy of the brain, is caused by the rupture of a blood vessel in that organ. The effect depends on the size of the brain area involved. Paralysis may occur in only one limb, or the whole side of the body may be involved. Only by awaiting the resolution of the blood clot can one tell whether or not the dog will recover completely. Medicines seem useless.

The Blood. Some blood ailments may be recognized by pet owners. Anemia, excess urea, excess sugar, and excess bile can be easily determined. Various larvae and micro-organisms can also be detected with a microscope. These have been discussed under parasites.

ANEMIA. This is a blood condition caused by too little blood, too few red cells, or insufficient hemoglobin to enable the blood to take up its normal load of oxygen from the lungs. The dog's gums and tongue are pale, his endurance poor. Depression is marked in severe anemia. The dog's eyes become sunken, the appetite feeble, and emaciation progressive.

In case of hemorrhage, the dog may lose enough blood to die or be close to death. The blood may be lost externally or it may flow into the abdomen or chest cavity. After the blood clots in cavities, the fluid component returns to circulation and may save the dog's life. The clot eventually hemolyzes and is picked up by the blood and passed out in the urine. When the danger of hemorrhage has passed, a transfusion may save the dog's life. Transfusions have also saved the lives of many dogs made anemic by lice, hookworms, and whipworms.

Treating anemia is usually a matter of finding the cause, removing it, and supplying the food to stimulate blood building. Iron is essential. Meat or liver, dried or fresh, will help greatly. A very little ferric and ammonium citrate is excellent. Curiously enough, diets especially planned to cure anemia sometimes do not have sufficient salt. All dog food should contain at least 1 per cent salt, and a little more can be fed to good advantage to anemic dogs. See Table I for good sources of iron.

HEMOPHILIA. A few cases of "bleeding" after the pattern of humans who inherit the tendency have been reported. It has been found that the defect runs in families, being inherited through the dam from grandfather to grandson, thus seeming to skip a generation. Females are almost never bleeders. A dog with hemophilia bleeds for days from insignificant cuts which in a normal dog would stop bleeding in a matter of minutes. Severe cuts may result in death unless surgical treatment is given.

LYMPH GLAND ENLARGEMENT. In discussing this malady, we include the spleen among the lymph glands. A great deal has been written in veterinary literature about a disease not infrequently found in dogs which causes tremendous enlargement of the spleen and generalized enlargement of all the lymph glands of the body. This disease is often called Hodgkins disease or leukemia. It may not be either. The author has done considerable work with it, and in all the cases studied there have been no blood changes comparable to those in the blood of humans afflicted with leukemia.

Some dogs' glands swell until they practically choke the victim to death. The swellings in the lymph nodes or glands can be felt enlarging day by day. A drug now being tested shows great promise in alleviating this condition, and removal of the spleens of affected dogs has produced rapid cures. Lymphosarcoma, a form of cancer, may be one cause of the swellings.

20. The Skin

IT HAS been the practice of veterinarians who have written about skin diseases in dogs to consider them as if they came from the same causes —internal as well as external—as do skin diseases in human beings. In other words, they have used the same definitions and assumed that the same conditions affected both species. Thus we often find such things as allergies and vitamin deficiencies included as causes of skin troubles in dogs, just as in persons. Possibly we should classify skin diseases of dogs in this fashion, but I question it. After having treated thousands of cases of skin diseases in dogs and having cured them from the *outside,* I feel I can say with assurance that, if there are internal causes, they are so rare that the layman can disregard them.

Discoveries based on the study and observation of other species have been applied to dogs without justification. I can remember, as you perhaps can, when some so-called experts advised giving dogs orange juice to cure skin diseases, because orange juice cured scurvy in guinea pigs and in humans. Then it became known that dogs synthesized their own vitamin C, and therefore that it need not be supplied from outside sources. Because a vitamin G deficiency caused rats to lose their hair at the elbows, dog owners were advised to use vitamin G to cure skin diseases. Dogs were supposed to be "allergic" to certain foods. It even became the style to have the dog owner bring his pet to the veterinarian to check on whether the skin disease could be cured if particular kinds of meat were dropped from the diet. No beef was fed for one week. The following week no pork would be fed; the next, no chicken, et cetera. Finally I became so annoyed at this practice that I wrote an article in which I said that if you are feeding a *complete diet* when your dog breaks out with a skin disease and your veterinarian tells you your dog needs a change of diet, what you really need is a change of veterinarians. I still feel the same way. I have never seen a case of skin disease on a dog which was cured by a diet change.

If dogs do show allergic reactions to food, it is an extremely rare phenomenon. I realize that many cases of so-called allergy have been reported, but in every such case about which I have read or heard some external medicine was used in its treatment—and generally not given the credit for cure which it probably deserved. If a dog does show a rash after eating some specific protein (the term "allergy" is not used in connection with fats or carbohydrates), it is proper to say he exhibits a food idiosyncrasy rather than an allergy. However, in all the thousands of dogs I have handled, I have never known of a case where a skin disease was the reaction to any article of diet. I *have* seen dogs swell up in the face and show blobs of swelling all over the body after eating eggs. It has always been eggs which produced the swelling, and it always subsided within twelve hours. But that is not a sensitivity to eggs, because those same dogs ate eggs regularly. They had never exhibited such symptoms before, nor have they since. It is probably the reaction to a bacterial toxin elaborated in a certain egg.

Today up-to-date veterinarians very seldom tell anyone to change diets to cure skin diseases. Instead they give medicines for external application. But many laymen still speak of food allergies in their pets causing skin trouble and harbor other notions which have been proved to be misconceptions.

Let us consider the more common skin afflictions of dogs. Dermatitis might be the best general term to use in describing almost all active skin diseases. All that the word means is "inflammation of the skin." A burn with heat, such as sunburn, and an acid burn are both cases of dermatitis, because with both conditions the skin becomes inflamed. It can be caused by insect bites as well as by the rubbing and chafing of chains, ropes, or rough collars.

A few words about the treatment of skin disease may not be out of place here. You probably wonder why your veterinarian urges you to keep on treating your dog for some time after he seems completely cured. The reason is simple enough once you understand it. The dog's skin is thicker in some places than in others. If the infection is deep in the skin—at the bottoms of the hair follicles, for instance—the upper layers may be "cured" while the infection still remains far down in those follicles or glands. When the curative drug is no longer present on the skin, these infectious organisms increase again. This is especially true of red mange and fungus infections. Only persistent dosing effects a permanent cure.

ECZEMA

In the true sense there is no such thing. The word "eczema" is derived from the Greek "to boil out," and the old idea was that food somehow heated the blood, the blood boiled and came out through the skin as a rash. We still hear the absurd phrase about certain foods, "they are too heatening to the blood." It is strange that even today it is necessary to repeat: Blood does not overheat; it does not boil out.

But there is a skin disease characterized by *moist* discharges which scale over. This causes itching, and the dog scratches and chews at the affected area constantly. This disease is generally called eczema, even though the name is inappropriate. In other cases a condition of dryness (as contrasted with the moist form) occurs and causes itching. It spreads rapidly and the hair falls out. This is often called dry eczema—again badly named.

Both types of eczema are much worse on some breeds than on others. Scottish terriers, Sealyhams, West Highland whites, and other terriers are among those most often found infected. Eczema is often called "Scotch itch." In St. Bernards, collies, and other long-haired breeds it can be insidious, starting on the skin well hidden from view and spreading over large areas before it is detected.

In sections where there are screw-worm flies and other flies whose maggots relish the infected spots, it is not unusual to find masses of maggots eating holes in the dog's skin and even causing death. These are, of course, extreme cases complicated by the maggot poisoning.

Both dry and moist eczema are found on dogs of all breeds. They occur most often in the warm, damp days of summer, just when fleas are starting to be most prevalent. It has been thought that insect bites irritate skin areas which the dog chews and makes even moister. In these spots fungus spores find a perfect place to incubate, and they are the principal cause of the disease. This would seem to be proved by the fact that fungicides generally cure the trouble quite simply and insecticides combined with fungicides seem to help greatly in preventing the infections from starting. The whole story of the cause of eczema is not yet known. Possibly many organisms are responsible for eczema, and even viruses may yet be found among them.

Your veterinarian should be able to give you a remedy to be applied externally for the control and cure of both forms of eczema, unless complications such as we have mentioned have set in.

ALOPECIA

This is baldness or an insufficiency of hair. It is a condition, not a disease. It may be hereditary, as in Mexican hairless dogs or in certain untypical representatives of breeds. I have seen many dogs with fuzzy coats when all their brothers and sisters had normal ones. They lacked the long guard hairs.

Alopecia is often seen in dogs with incipient diabetes. The hair on the ears, head, and back of the hind legs thins noticeably. It is also seen in dogs with testicles that have degenerated and sometimes in dogs with testicular tumors. I have known nude dogs to grow luxuriant coats when their testicles were removed, and I have seen others grow fine coats with no external treatment whatever after they were given large doses of female sex hormone. The exact reason for this occurrence is not known.

ACNE

This is an inflammation of the glands of the skin—the glands which secrete wax or sebum. When little pimplelike eruptions occur in the skin but the whole surface is not red, it may be that the sebaceous glands are infected. The little enlargements may contain pus which, upon rupturing, forms a scab. It is thought that dirt sometimes clogs the pores, causing bacteria to multiply underneath. This type of skin disease is usually found under collars and on the belly. Possibly the pressure of collars and harnesses prevents the waxy secretion from moving out of the glands, with the result that the surface becomes impacted, making a covered well of bacteria.

It is well to squeeze the little nodules and rupture them, treat the area with a good wax solvent, such as ether or alcohol, and then apply a healing lotion. Irritating drugs like phenol had best not be used.

DANDRUFF

This is a term used to designate constant flaking of the skin. All dogs like all human beings, are constantly shedding off the outer layer of the skin which is being replaced as the skin grows outward. Finding of even a small number of scales gives some dog owners concern.

A good brushing with a coarse brush will very often rid the hair of flakes. If the dog is scratching, however, it is another matter, and an infection is probably the cause. This may be equivalent to pityriasis in persons. Often dog owners are advised to feed cod-liver oil, wheat-germ oil, and raw eggs, and told not to feed starchy foods. Vitamins are concerned with skin health, to be sure, but special food supplements seldom effect cures. Some of the unsaturated fatty acids, certain building blocks of fat, are necessary for skin health in rats and children, but whether these food ingredients help coat health in dogs remains to be proved. Linoleic, linolenic, and arachnidic acids are quite abundant in nature. Linseed oil is rich in them, and a few drops a day is enough for a dog.

Dandruff seems to be a seasonal thing in some dogs. One house dog I know never shows any in the spring or fall but sheds scales continually during the summer and winter. You may read that crude caustic soaps produce dandruff, yet dogs treated with the daintiest soaps may be the worst offenders. Again it is said that the dry atmosphere of a heated house is conducive to dandruff; yet it is seen in kennel dogs which have never been in heated rooms. It appears to be a normal occurrence, and, as we have said, it can be helped by hard, vigorous brushing.

PSORIASIS

This is sometimes called elephant skin by dog owners. The skin becomes thickened, gray, and coarse. Often, by squeezing, one can express small drops of pus. It appears most commonly on the tails of dogs, especially great Danes, and on the elbows and sides of the legs. It should not be mistaken for calluses, because it does not necessarily appear on areas which are subject to friction. I have even had cases on the noses of dogs brought to me for treatment.

Only by keeping the area soaked with a penetrating lotion can cure be effected. Because the dog is so likely to rub the lotion off the legs when he lies down, it may be desirable to apply bandages soaked in the solution. The cause of the disease is not known.

RINGWORM

This skin ailment is easy to detect because it grows in such neat areas with well-defined boundaries. Many persons labor under the misapprehension that it grows in a perfect circle. It may be quite irregular, but tends to grow in an oval. When it reaches a certain size, it stops. The hair falls out and the area becomes cured automatically. Then it appears in a new place. In severe infections the areas may run together into one large spot. Frequently the first noticeable spots are in the short hair of the face, but it may appear anywhere on the body. Short-haired dogs are more susceptible than long-haired breeds.

Another way to recognize that the trouble is ringworm is to examine the members of the family. It has been my experience that in most cases dogs with ringworm contracted it from a person. They give it back, too, to other dogs and to cats, and to the children and Mother and Dad. Ringworm is caused by a definite fungus. It is easy to cure. Iodine-and-glycerine is one familiar remedy which effects a cessation of growth. The difficulty in treating it is in the prevention of new spots. Fungicides applied liberally are quite effective in this. Powders with fungicides added can be bought in pet shops and drugstores and, if used liberally, are the simplest method of ending the infection.

IMPETIGO

So many children have impetigo that parents frequently ask whether dogs have it too. So far it has not been reported as growing on the skins of dogs.

SARCOPTIC MANGE

This is a skin disease which quite definitely is transmitted back and forth from man to dog. (For the life history of the causative mite, see page 81.) After the war many soldiers came home with itchy patches on their arms or legs. Frequently their dogs contracted it from them. Now one sees it less and less.

At first glance, without a microscopic study, sarcoptic mange resembles dry eczema. The hair comes out, leaving bald areas which become inflamed from the irritation and itch intensely. In a group of cocker spaniels I knew well, some of the dogs had one, some the other, and some both of these skin ailments. It was interesting to see that experienced dog men and several veterinarians couldn't tell which was which. Because of the similarity of symptoms in the two diseases, I will not trust my judgment in diagnosis unless a careful microscopic study has been made.

Finding the mites is not an easy matter. A fold of skin in the infected area is squeezed. A sharp scalpel or knife is scraped across it, the scurf-skin discarded, the fold pinched harder until serum exudes, and this is scraped again. The material is saved on a microscope slide and the process is repeated in several places. The accumulated substance can be mixed with mineral oil on the slide, spread thin, and studied for mites. If none is found, it is sometimes profitable to try again. Sarcoptic mange mites are much more difficult to find than the mites causing red mange, which we will consider next.

Once it has been diagnosed, there are few skin diseases easier to cure than sarcoptic mange. Even axle grease and finely powdered sulphur will do it. Lard-and-sulphur was one of the old remedies. Every drugstore has several effective sarcoptic mange remedies.

RED MANGE

This is a serious disease. It was only a few years ago that the appearance of a spot of any size was sufficient reason for destroying the dog. Veterinarians sometimes used to cut the spots out like cancer and hope that no mites were left. Dogs were killed to prevent the spread to other dogs. But with the discovery of effective modern remedies, the disease has lost its terror.

Red mange (demodectic or follicular mange) starts so innocuously that the dog owner pays very little attention to it. In our hospital we show the newly infected areas to the owners far more frequently than they show them to us, often when the pets have been brought in for some other ailment.

Usually red mange starts with a baldish spot on the face or forelegs, though exceptions are numerous. The spot spreads and becomes nude.

Other spots of irregular shape appear and join into large areas. The skin begins to itch; the scratching and the mites cause inflammation. The skin thickens and reddens, finally becoming raw. The name red mange fits it to a T at this stage, but until this point is reached, owners can scarcely believe their dogs have it.

Red mange is a strange malady. Sometimes dogs have it in a mild form and infect puppies. I told the owner of one bitch to cure such a mild case before the dog was bred. He didn't, and of six puppies only two contracted it. But they died needlessly. They were not treated in time and they would not have been infected if their mother had been cured.

Can people catch it? Dermatologists say that they can, on the cheeks beside the nose. Can the mites live away from the dog for long periods of time? Probably not for more than three days, so it is certainly safe to bring a new dog into a home where a dog previously had red mange a week after the first dog has gone.

Diagnosis with a microscope is simple. A fold of skin is squeezed tightly and scraped hard with a knife edge while the pinching continues. The exudate removed is spread thin on a microscope slide, mixed with mineral oil, and studied. The cigar-shaped insects are easily visible at one hundred magnifications.

Curing the disease is relatively simple now that we have rotenone, DDT, and benzene hexachloride. If any one of these drugs is mixed with a good penetrating oil or a salve, it kills the mites in the follicles. The difficulty is in discovering new areas. Some new data seem to indicate that heavy dusting with good flea powders containing rotenone will keep new areas from becoming infested while the known areas of infestation are being treated.

HOOKWORM DISEASE OF THE SKIN

This has been seen in dogs kept in pens heavily infested with hookworm eggs. When it gets very muddy, if a dog tracks in much of the infested mud to his bed and then lies in it, he incubates the eggs by the warmth in his body, and in time the larvae bore into the skin, making a red, raw area corresponding to the area on his body which was muddy. I have scraped the skin of such dogs and found large numbers of larvae.

Antiseptic baths in warm water cure the condition quickly. One bath is usually enough. The soil in the runs or about the doghouse should be replaced with new sand or earth and the bedding changed often enough so that the dogs do not lie in soil which they track in.

21. Bones, Joints, and Muscles

THE VARIOUS parts of the skeleton are vulnerable to a number of ills ranging from mild to serious. Bones may be diseased, malformed, broken, or dislocated at the joints. The joints, in turn, may be diseased, inflamed, sprained, ankylosed, twisted, or distended due to pressure of the fluid lubricating them. Muscles may become inflamed, diseased, broken or torn, infected with trichina, atrophied, or paralyzed.

RADIAL PARALYSIS

Radial paralysis is an injury which often appears to be a dislocation. In one sense it is, because the whole shoulder droops yet all the true joints remain intact. This is due to the breaking of the radial nerve. A heavy blow against it may cause a permanent break or bruise which, temporarily, produces the same result.

Because this nerve controls the motion of the front of the forearm, lack of its influence, plus the activity of the nerves on the back of the forearm, causes the foot to pull backward. This bending backward, plus the dropping of the shoulder, makes the front leg, from the wrist downward, drag on the ground, and if it is unprotected, the skin will in time wear away. In cases of radial paralysis the affected legs are often amputated to prevent the sores from becoming infected.

A few physiologists are equipped with electrical devices and an exact knowledge of the location of nerves, which enables them to determine the exact extent of the injury. If the nerve is not too badly impaired, the dog's leg should be placed in a splint to prevent it from twisting and the tendons from becoming shortened, so that when normal motion has been restored, the dog may walk normally again.

CANCER OF THE BONE

Bones are subject to many growths, the most common being two forms of bone cancer. One form, which grows in the shaft, weakens it by replacing the hard substance with soft cancerous growth until the bone collapses at this point. This is usually an *osteosarcoma.*

Another highly malignant form, the *periosteosarcoma,* spreads rapidly by liberating cells which are carried by the blood all about the body and grow as metastases. It originates in the "bone skin" (periosteum). This form generates bone, so metastatic growths contain bony tissue no matter where they are found.

JOINT AILMENTS

Besides being subject to dislocations, joints are liable to infections of various kinds, to *ankylosis,* to joint "boils," et cetera. Arthritis is inflammation of the joints, usually caused by the presence of infectious organisms. Sometimes sharp objects which penetrate the joints push bacteria into the joint capsules, and the result, if not treated, can be an immobilized (ankylosed) joint.

It is not necessary to destroy pets with joint ills. Most of them recover, though in some the joints are permanently disfigured. Surgery is often valuable. A very careful inspection of the heart is important, because it has been found that heart disease (especially endocarditis) is frequently an accompaniment of joint infections, especially when they are generalized.

Before the discovery of sulfas and the antibiotics it was the practice to apply strong liniments to joints, even blisters, such as are used for horses. Now it has been found that the newer drugs destroy a good many of the organisms that affect joints, and therapy today involves their use with considerable success.

Injury from Accident. When a joint is opened in an accident, by a bullet wound or by a penetrating wound of any kind, there is danger of infection. If it is kept thoroughly cleansed and heals properly, it may be as good as new. I have repaired many joints which were wide open, necessitating suturing of the joint capsules as well as the covering tissues above them. They fill with joint fluid generated by the natural secretive tissue, and in time the animal has all the flexion he had before the injury.

Infections of Young at Birth. In many species of animal, infections of the young at birth occasionally settle in the joints. All horsemen know of the serious results to colts when the navel becomes infected, but few dog owners realize that the same thing may occur to their pets. Any infection which settles in joints and grows there causes irritation. The capsule may fill with a yellow or reddish material composed of pus and blood. Connective tissue naturally forms in time, and the joint is thus stiffened, even if the bacteria are killed. You can feel the heat in such joints with your hand. They show all the four indications of inflammation: heat, redness, swelling, and pain. There are a variety of such infections, and you will be well advised to let your veterinarian prescribe after he has determined just which one is involved.

Ankylosis. This is the immobilizing of joints. A joint may be said to be ankylosed even when partial movement is present. A joint is sometimes purposely ankylosed to prevent a leg from being too long or too short or permanently dislocated as a result of an accident. Many cases of accidental breaks near joints may be expected to set with permanently stiff joints. In complicated breaks there is often no way to prevent this, but fortunately it seldom causes the dog great discomfort.

Joint "Boils." Injuries which cause the capsule to become distended with the joint fluid—a viscous material which looks like tough egg white—may produce disfiguring bulges. This is the equivalent of so-called "water on the knee," which humans sometimes develop after knee injuries. In dogs, especially great Danes, these bulges develop over leg joints which have been injured by the heavy dogs' lying on hard, bare floors. The elbow joint—the joint below the shoulder—sometimes puffs out as large as a baseball. You can feel the viscous fluid inside if you squeeze the lump. If the dog is made to lie on a mattress or in a box with a deep bedding of straw or hay as soon as the bulges begin to appear, the lumps will disappear. If the dog continues to irritate them, the lumps—which are really extensions of the joint capsule—will solidify slowly by the accumulation of connective tissue until they are almost solid with only a small amount of fluid in their centers. Such disfigurements are seen in other leg joints of large dogs, but not so frequently. They are rare in small breeds.

Once the bulges become established, surgery is the only remedy, and this is not without risk. If the joint capsule becomes infected, a serious condition develops. The leg may become stiff even after it is cured of the infection. Moreover, an operation, in order to be successful, demands the co-operation of the dog, the owner, and the veterinarian. The dog must be restrained from chewing at the bandages; he must have a soft place to lie; his operative site must be padded as well as bandaged, because there will be times when he will lie on hard surfaces in spite of the owner's best efforts to make him lie on his mattress. The incision must be dressed regularly; the stitches have to be removed; and for a few weeks afterward the dog must be watched to see that he does not plunk down his bruising weight on the elbows and start the trouble all over again, or keep the joint inflamed. Light fawn-colored dogs must be nursed with special care after such an operation. If the incision has to be resutured and scar tissue fills it, there will be a black telltale mark to show.

MUSCLE AILMENTS

Perhaps it would be more accurate to describe most of the muscle ailments under the general topic of nerves, because an ache in a muscle is really a nerve ache. However, if the muscle were not injured or infected, the nerves would not be registering the disturbance.

What are the most frequent muscle ills? Ruptures, tears, wounds, infections, tendinitis, bruises, fatigue. All these ailments need veterinary attention and good nursing. Perhaps heat treatments are indicated; surgery may be necessary, or vitamin therapy, or abscess draining and flushing. You may treat your pet at home under your doctor's instructions and generally you may expect improvement.

Muscle Fatigue. Muscles do the work of the body. Some are quiet most of the time; some, such as the heart, are constantly at work. Sugar and oxygen supplied by the blood are the energy or foods of muscles, and the waste products, such as carbon dioxide and sarcolactic acid, are carried away. It is the accumulation of wastes which causes muscular exhaustion, rather than actual exercise. Muscles can increase in size and strength when accustomed, over a period of time, to certain work—witness the tremendous thigh muscles of well-trained racing greyhounds in contrast to those of representatives of the breed maintained in apartment houses. Or compare the large, hard muscles of working sled dogs with the smaller, unused muscles of pets of sled-dog breeds.

It is wrong to expect any untrained dog to do the work of trained and hardened ones. I have seen well-conditioned foxhounds run well over two hundred miles in twenty-four hours while other untrained hounds, whose spirits were strong but whose muscles had not been hardened, ran until they had to be carried home. Such strain on the heart muscle and skeletal muscles is cruelty and should not be permitted. Every dog should be conditioned gradually to the work he is to do. If he is not, the muscles may become clogged with waste products until some may be put out of commission for a long period of time.

Injuries. When the sheath around the muscles, the tendon attaching it to the bone at either end, or the muscle substance itself is torn, the gap usually can be felt. The tendon may knot up in a lump a considerable distance from the usual point of attachment. Surgical repair of this condition should be attempted at once or the muscle may become so short that the tendon cannot be pulled back into position. Muscles can be pulled together, too, and the sheaths sutured, after which they become efficient. But in such repairs the area must be kept immobile for several weeks or muscular contraction is likely to pull the stitches out before healing can take place.

Muscles owe part of their bulk to nervous energy. When a nerve supplying any muscle or set of muscles is cut, the area becomes atrophied, or shrunken. Disuse produces a similar effect. After a splint has been removed from a pet's broken leg, the muscles will have become so atrophied as to be perhaps half the normal size. Unused muscles can be brought up to form quickly, but those atrophied from nerve blocks or breaks may never regenerate.

Pressure. Pressures over muscles may cause such ill effects that the muscles become filled with connective tissue and harden. This is seldom seen in dogs, except those doing hard work and wearing harnesses. Such muscles serve almost as calluses.

Bruises. Aside from the skin, animal muscles are the most likely parts of the body to be bruised, yet it is amazing what punishment they can stand and still not show any ill effects.

When muscles are badly bruised they turn black in their substance because of the blood engorging the area. Many days are sometimes required for the bodily forces to repair a damage of this sort.

Infections. Muscular infections sometimes develop. Rheumatism caused by the inflammation of connective tissue throughout the muscle may be more common than we know. Abscesses are frequently found deep in muscles.

Tumors. Growths called myomas are reported in dogs as well as mixed tumors embodying muscles and connective tissue; and tumors of other origins, such as fatty tumors and malignancies, are found invading and displacing muscle tissues.

HERNIAS

A hernia is a protrusion of tissue, organ, or organs through an abnormal opening. Hernias, or the tendency to have them, are frequently hereditary. There is a strong breed tendency for perineal hernias, Boston terriers being especially prone. There is a strong tendency to umbilical hernias among strains of cocker spaniels, and a very high percentage of certain lines will be afflicted. The umbilical variety is usually not operated on unless it is large. The small, hard lumps perhaps up to the size of half an English walnut cause no trouble.

Umbilical. The most common forms are hernias through the abdominal wall. And of these, the navel or umbilical hernia is found many times more frequently than any other form. At least 10 per cent of the dogs of some strains will be found to have this type. It may show as a small bubblelike protrusion at the usual site of the navel, or it may be several inches across. Repairing one consists of opening the skin, dissecting out the sac made by the protruding peritoneum and replacing its contents within the abdomen. The peritoneum is then sutured, the edges of the muscles are trimmed and brought together to close the defect, and the skin is finally sutured.

Inguinal. Inguinal hernias occur in the ring of muscle through which the spermatic cord descends. The ring may tear and allow intestines, omentum, and even the bladder to enter the hernial opening. In repairing the inguinal, the same general principles apply. However, it must be remembered that the spermatic cord passes out of the abdomen at this point, and in suturing the muscles one must leave room for the cord.

Diaphragmatic. Ruptures of the diaphragm occur commonly after accidents. The rent may be an inch long or even longer. Part of the liver, the intestines, and other organs may work through and interfere with the function of lungs and heart. The animal breathes with difficulty, using its chest muscles to help compensate for the loss of abdominal function. Temporary relief may be afforded to the pet by holding his front legs and standing him on his hind legs, so that the misplaced organs will slide back into place. Repair is possible if the veterinarian has access to an apparatus to administer air to the dog via his windpipe; without it the operation cannot be done because the lungs will collapse.

Abdominal. Rents elsewhere along the sides and bottom of the abdomen occasionally result from accidents. They may leave only the skin to hold the sac filled with intestines and omentum or possibly the spleen. The injury looks most serious and it usually surprises the owner to learn that even very long rents may be repaired successfully. The skin is opened; the peritoneum is joined with gut; the skin is closed and recovery is often complete in a week. A few gut sutures are used to hold the muscle layer.

Perineal. When a dog's prostate gland enlarges, as it so often does in older animals, there is a feeling in the pelvic region as of a stool occupying the bowel. The dog strains continually, as if he were trying to pass it. This constant pressure at length weakens the peritoneum and muscles from the anus to the surrounding tissue and a small tear may occur. Gradually the tear lengthens. Next a loop of bowel may enter the opening and form a sac under the skin. The pressure on the prostate gland causes the tear to enlarge still farther and more intestines to occupy the opening. At length the prostate itself may be forced out, dragging the bladder with it. If this occurs, the dog is doomed unless the bladder is tapped, the urine withdrawn, and the organs squeezed back into place. In time such a hernia tears the tissue all around the anus, causing a great disfiguring bulge to appear.

In the case of perineal hernias two operations generally are necessary to produce a successful result. The dog can either be placed on a dosage of the synthetic female sex hormone, stilbestrol, for several weeks, until the prostate has reduced considerably and no longer causes straining, or he can be castrated, which produces the same result. Then, with no further compulsion for straining, the operation to suture the rent can be attempted with a fair degree of success, if many silk sutures are buried. Those cases where the entire circle around the anus is ripped have less chance of being operated on successfully.

AFTERTREATMENT: The aftercare for any hernia operation consists of feeding light diets, and the application of antiseptics to the sutures to prevent infections, for it must be remembered that the areas are dirty, because the dog sits or lies on them, constantly exposing the sites to infection. A pair of dog-sized pajama bottoms can be used to good advantage. They must be removed, of course, each time the dog defecates. A diet which produces a soft stool is essential.

22. The Ear and the Eye

THE EAR

THE EAR afflictions most commonly encountered are canker, ear mites, middle-ear abscesses, and ear-flap injuries.

Canker and Ear Mites. Canker is a term covering many ear infections manifested by the accumulation of excess waxy secretions. It may be due to dirt or irritation caused by bacterial growth. Canker can be recognized by a cheesy odor, a gummy wax in the ear, and frequent scratching. Ear mites, which cause the same symptoms, usually produce a drier, grayer, crumbly wax with less odor. By their irritation, which often drives a pet frantic, they cause symptoms of general sickness, with loss of appetite, loss of weight, and frequently hematomas in the ear flap, from the batting and bruising of the ear when the dog scratches it.

A reading glass will help to distinguish the mites. If a little of the crumbly wax is spread in some mineral oil on a piece of glass and observed with the reading glass, even a magnification of eight times will enlarge them sufficiently to make them visible as moving dust particles. A veterinarian can diagnose them at 140 magnifications so that they look like crabs, and their eggs, too, are visible. Often when mites are not found in profusion the eggs alone are sufficient for diagnosis.

Curing canker can generally be effected by flushing out the wax with alcohol and ether and inserting a sulfa-drug solution in propylene glycol, or dilute phenol or iodine in glycerine. Some veterinarians prefer an oily base with an antiseptic.

Curing mite infestation consists of flushing the ear with peroxide, or a mixture of ether and alcohol, to dissolve the wax. This is followed by an oily solution, or propylene glycol, containing an insecticide with rotenone, or benzene hexachloride. The mites are usually killed in one application, but there may be some on the hair about the ear flap which will crawl back inside the ear after the insecticide has been eliminated and start the infestation again. Treatment once a week for three weeks will effect a cure, but you must watch out for companion pets reinfesting the cured one.

If the ear flap itches, it may have skin disease, the outer edge may be crusted, and a thickened fluid-filled lump (hematoma) may develop in it. These must all be treated by a veterinarian. Hematomas require prompt attention or they may cause a cauliflower ear.

Pendulous ears, such as those of hounds and setters, are more frequently infected than are bat ears, such as those of Boston terriers and German shepherds. Bat ears are prone to diseases around the rim of the flap, while pendulous-eared dogs have more canker and interior infection.

In bathing dogs, if water runs into the ears it does not cause canker. The ear has a lining of wax which helps protect it.

To cure persistent canker, the chronic, seemingly incurable kind, an operation has been devised which consists of opening the ear canal to its lowest point on the side of the face and suturing the skin to the skin lining of this canal. A V-shaped opening is thus left, from which the discharge can drain and into which air can penetrate. The surgeon may find that irritation has continued for so long that the canal is solid and the cartilage may be turned to bone. At least the owner will have access to the area and can flush it daily so that the infection itself can be eliminated.

Ear Flap Injuries. The unhealing notch so often found in hounds at the ear tip may develop into a serious injury. It starts from a small cut but is made steadily worse and deeper by the shaking of the dog's head. The end of a long ear travels at a high speed as it rotates when a dog shakes his head. When the tip is struck against a hard object, such as a buckle or the side of the doghouse, the cut may tear. Sometimes a fairly large blood vessel scarcely has time to seal itself off when it is struck and reopened. Not only do these tears leave ugly scars, but they bleed profusely and, in summer, invite maggot infestations. If your dog has a notch of this kind, see that it receives (or give it) immediate attention.

Cauliflower Ears. Hematomas, unless opened, will cause a "cauliflower ear" which puckers and thickens. There is another kind common in dogs which grows as a spongy protrusion in the ear canal and part way out of the ear. At length the ear becomes filled until drainage from the lower canal is prevented. The odor is obnoxious. The veterinarian can remove these growths a few at a time, taking only enough each time so that skin can cover the area, until the ear appears quite normal. Medication must be applied during and after the procedure.

THE EYE

The common eye symptoms which accompany generalized diseases have already been discussed. Bluing of the cornea, mucous discharge, and sticking together of the lids, when a part of a disease picture, are not primarily eye ailments at all and cannot be treated as such. Nor can we properly classify as ailments conditions such as "scratchy" eyes, which affect a dog after a hunt, when dust, grass seed, and tiny foreign bodies cause irritation to the eyes for a day or two. Here we are concerned only with infections or injuries which directly affect the eye or parts of the eye.

The Lids. In examining an eye which appears to be ailing, look first at the lids. Are they infected with skin disease or mange? Does the dog paw at them and increase the irritation? Do one or both of the lids roll inward so that the lashes rub on the eyeball? Is there a little wart growing on the inside of one lid? Is there a wound?

For skin disease, the treatment must be directed toward the cause. A mite-killing drug in a sticky vehicle is most effective in cases of mange; a fungicide should be employed in cases of fungus diseases.

In the case of inturned eyelids, surgery can generally correct the condition. A crescent of skin is removed below or above a lid, and when the skin is sutured the lid rolls out where it should be. Warts are also removed surgically by dissecting the wart, roots and all, from the lid while the patient is anesthetized. Wounds are sutured if necessary.

Aftercare consists of the use of an eye ointment, such as sulfa or penicillin ointments made with special bases.

The Conjunctiva. The layer under the lids and around the eyeball—the conjunctiva—is often wounded, inflamed, or diseased. The nictitating membrane (third eyelid) is usually considered part of it. Inflammation of this tissue may be so intense that the eye will close and the membrane fold outward over the lids. The irritation is intensified by the dog's rubbing the eye.

Examine closely for cuts, scratches, and foreign bodies, such as little thorns or bits of glass or wood. If you find no indication of injury, the condition may have been caused by bee stings or insect bites, which recover without treatment. Or the gland of Harder, in the inner angle of the lids, may be swollen and inflamed.

FOREIGN BODIES: Remove all irritating material. Apply an eye ointment containing an antiseptic and an anesthetic. Sulfa and butyn or metaphen and butyn are often used. Sedatives to prevent the dog from harming itself are valuable.

INFLAMED GLAND OF HARDER: See Chapter 7.

Pink-eye. A common ailment of dogs as well as of many other pets is called pink-eye. It is one of the diseases that is possibly contracted from humans and affects the dog in much the same way. The whole eye becomes inflamed. Probably pink-eye is one of the causes of conjunctivitis, since its symptoms are identical with some forms of that condition. Nevertheless, a bacteriologist can demonstrate the streptococcus organisms which produce this specific infection. In severe cases the cornea may become opaque, starting with a pale graying and ending with such denseness that the dog can no longer distinguish forms and becomes blind.

Treatment consists of the application of any one of the streptococcus-killing agents which have been demonstrated to be harmless to the eyes, combined in an ophthalmic-ointment base. Sulfa drugs, even sulfanilamide, are adequate. Those most often used are sulfathiazole and sulfadiazine. Penicillin and other antibiotics, such as Bacitracin, are excellent. If medication is applied at least once a day (preferably three times a day), cure and resolution of the inflammation may be expected within a few days.

The Eyeball. Many ailments affect the eyeball. Most of them are of such nature that they had best be left to the expert for treatment.

GLAUCOMA: There is no treatment for this because it is usually a hereditary ailment, first appearing when the dog is over four years old. It does not skip a generation but passes from parent to offspring. Because it does not start until middle age, it is passed on and on by dogs which are bred in early life. The eyeball develops an internal pressure which eventually causes enlargement. The dog is in some pain. The lens may drop down from behind the pupil and the eyes grow so large that they look like headlights. Surgical removal of the eye is effective when only one is diseased, but it should be performed by an expert. The operation is delicate, and infection within the sutured lids is always a danger until healing is complete. A well-performed operation leaves a dog with lids intact, but the dog appears to have his eye closed.

OPACITY: When the eyeball is injured, a whiteness which may cover the transparent part of the eye generally develops. This is due to the presence of white cells which are attempting to promote healing. After the scar forms over the injury, a white spot may still remain. The whiteness or blueness often disappears from the outer parts of the eye first and later from the scar itself.

The dog must be prevented from rubbing an injured eye by taping his front legs together, if necessary, or by administering sedatives. Eye ointments should be applied. An unattended injury may etch away so much of the cornea that the aqueous humor will escape and make healing impossible. Prompt attention is essential.

CATARACT: This is a whitening or bluing of the lens due to causes yet unknown. The natural slow lightening of the deep blue color seen in the pupil comes with age and is not a cataract.

Your veterinarian may inject sterile milk, which sometimes produces an astonishing improvement. In some cases, however, this treatment does not help. Needling of the lens with a special cataract knife such as that used on human patients in some cases clears the cataract when the lens heals.

Injuries to the Eye. In accidents in which the arch of bone which protects the eye is fractured, the eye itself is sometimes seriously injured. It may be completely pressed out of its socket and left hanging by only a few muscles, the socket filled with grime. In less severe cases the eyes may be merely pushed out of the lids. Dog fights also may result in such injuries.

The treatment depends on the type of injury. Eyes which are very seriously damaged need major surgery, while those which are only outside the lids can be replaced with local anesthetic. The injection is made at the outer angle of the eye, and an incision at that point widens the opening so the ball may be gently pushed back into place. In all cases quick action is urgent. If the socket behind the eyeball becomes filled as a result of hemorrhage, it is unlikely that the eye can be saved. Be sure the eyeball is not allowed to dry. A soft, moist cloth can be kept over it until the veterinarian is consulted.

23. The Nervous System

WHAT we think of as the nervous system consists of the brain and the spinal cord together with all the larger and smaller nerves emanating from and leading to them, down to the tiniest terminal branches. The system is affected by various troubles, ranging from injury to the terminal branches to the involvement of the brain itself by viruses, bacteria, protozoan organisms, toxins, and mechanical injuries.

To appreciate all the chances for nerve injury to which a pet is liable one need only consider for a moment the innumerable ramifications of nerves about an animal's body. Aside from the possibilities of mechanical injury, the nerves are governed by secretions of the ductless glands and manifest odd and abnormal behavior when the glands fail to function properly. If the pancreas, for example, fails to secrete insulin, the blood fails to store sugar in the liver; if the blood becomes overwhelmed with sugar, a nervous manifestation—a convulsion—occurs. If there is too much thyroid secretion, the animal becomes nervous and overactive; too little, and he is sluggish. Interfere with the function of the parathyroids and a different kind of convulsion occurs. And when the pituitary is disturbed, a whole host of abnormalities in behavior develops. These manifestations are all nervous and all are controlled by or due to chemical secretions.

Drugs taken through the mouth will affect the nerves. A dog poisoned with strychnine trembles violently, then rests a moment and trembles again. Put his nervous system out of commission with an injectable hypnotic and the trembling stops, showing that the nerves were directly affected by the poison.

In other sections of this book we have already considered many of the common nervous complications in connection with the functions of other parts of the body. We have seen the effects of poisons on the nerves (page 148). And in Chapter 2 we discussed the relationship between the glands and the nerves. We have seen that nerves can regenerate and animate tissue to which the nerve trunk has been severed.

Although much of the material that might well have been treated in this chapter has already been covered elsewhere in this book, one general group remains—those important nervous maladies which we lump together under the heading of fits or convulsions and which are worthy of special attention.

CONVULSIONS

From about 1920 or a little earlier until comparatively recently, an epidemic of running fits was prevalent in the United States and to some extent in other countries, notably England. Dogs had violent fits for which no cause could be assigned—no parasites, fever, or sickness of any kind. The dog would run about yelping or crawl cowering and quivering under some protected place, and finally stretch out stiff while his jaws clamped together and froth whipped up in his mouth. He usually urinated and defecated. The general conception was that these running fits were due to some deficiency in diet. Minerals, vitamins, proteins, orange juice, and dozens of other things were tried.

A change of diet often cured it—provided the change was away from dog biscuits and kibbled food. Because of this, I was convinced that there was something *in* dog biscuits which was to blame. In my experience no case developed when dogs were taken off biscuits and fed a different food which furnished a balanced diet. Working on this premise, we set out to find *what* there was *in* the biscuits. Some time later I published some material on this theory and it was ridiculed. We studied molds in kibbled biscuits and found no harmful ones. No harmful bacteria were found. But everyone who asked my advice was told to give up kibbled biscuits. Invariably the fits stopped in their pets.

The substance in the kibbles was not found then, but in 1947, Mellanby, the same English scientist who discovered vitamin D, found that nitrogen trichloride, the bleach used to whiten flour, was the causative agent of these running fits. The use of bleached flour has since been discontinued, and thus one major cause of running fits in dogs has been removed.

WORM FITS

In puppies any form of worms in large numbers may produce fits. Elimination of the worms stops the fits. In older dogs severe roundworm infestations are so rare they can be disregarded as a cause of fits. But hookworms, both from the anemia they cause and from their toxins, can and often do bring about fits.

Whipworms, too, are a frequent cause of fits, especially in dogs which are exercised. When infested dogs are taken hunting, no matter what their age, they may have half a dozen fits in a night. Fear of the fits has caused many a fine hunting dog to lose his enjoyment of hunting. To have a terrifying experience like a fit strike him just as he becomes excited over his chase and nicely warmed up is sufficient to spoil his pleasure in hunting.

Tapeworms in numbers debilitate and secrete poisons which produce fits. Elimination of any of these parasites may end the fits within twenty-four hours.

FEVER FITS

These occur in the initial phases of infectious diseases which raise the temperature. In Carré distemper the visible symptoms may be ushered in by a few days of fits. This holds only with the diseases accompanied by high fevers. Housedog disease, in which the temperature runs 102.6°, seldom produces a fit. When canine influenza was rampant it was marked by fits which lasted a few days and then disappeared.

INFLAMMATION

Encephalitis fits are of a different nature. There is less tendency to run. The dog is more likely to stand, sit, or lie in one spot until the fit is over. Also, as you will remember, the convulsions come at closer and closer intervals until the dog may die in a long, almost continuous convulsion. Or his convulsions may stop and a twitch develop, depending on what part of the brain or spinal cord is damaged. Rabies is a primary encephalitis. Meningitis, too, produces fits and sometimes twisting of the back. It may be cured with sulfa or antibiotics.

EPILEPSY

Dogs are believed to suffer from epilepsy of an incurable nature. No treatment which I know of cures such epileptiform convulsions.

ECLAMPSIA

What may give the impression of a fit to the uninitiated is a malady common to all species during the lactating period—eclampsia, also called milk fever. The bitch, whose blood calcium has been partially exhausted by her nursing puppies draining it away in milk, starts to quiver, develops a wild, startled expression, and then shakes violently. Bitches with eclampsia do not froth at the mouth. Sometimes they develop quite high temperatures; their muscles remain rigid, and the whole picture is alarming.

This condition is easily and quickly relieved by the injection of calcium gluconate into the vein. One cubic centimeter of a 27 per cent solution for each two pounds of weight of dog brings relief in ten or fifteen minutes.

FOOD POISONING AND CHEMICAL POISONING

These, as we have seen, affect the nervous system. For treatment, see pages 148–49.

TETANUS (LOCKJAW)

This produces convulsions, but they are not accompanied by frothing. The lips are pulled downward by the muscles so that there is the appearance of a sickly grin. The gait is stiff, head stretched out in front and tail held stiffly behind. The third eyelid (nictitating membrane) nearly always becomes especially prominent.

DIABETES AND UREMIA

Convulsions occur from too much sugar in the blood, caused by sugar diabetes (*diabetes mellitus*), and also from uremia, caused by acute or chronic kidney disease. In the latter case the temperature is usually subnormal and albumin is present in the urine.

SUNSTROKE

This can produce what appears to the layman to be a convulsion. The dog is trying so desperately to breathe and his breath is coming in such rapid gasps that the owner may believe he is having a fit and not recognize the cause of the trouble. With sunstroke the temperature is very high, sometimes 109°, the dog exhales and inhales fast, the tongue and gums may be purple or blue (see page 135).

FOREIGN BODIES

Some dogs will have fits from foreign bodies in their stomachs. I have seen puppies have fits after meals of dog biscuits which they did not chew into small enough pieces. Stones, lumps of coal, bones, and other hard objects that have been swallowed often produce fits. A dose of peroxide soon brings relief.

Bones or sticks which wedge across the roof of the mouth, between the teeth, may cause such misery and fright that the dog gives every indication of having a fit. I have known dogs to roll down flights of stairs, run about pawing at their faces, frothing at the mouth, and exhibiting such symptoms as to frighten anyone.

NEURALGIA

Dogs are subject to nerve inflammation attended by pains in the nerves much like those we feel, if similarity of symptoms is any indication. They may become stiff, seem to ache, cry out with pain, be unable to go up or down steps—or, upon occasion, be able to go up stairs but not down, or vice versa. Pressure on certain areas in lifting them may elicit dismal howls of pain.

Heat very often helps materially. After suffering during the damp spring days, some dogs will become animated and happy and apparently without pain on the hot, bright days of summer. When a cool, damp spell of weather comes, the trouble is again evident.

Vitamin B injections have seemed to afford relief in some cases. Fowler's solution of arsenic, a drop a day for each seven pounds of weight for a week, increased to a drop for each five pounds the second week, has been recommended highly. Aspirin, one five-grain tablet to a fifty-pound dog, or in proportion, apparently eases the pain considerably.

PARALYSIS

The most baffling nervous disease which veterinarians are called upon to cure is posterior paralysis. When complete, the paralysis leaves the hind quarters dangling if the dog is lifted. He may be able to pull himself along with his front legs on the ground or floor, the hind legs dragging behind. In some cases paralysis requires several days to become complete, the dog going through a period of acute pain and showing great anxiety. This state passes and the ensuing paralysis gives relief from the pain. In some dogs, this paralysis creeps forward, paralyzing all the dog's legs and usually resulting in death.

The dog may sometimes be paralyzed in one leg or both legs on the same side (hemiplegia), as happens in a stroke where a blood clot presses on a small area of the brain. In time he may recover completely.

A form of paralysis which occurs once in a thousand cases is the spastic type. It is so rare that you are unlikely ever to own a dog so afflicted. Spastic paralysis stiffens the striped muscles all over the body. The whole body stiffens as with tetanus, but from a different cause—a damage to the brain. In flaccid paralysis, the damage is in the cord. In tetanus, the paralysis is caused by a bacterial toxin. Your veterinarian can distinguish between the spasticity caused by encephalitis and that caused by a brain injury by injecting a sedative drug such as sodium pentobarbital and noting the reaction. If the dog remains rigid after anesthesia has begun, it is not encephalitis spasticity.

Often the cause of paralysis is unknown, but several factors are known to produce it, among them potassium deficiency, lack of biotin (a vitamin found in yeast, part of the B complex), mineral deficiency, and inadequate protein. Moreover, we know that blows on the spine, autointoxication from long spells of constipation, heavy infestations with ticks, great accumulations in the anal glands, and damage from disease can cause it. Tumors in the spine and blood clots are possibilities if not probabilities.

TREATMENT: If you find your dog suddenly paralyzed, apply a muzzle first and then feel to see if his back is broken. If it is, put him gently on a flat surface and take him to the veterinarian. He may be able to operate and set the back, and if the spinal cord has not been injured, your pet may be well again in time.

If your dog has developed paralysis slowly, your veterinarian will suggest treatment. And here more patient nursing is needed than in any other ailment your dog may develop. Start with the possibility in mind that recovery to normal may never occur. Be grateful for every bit of improvement shown. You may have to build a carriage for your pet's rear quarters. He will have to be kept on some absorbent material which must be changed frequently or the urine he passes may burn his skin. Bed sores develop easily. His feces must be removed. He may have just enough nerve life in his back legs to hold his weight. This simplifies matters greatly, because he can be taken outside and taught to urinate and defecate when he feels the pressure of your fingers over his bladder on each side of his abdomen. Such a dog is a good patient and remains housebroken, but a completely paralyzed dog is a great care and only a loving master will have the patience to see such an illness through.

Definite nerve destruction on a large scale cannot be repaired, and the posterior paralysis following Carré distemper or housedog disease unfortunately is often hopeless. Your veterinarian will be able to give you some idea of the extent and progress of the disease.

Chastek Paralysis. This we consider separately, because it is a distinct form with a known cause. It is produced by the consumption of raw fish in quantity. In raw fish there is a vitamin B_1 (thiamin) inactivator. Therefore the disease is really a thiamin deficiency. It is relieved by adding the vitamin to the diet and by feeding only cooked fish, since cooking destroys the inactivator.

COLLAPSE

Nervous collapse following an accident or serious surgical operation is called shock. In it, the dog is debilitated, the pulse is weak, the color in the gums is pale and anemic.

Some dogs lie as if they were dead; others may show signs of nervousness and tend to bite if touched. Treatment of shock has already been discussed on page 135.

NERVE TUMORS

Actually the neurofibroma is a tumor of the sheath and not of the nerve proper. I know of no true nerve tumors as yet having been reported in pets. But these tumors of the sheath grow rapidly and form large lumps. They require treatment by your veterinarian.

24. Fifty Questions Frequently Asked by Dog Owners

1. Q. What causes a dog to start shedding?
   A. The lengthening of the day.

2. Q. Can mature dogs do without certain vitamins?
   A. Yes. Vitamins C and E.

3. Q. Does a dog need lean meat?
   A. No. He can live on dehydrated meat or without any meat at all.

4. Q. Could a dog live on a vegetable diet?
   A. Possibly, but not practically.

5. Q. Does milk make worms in dogs?
   A. No. Milk is an excellent food for dogs.

6. Q. Do dogs eat grass to obtain vitamins?
   A. No. They probably eat it to cause vomiting.

7. Q. At what age do bitches first come in heat?
   A. At six to twelve months, depending on breed and rapidity of growth.

8. Q. Does ground glass kill a dog quickly?
   A. It usually doesn't even bother him, passing through without damaging the digestive tract appreciably.

9. Q. Can you tell the age of a dog by his teeth?
   A. His second set starts to erupt at fourteen weeks of age and are all in by five months. Beyond that, teeth are a poor indication of age.

10. Q. Is distemper the only disease which leaves pits in the tooth enamel?

A. No. There are a number of diseases puppies can have at teething time which leave pits.

11. Q. Do dogs have eczema?
A. They have a skin disease which is called eczema.

12. Q. How can one tell if a dog has kidney disease?
A. By boiling a small amount of urine in a test tube. If a white cloud or precipitate develops, it probably is albumin, which is an indication of kidney disease.

13. Q. When a dog sits down and drags himself along with his front legs, does it mean he has worms?
A. Not necessarily. He may have worms, but this particular action means that he is trying to squeeze out some of the accumulation in his anal glands.

14. Q. Do worms cause anemia?
A. Yes. Hookworms cause it by drawing blood; whipworms by their toxins.

15. Q. Do dogs have collarbones (clavicles)?
A. No. Among pets, only birds have them.

16. Q. What is a roundworm?
A. It may be any of a class of nematodes—hook, whip, ascarid—or it may be a specific ascarid usually called roundworm. It is three to five inches long, one sixteenth of an inch thick, and pointed at both ends.

17. Q. Are hookworms so named because their ends are shaped like hooks?
A. No. They are called hookworms because of the very small hooks around their mouths, by which they hold onto the intestinal lining. Hookworms are five eighths of an inch long and about as thick as heavy thread.

18. Q. How do dogs acquire tapeworms?
A. Principally by eating fleas and rabbits, each of which is host for a specific kind of tapeworm.

19. Q. Can a veterinarian find tapeworm eggs by a fecal examination?
A. The eggs of the flea-host worm are seldom found, but the eggs of the rabbit-host worm are always evident.

20. Q. Are dogs subject to any infectious liver disease?
A. One type is caught from rats—leptospirosis.

21. Q. When a dog has blacktongue, does his tongue really turn black?
A. Blacktongue, caused by niacin deficiency, produces a condition in the mouth in which the tongue turns black *after* death.

22. Q. Do dogs have bladder stones?
A. Often. They may range in size from minute to stones three or four inches in thickness.

23. Q. Is there any way to stop an old bitch from dribbling urine?
A. Many spayed bitches have weak bladder sphincters. Small doses of stilbestrol given at regular intervals will cure the dribbling.

24. Q. What causes dogs to have fits and then chorea?
A. Carré distemper and housedog disease, with about equal frequency.

25. Q. Do dogs get cavities in their teeth?
A. Very rarely.

26. Q. Does food cause skin disease in dogs?
A. So seldom that it can be disregarded as a cause.

27. Q. Do dogs get stomach ulcers from worry?
A. Dogs very seldom have stomach ulcers from any cause.

28. Q. What causes a dog to drag a front leg? Is it curable?
A. An injury to his radial nerve. It is seldom curable; usually the nerve fails to regenerate.

29. Q. Is coccidiosis caught from chickens or rabbits?
A. Neither. The dog has three forms, none of which is contracted from chickens or rabbits.

30. Q. Do bitches have cancer of the ovaries?
A. No case has been reported.

31. Q. Why are puppies of white breeds so frequently deaf?
A. Usually from careless breeding. Deafness is not necessarily associated with color, except in pups from two harlequin-colored dogs.

32. Q. What is dog plague?
A. That is an old and seldom-used name for Carré distemper.

33. Q. How long should a bitch be allowed to attempt whelping before it is necessary to use instruments?
A. Until a puppy is down in the pelvis and is obviously too large to be passed normally.

34. Q. Do only dogs with lop ears have troubles?
A. No. Bat-eared dogs often have them, including canker and ear mites. Bat-eared dogs have their ear tips irritated by flies more than dogs of lop-eared breeds.

35. Q. When a dog's eyelids turn in and the hair rubs on the eyeballs, can they be fixed?

A. Yes, by an operation which removes a crescent of skin below and above the eye, thus pulling the lids out to their proper position.

36. Q. What can be done to remove the small tumor so often seen in the inside corners of the eyes of Boston terriers and cocker spaniels?
A. It can be removed by surgery successfully and quite simply.

37. Q. How does a fecal examination determine the presence of worms?
A. By demonstrating the eggs of worms. Knowing which worm lays eggs such as are found, the technician knows which worm the dog is harboring.

38. Q. Do fleas breed on the dog?
A. Fleas copulate and the female lays eggs while on the dog. The eggs fall to the ground, into rug nap, overstuffed furniture, cracks in the floor, and hatch when the weather is warm and damp. A worm emerges and grows, eventually spins a cocoon, pupates, and emerges as a flea which jumps on the first thing moving past it—dog, cat, or person.

39. Q. Do lice breed on the dog?
A. Yes.

40. Q. Is red mange curable?
A. Quite easily, with persistence.

41. Q. Is glaucoma hereditary?
A. Definitely. It never skips a generation.

42. Q. Do dogs have hernias?
A. Yes. The most common is the small navel (umbilical) hernia often found in cocker spaniels.

43. Q. What makes an occasional dog's eyes reflect red at night?
A. A rare hereditary characteristic. The eyes are like those of a raccoon in this respect.

44. Q. Do dogs have lockjaw?
A. Yes, for which reason tetanus antitoxin should be administered in cases of penetrating wounds which the air cannot reach.

45. Q. How many successful ways are there of vaccinating dogs against distemper?
A. At least ten.

46. Q. Is mange transmissible from dog to man?
A. Sarcoptic mange is transmissible from dog to man and also from man to dog.

47. Q. Do dogs have many forms of cancer?
A. Probably as many forms as human beings have.

48. Q. Can a dog get fat in any way other than by eating too much? How about glands?
A. Glands help to regulate the use your dog makes of the food he eats. Eating is the only way he can get fat.

49. Q. Do dogs have venereal diseases?
A. Not the kind human beings have, but there is a cancer transmissible by copulation.

50 Q. Will a dog infect his wounds if he licks them?
A. No. He licks any dead tissue away, along with bacteria.

Index